U.S. ENERGY POLICY AND
U.S. FOREIGN POLICY
IN THE 1980s

U.S. ENERGY POLICY AND U.S. FOREIGN POLICY IN THE 1980s

REPORT OF THE ATLANTIC COUNCIL'S
ENERGY POLICY COMMITTEE

JOHN E. GRAY, *Chairman and Co-rapporteur*

HENRY H. FOWLER, *Co-chairman*

JOSEPH W. HARNED, *Co-rapporteur and Project Director*

Foreword by
KENNETH RUSH

BALLINGER PUBLISHING COMPANY
Cambridge, Massachusetts
A Subsidiary of Harper & Row, Publishers, Inc.

International Standard Book Number: 0-88410-902-X

Library of Congress Catalog Card Number: 81-12810

Printed in the United States of America

Library of Congress Cataloging in Publication Data

Atlantic Council's Energy Policy Committee.
  U.S. energy policy and U.S. foreign policy in the 1980s.

  Includes index.
  1. Energy policy—United States—Addresses, essays, lectures.
2. Power resources—Addresses, essays, lectures. I. Gray, John E.
II. Fowler, Henry H., 1908–   III. Harned, Joseph W. IV. Title.
HD9502.U52A87 1981   333.79'0973   81-12810
ISBN 0-88410-902-X   AACR2

CONTENTS

Members of the Atlantic Council's
Energy Policy Committee ix

Foreword— *Kenneth Rush* xiii

Preface— *John E. Gray* xv

List of Figures xix

List of Tables xxi

Chapter I
U.S. Energy Policy and U.S. Foreign Policy
in the 1980s
— *Atlantic Council Energy Policy Committee* 1

Executive Summary 1
I. Introduction and Purpose 10
II. Perspective on Future International Energy Supply 12
III. U.S. Energy Policy and International Energy Relationships 14
IV. Issues for the 1980s 22
V. Energy Policy Decisionmaking in the United States 39

VI. General Observations and Conclusions   47
VII. POLICY RECOMMENDATIONS   50

Chapter II
International Energy in the 1980s
— Melvin A. Conant   63

I. Introduction   63
II. World Energy Trade   66
III. Considerations Affecting Oil Supply in the 1980s   77
IV. The International Oil System   91
V. Prospects for the World Oil Market — the 1980s   95
VI. New Claimants for Oil   98
VII. Debt Financing of Energy-importing Developing
    Countries   103
VIII. The Perspective from the United States in the 1980s   108

Chapter III
U.S. Energy Relations With The Arab
Oil-producing States Of The Gulf
— Richard D. Erb   11

Introduction   111
I. Postwar Trends and Events in the 1970s   113
II. Factors Influencing the Oil Price and Production Decisions
    of the Arab Producers of the Gulf   120
III. U.S. Interests and Policy Recommendations   127

Chapter IV
U.S.-Canadian Energy Relations
— Edward F. Wonder   137

Introduction   137
I. The Context of Canadian Energy Policy: Resources
    and Politics   140
II. Bilateral Energy Relations in the 1980s   153
III. Conclusions   173

Chapter V
U.S.-Mexican Energy Relations
—*Edward F. Wonder* 177

Introduction 177
I. Mexican Energy Resources 179
II. Energy Policymaking and Mexican Oil and Gas 185
III. Recent Trends and Issues in Bilateral Energy Relations 194
IV. Bilateral Energy Relations in the Next Twenty Years 202
V. Conclusions 212

Chapter VI
U.S.-Venezuelan Energy Relations
—*Edward F. Wonder* 217

Introduction 217
I. Venezuelan Energy Resources 219
II. Economic and Political Environment of Venezuelan
   Oil Policy 224
III. Recent Experience in Bilateral Energy Relations 231
IV. Energy Relations in the 1980s and 1990s 238
V. Conclusions 245

Chapter VII
U.S.-Japanese Energy Relations 247

Foreword—*John E. Gray and Yoshizane Iwasa* 247
Members of the Japan-U.S. Energy Relationships Committee 249
I. U.S.-Japan Energy Relations: An American View
   —*Milton Klein* 250
II. Japan-U.S. Energy Relations: A Japanese View
   —*Toyoaki Ikuta* 274
III. JOINT POLICY RECOMMENDATIONS—The Energy
   Policy Committee of the Atlantic Council of the United
   States, and the Japan-U.S. Energy Relationships Committee
   of the Committee for Energy Policy Promotion, Japan 287

Appendix   293

Glossary   295

Index   297

List of Members of the Atlantic Council's
Board of Directors   311

MEMBERS OF THE ATLANTIC COUNCIL'S ENERGY POLICY COMMITTEE

CHAIRMAN and CO-RAPPORTEUR

John E. Gray,[1] president, International Energy Associates Limited

CO-CHAIRMAN

Henry H. Fowler, partner, Goldman Sachs & Co.; former secretary of the treasury

CO-RAPPORTEUR and PROJECT DIRECTOR

Joseph W. Harned, deputy director general, Atlantic Council

CASE STUDY RAPPORTEURS

Melvin A. Conant, president, Conant & Associates Ltd.; former assistant administrator, Federal Energy Administration

Richard E. Erb,[2] resident fellow, American Enterprise Institute for Public Policy Research

Milton Klein, senior assistant to the president, EPRI; former director, Research Development and Technology Applications, International Energy Agency, OECD

Edward F. Wonder, senior consultant, International Energy Associates Limited

---

1. Italics indicate members who are also directors of the Atlantic Council.

2. Richard Erb served as rapporteur until his appointment as U.S. executive director of the Internal Monetary Fund.

ix

MEMBERS

Cortland Anderson, vice-president for corporate affairs, The Washington
Post Co.

Willis C. Armstrong, consultant; former assistant secretary of state

Robert T. Bonn, senior vice-president, Pacific Lighting Company

Peter C. Borré, principal deputy assistant secretary for international affairs,
U.S. Department of Energy

Emilio G. Collado, former president, ADELA; former executive vice-president,
Exxon

W. Donham Crawford, chairman, Gulf States Utilities Company

Floyd L. Culler, Jr., president and chief executive officer, Electric Power
Research Institute

Charles J. DiBona, president, American Petroleum Institute

Warren H. Donnelly, senior specialist for energy, Congressional Research Service,
Library of Congress

Sherwood L. Fawcett, president, Battelle Memorial Institute

William H.G. FitzGerald, vice-chairman, Financial General Bank Shares Inc.

George S. Franklin, Jr., coordinator, The Trilateral Commission

Robert W. Fri, president, Energy Transition Corporation; former administrator,
Energy Research and Development Administration

Lincoln Gordon,[3] senior fellow, Resources for the Future; former assistant
secretary of state

Joseph J. Jova, president, Meridian House International; former ambassador
to Mexico and the OAS

Julius L. Katz, former assistant secretary of state

Isaac C. Kidd, Jr., former supreme allied commander, Atlantic

John R. Kiely, executive consultant, Bechtel Corporation

William C. King, vice-president, corporate planning, Gulf Oil Corporation

George H. Lawrence, president, American Gas Association

Ian O. Lesser, M.S., London School of Economics; candidate for Master of Law
and Diplomacy, Fletcher School, Tufts University

Walter J. Levy, consultant

Clement B. Malin, assistant to the vice-president for strategic planning,
Texaco, Inc.

Harald B. Malmgren, president, Malmgren Inc.; former deputy special representative for trade

William McCollam, Jr., president, Edison Electric Institute

Alan B. McDougall, planning manager, Public Affairs Department, Exxon Corp.

Francis X. Murray, director, national energy programs, Center for Strategic and
International Studies, Georgetown University

---

3. Lincoln Gordon served as a member until his appointment as a member of the Senior
Review Panel, Central Intelligence Agency.

Henry R. Nau,[4] associate professor of political science, George Washington
    University
Paul H. Nitze, former secretary of the navy; former deputy secretary of defense
F. Taylor Ostrander, president, AMAX Foundation Inc.
Gary J. Pagliano, analyst in energy policy, Congressional Research Service,
    Library of Congress
Robert V. Price, executive vice-president, National Coal Association
Myer Rashish,[5] consulting economist
Charles W. Robinson, chairman, Energy Transition Corporation; former deputy
    secretary of state
Marcus A. Rowden, attorney; former chairman, Nuclear Regulatory Commission
Brent Scowcroft, former assistant to the president for national security affairs
Nelson F. Sievering,[6] principal consultant, International Energy Associates
    Limited
Timothy W. Stanley, president, International Economic Studies Institute
Ralph I. Straus, consultant
Franklin Tugwell, deputy assistant administrator, energy, environment and
    natural resources, Agency for International Development
Steven J. Warnecke, visiting scholar, Middle East Institute, Columbia University
Mason Willrich, vice-president for corporate planning, Pacific Gas & Electric
    Company
Carroll L. Wilson, director, World Coal Study, Massachusetts Institute of
    Technology
Watson Wise, petroleum industry entrepreneur; former U.S. delegate to the
    United Nations
Lawrence M. Woods, executive vice-president, planning and economics, Mobil
    Oil Corporation
Eric R. Zausner, senior vice-president, Booz Allen & Hamilton

EX OFFICIO MEMBERS
Theodore G. Achilles, vice-chairman, Atlantic Council
Kenneth Rush, chairman, Atlantic Council
Francis O. Wilcox, director general, Atlantic Council

PROJECT ASSISTANT
Eliane Lomax, staff member, Atlantic Council

---

4. Henry Nau served as a member until his appointment as a staff member of the National Security Council.

5. Myer Rashish served as a member until his appointment as under secretary of state
for economic affairs.

6. Nelson Sievering served as a member until his appointment as deputy director general
for administration of the International Atomic Energy Agency.

RESEARCH ASSISTANT

Mildred Turnbull, M. Litt. candidate, University of Glasgow

STUDENT INTERNS

Neile L. Miller, senior intern. M.S.F.S. candidate, Georgetown School
    of Foreign Service
William K. Griffiths, Michigan State University
Sheri Hoptman, Smith College
Alene McMahon, Principia College
Patrick O'Neil, Michigan State University
Maria Papathanassiou, Trinity College
Ousa Sananikone, Trinity College
Benjamin Tysch, University of California at Los Angeles
Lloyd Widom, Dartmouth College

FOREWORD

Few problems we will face over the next decade are more important than the supply and use of energy and the international energy relationships of the United States that affect the adequacy and security of that supply as well as the efficiency of its use. Energy supply and use will continue to involve uncertainties of a political, strategic, economic, and technological nature, as well as the unavoidable certainty of finite resources. The outcome for all nations will be heavily influenced by actions taken in the 1980s.

The outcome will depend in large part on the interrelated domestic and foreign policies of the United States. As the *Atlantic Council's Energy Policy Committee* concludes:

Much can be done in the 1980s to bring about fundamental changes in U.S. and world patterns of energy supply and use and thus to work out the problems we now face. There have been serious deficiencies in U.S. energy policy decisionmaking and in the U.S. government's pattern of interaction with the private sector. If energy policy in the United States is quickly characterized by better decisions with respect to all domestic sources, there is a good chance that the vulnerability of the United States and its allies can be reduced significantly by 1990. . . . Differing vulnerabilities and perspectives among the United States and its allies may complicate attempts to develop a consensus on how to deal with common energy concerns in a coordinated and concerted manner. The actions on energy matters that the United States, Japan, and the nations of Western Europe take individually and together will constitute a major element in their future relationships and future world order.

Those actions are proposed in the recommendations section of the first chapter, to which I add my own commendation.

I want to express our deep appreciation to John E. Gray, chairman and co-rapporteur; Henry H. Fowler, co-chairman; Joseph Harned, co-rapporteur and project director; the authors of the case studies, Melvin Conant, Richard Erb, Milton Klein, and Edward Wonder; the other members of the Energy Policy Committee; the numerous correspondents, discussants, and issue paper authors around the world; and the student interns, who together approached this eighteen-month task with continued interest and enthusiasm and who individually advanced constructive ideas that should prove helpful to all concerned with the future of international energy relationships. Special thanks go also to the U.S. Department of Energy, the Tinker Foundation, the Battelle Memorial Institute, and the many corporations and individuals without whose support this project would not have been possible. The partial financial support for the project from the Department of Energy does not imply that the assessments, conclusions, and recommendations expressed in this chapter or this volume necessarily reflect those of the department.

I should add that the views expressed in Chapter I are those of the Energy Policy Committee and not necessarily those of the Atlantic Council as a whole. It should be clear also that while Chapter I sets forth the overall views of the committee, no particular member of it should necessarily be assumed to subscribe to all the specific views presented. The views expressed in the case studies that form the subsequent chapters of this book are those of the respective case study authors, though each case study has been reviewed by the committee in draft form and reflects members' comments. The case study of U.S.-Japanese energy relations includes both a U.S. perspective and a Japanese perspective, as well as a series of joint policy recommendations developed by the Energy Policy Committee with its Japanese counterparts, who are identified on page 249. The Atlantic Council is pleased to present these analyses and findings for public discussion and debate.

Kenneth Rush
Chairman of the Board
Atlantic Council

PREFACE

In the fall of 1979, the board of directors of the Atlantic Council decided to examine the international energy relationships of the United States, in order to advance understanding of the importance of those relationships to U.S. domestic energy policy and to help clarify the interrelationship of U.S. energy policy and U.S. foreign policy. Thus a very broad scope study was initiated. Ultimately the purpose of the study became to identify key issues associated with U.S. international relationships on energy and to recommend actions for the United States and its allies to take in the 1980s.

The Council's Energy Policy Committee was reconstituted, and with some fifty-three individuals being invited to join in this new work of the committee. These members are listed on pages ix–xii.

The work of the Committee began early in 1980 with the formulation of its approach to identification and understanding of issues and options. Subsequently, with Melvin Conant as rapporteur, we undertook as a case study a "macroassessment" of the international energy situation in general and world oil trade in particular. At the same time, case studies of U.S. bilateral energy relationships with Canada, Mexico, and Venezuela were undertaken with Edward Wonder as rapporteur for each of these, and with Japan, with Milton Klein as rapporteur. A sixth case study was added thereafter—energy relations with the oil-exporting countries of the Persian Gulf, with Richard Erb as rapporteur. Our intent was to use the case studies as building blocks leading to the preparation of a policy paper. This was done, and the case studies are published here as supporting chapters of the policy report (Chapter I).

In addition to the case studies, we invited informal statements on specific issues related to certain nations, regions, institutional, political, and economic matters. Contributors of "issue papers" and other invited commentary include Melvin Conant[1]; Marcel Kramer of NATO; Hanns Maull of Bayerischer Rundfunk; Steve Warnecke; John Kiely; Dennis Bakke of the Mellon Institute; Warren Donnelly; Robert Fri; Frank Tugwell; Ryukichi Imai, Japanese ambassador to Kuwait; Juan Eibenschutz of the Mexican Comision de Energeticas; Ian Watson, Canadian member of parliament; Ronald Ritchie, Canadian energy consultant; R. Horsfield of Imperial Oil of Canada; Sheikh Saud al Soyel of United Saudi Industries; Alfonso Ravard of Petroleos de Venezuela; Emilio G. Collado; Myer Rashish; E.A. Baetz of Exxon; George McGhee, former under secretary of state; Adolph Schmidt, former ambassador to Canada; Tamaki Ipponmatsu of the Japan Atomic Power Company; D. Joseph Wood and Michael Gillette of the World Bank; and Arthur Heyman and Frank Gannon of the Organization of American States.

The resulting "issue papers," as well as the macroassessment and the case studies, were used in formulating the evolving drafts of the policy report (Chapter I). Its final text was prepared by the chairman and the project director, taking fully into account the extensive comments and limited dissents. Those that were not treated in the text are found in footnotes.

The Committee's examination of U.S.-Japanese energy relationships elicited a proposal from the Institute of Energy Economics and the Committee for Energy Policy Promotion, both based in Tokyo, to upgrade the Committee's case study to a joint project. Mr. Yoshizane Iwasa, councelor of the Fuji Bank, became chairman of a committee of Japanese experts organized as a counterpart to the Atlantic Council's Energy Policy Committee. He was assisted by Mr. Mamoru Sueda, secretary general of the Committee for Energy Policy Promotion, and Dr. Toyoaki Ikuta, president of the Institute of Energy Economics. The complete list of members appears on pages 249-250. The Japanese counterpart commiteee produced a working paper to parallel the case study written for the Atlantic Council by Milton Klein. Representatives of both committees then met on several occa-

---

[1] Members of the Energy Policy Committee listed here are further identified on pages ix-xii.

sions to review the two working papers and to formulate a series of joint U.S.–Japanese policy recommendations. The U.S. and Japanese working papers and the joint policy recommendations are published here as Chapter VII. We deeply appreciate the extent and value of the exchanges with our Japanese associates and the prospect that we may contribute to enhanced relations between Japan and the United States in the context of overall U.S. relations.

We are pleased that Gary Pagliano, Marc Rowden, and Steve Warnecke could join the Committee in the course of the project and regret that Adolph Schmidt and Bob Schaetzel were compelled to withdraw from the Committee owing to the pressure of other assignments. Nelson Sievering served on the Committee until his appointment as deputy director general for administration of the International Atomic Energy Agency in Vienna, Austria. Lincoln Gordon served until his appointment as a member of the Senior Review Panel, Central Intelligence Agency. Myer Rashish served until his appointment as undersecretary of state for economic affairs. Henry Nau served until his appointment as a staff member of the National Security Council. Richard Erb served as Rapporteur of the Committee's case study on U.S. Energy relationships with the oil-exporting countries of the Gulf until his appointment as U.S. executive director of the International Monetary Fund.

Our Committee worked hard and well to produce from diverse experience and often divergent points of view this collegial policy report and the related case studies. Given the breadth of the issues and the range of the options, we are pleased to have concluded the work with substantial consensus on the part of the members of the Committee. We recognize that we have done so, in some instances, by sticking to general principles rather than presenting detailed solutions. But we are most grateful for the opportunity to have participated in the work of a group of highly knowledgeable people willing to contribute their time and expertise in such a constructive and harmonious manner. We especially thank our project director, our rapporteurs, and each of the other members of the Energy Policy Committee for their extraordinary efforts over the past eighteen months.

John E. Gray
Chairman and Co-rapporteur
Energy Policy Committee

Henry H. Fowler
Co-chairman
Energy Policy Committee

LIST OF FIGURES

7-1   Energy Consumption Patterns, 1979   253
7-2   Total Primary Energy Requirements per GDP, 1979   254
7-3   Total Primary Energy Requirements per Capita, 1979   255

LIST OF TABLES

1-1   Potential World Primary Energy Production   13

2-1   Summer 1980 Estimates of OECD Energy Balances,
       1985-1990   67
2-2   Total Estimated Free World Oil Production,
       1985-1990   67
2-3   Fall 1980 Estimates of Demand for OPEC and
       Gulf Oil   69
2-4   Hypothetical Level of OPEC Oil and LNG Production
       to Meet Estimated Free World Demand   69
2-5   Countries Possessing the Oil Reserve Base to Expand
       Oil Production in the Near Term (to 1985)   70
2-6   Natural Gas: Market Status of Proved Reserves   72
2-7   International Coal Trade, 1960-2000   73
2-8   Outlook for OECD Coal Production: Demand
       and Imports   74
2-9   OECD Nuclear Power Projections   75
2-10 Estimated Current Supply Positions of the Seven
       Major International Oil Firms   94
2-11 Current Balances of Major Country Groups   104
2-12 Non-OPEC Developing Countries: Financing of
       Balance of Payments Deficits, 1974-1978   105

4–1   Canada's Discovered Gas Resources and Estimated
      Additions, 1978   142
4–2   Canadian Uranium Resources   145
4–3   Canadian Petroleum Supply   152
4–4   Canadian Marketable Gas Supply   154

5–1   Mexican Oil Exports, by Destination   198

7–1   Primary Energy Supply Patterns, 1977   252
7–2   Key Energy Indicators and Data, Japan   256
7–3   Key Energy Indicators and Data, United States   259
7–4   Agreements in Energy RD&D Between Japan and
      the United States   271
7–5   Primary Energy Consumption of Major
      Countries, 1979   275
7–6   Oil Imports of Japan, the United States, and
      Western Europe by Source, 1979   276
7–7   Japan's Trade with the United States   282
7–8   Total Energy Requirements of Major Countries
      per Capita, 1978   285
7–9   Total Energy Requirements of Major Countries per
      Unit of GDP, 1978   285
7–10 Japan's International Trade   286

U.S. ENERGY POLICY AND U.S. FOREIGN POLICY IN THE 1980s

Atlantic Council Energy Policy Committee

EXECUTIVE SUMMARY

The world structured its post–World War II economic development on the premise that oil supply, internationally, would be adequate, economic, and reliable. The world has now learned that this premise is incorrect and that there are serious political and economic constraints on that supply.

The international energy problem today is oil. Oil is a security problem, an economic problem, and above all, a shared problem. Essentially, all the oil-importing – developed and developing – nations are vulnerable to supply interruptions and price increases. The developing nations suffer both the direct burden of oil costs and the indirect effects of the collective vulnerability of more mature economies. Even among producers, oil is a source of internal instability and fears of outside intrusion.

In the end, the interests of all nations converge on resolving the problems of dependence on oil. The thesis of this policy paper is that the problems must and can be solved and that a high and intensive order of international collaboration and cooperation is essential to a solution.

The preconditions for a solution are clear enough – a credible and determined program to assure a more secure and economic supply of oil while simultaneously developing means to use less oil, develop alternate energy supply and use programs, and reduce vulnerability to oil supply interruptions.

No such program is possible without leadership from the United States. And no U.S. leadership is possible unless there is a strong and consistent domestic energy policy that complements, and is complemented by, U.S. foreign policy.

Much of the discussion of energy issues in the United States since 1973 has focused on problems and courses of action within our borders. While there has been growing recognition that the oil problem is the result of foreign developments, there has been until recently little understanding of the international effects of U.S. action or inaction.

Such actions will continue to affect consuming and producing countries abroad. To the extent that the United States reduces its imports of oil, it removes some element of uncertainty from the availability of oil to other nations. To the extent that the United States develops and makes available alternative energy supplies and technology such as coal, nuclear, and synthetic fuels, it provides an alternative to the importation of crude oil for all countries. To the extent that the United States develops and makes available alternate energy end use technologies, it provides broader supply choices. And such actions by the United States can redound to the advantage of its economy, balance of trade, and private institutions. Moreover, they will affect development not only in the industrial democracies that are our allies but in the less-developed countries that are heavily dependent on imported oil.

U.S. energy and foreign policy goals will be served best by embarking urgently on the road to enhanced energy supply security. The actions the United States takes—or fails to take—in this decade with respect to energy will have far-reach effects on itself, on the position of the United States in the world, and on world order. The purpose of this policy paper is to identify related issues and to recommend actions for the United States and its allies to take in the 1980s.

Section two of this chapter, "Perspective on Future International Energy Supply," provides a brief perspective on future world energy production. It is noted that this forecast shows significantly reduced future dependence on conventional oil relative to other energy sources and that reduced dependence on oil is required in any event as world energy demand increases.

Section three discusses U.S. energy policy and foreign policy relationships in terms of international impacts of U.S. energy policy; impacts of international developments on U.S. energy policy; impacts of nonenergy issues such as trade conflicts, regional conflicts, strategic conflicts, and population growth; international energy supply security; and U.S. options in an international supply shortage.

In the fourth section, issues for the 1980s are developed under the following headings—international security; bilateral issues in the energy context; multilateral cooperation; incentives to producers; recycling; diversification of sources; allocation; and energy in the developing countries.

In Section V, energy policy decisionmaking in the United States is discussed, first in a background statement and then in terms of principal problems dominating U.S. government policy and decisionmaking; international energy policy decisionmaking; and finally, U.S. energy policy and the U.S. energy industries.

Section VI presents general observations and conclusions and may be summarized as follows:

- Throughout this decade, oil will remain the single most important commercial fuel, while such other primary and secondary energy sources as natural gas, coal, nuclear power, electricity, and energy from renewable sources must be relied upon increasingly.

- Reducing demand for energy and securing access to oil while developing other sources will continue to be the major energy preoccupation of the United States and other governments.

- There will be no significant short-term relief for the United States from dependence upon oil imports, given the lead times required to develop existing resources and alternative energy sources on a sufficient scale, achieve significant conservation, and generally alter the pattern of energy end uses. The strategic implications of this continuing dependence will bear increasingly on U.S. leadership of the alliances.

- Until the United States can clearly demonstrate both the capability and the will to fully develop alternatives to oil, as well as its remaining oil resources, and thus reduce the leverage of the exporters, it is probable that oil exporters will continue to employ oil as a means to achieve political as well as economic objectives.

- Increasing domestic energy production and decreasing U.S. imports will keep jobs and tax revenues in the United States, moderate U.S. inflation, and strengthen the U.S. economy. This has significant implications in regard to the conduct of foreign and defense policy.

- The increasing dependence of Western Europe on the Soviet Union for energy will become increasingly worrisome if the trend continues.

- New claimants for a share of oil in world trade—OPEC members' internal requirements for rapidly developing economic infrastructures, the developing countries generally, and perhaps the Soviet Union—will put greater pressure on world supply.

- The energy problems of the non-oil-producing developing countries, with the associated risk of political instability, will require special efforts, including innovative methods of financing.

- The prospects for an importer–exporter dialogue are severely limited. There are conflicting priorities among the exporters as well as disparate vulnerabilities among the importers.

- There will be no significant short-term relief for our European and Japanese allies from their dependence on oil imports. This may complicate attempts to develop a consensus on how to deal with common energy concerns in a coordinated and concerted manner.

- The actions on energy matters that the United States, Canada, Japan, and the nations of Western Europe take individually and together will constitute a major element in their future relationships and future world order.

- U.S. energy relationships with Latin America on a multinational basis can be effective, both politically and in terms of cost effectiveness.

- A fundamental element of U.S. policy for Central America should be assistance for oil exploration and for the development of hydropower, geothermal, and biomass energy resources.

- Latin America fuels from biomass, such as ethanol from crops and methanol from wood, may become a modest factor in energy commerce.

In Section VII, "Policy Recommendations," a strategy composed of the following principles and actions is recommended for the 1980s:

- Strengthen the capability of the United States to provide international leadership by:

  - Assuring that U.S. energy policy fully reflects the interaction of domestic and international energy interests and U.S. foreign policy.

  - Establishing a Council on International Energy Policy, reporting to the National Security Council and with commensurate authority, to provide for coordination of domestic and foreign policy on energy and energy supply security.

  - Assuring that U.S. government and energy industry strategy focus on reducing demand growth; increasing domestic and international supply; developing alternatives such as domestic and imported (non–Middle East) gas, coal, nuclear, and synthetic fuels and fuels from renewable resources; cooperating with other consuming nations on research, development, and demonstration of energy technology; diversifying sources and helping developing countries to improve their energy security.

  - Congress as well as the administration recommitting the United States to the emergency oil-sharing contingency plans of the International Energy Agency.

  - Providing for stable and consistent market-oriented federal government policy, to allow action on the part of the energy industries and the development of supportive regulation and public understanding.

  - Making DOE responsible for U.S. government research, development, and demonstration (RD&D) programs related to conservation; the supply and use of oil, gas, electric power, coal, nuclear, and nonconventional technologies; emergency planning and preparedness for imported oil supply cutbacks or shortages; and management of federally owned energy resources and supply activities.

  - The U.S. government undertaking no energy RD&D or supply activities in competition with the private sector. However, the

U.S. government should be prepared to support such activities where national security and foreign policy interests are served.

- Encouraging cost-effective conservation measures based on market pricing of energy combined with selective energy efficiency goals.

- U.S. industry and utilities vigorously pursuing development and use of U.S. coal resources, strongly supported by government policies and regulations to streamline coal leasing, mining, and use. Encouraging worldwide U.S. coal exports, along with the development of improved domestic transportation facilities, port and harbor facilities, and export-related transportation techniques and systems.

- Encouraging industry, utilities, and households to continue to substitute other energy sources for oil, influenced by price signals.

- Encouraging the use of gas in recognition of its growing supply potential. Gas prices should continue to increase to competitive fuel levels.

- U.S. government acting to (1) improve the nuclear regulation process to focus on overall safety and efficient and timely licensing; (2) standardize safety evaluation procedures; (3) together with industry, assure the safety and encourage the public acceptance of nuclear power; (4) demonstrate safe radioactive waste disposal and the feasibility of the breeder reactor; (5) assure the orderly and timely completion and operation of plants completed, under construction, and planned and the provision of an additional major increment of nuclear power by the year 2000.

- Presidential action establishing a task force to examine and recommend specific measures affecting the U.S. electric utility industry to the end that its structural and financial viability and future national supplies of electricity adequate to support the nation's needs are assured.

- Developing alternative energy sources—synthetic fuels, biomass, solar, geothermal, and so forth—in as rapid a manner as is economically efficient. The potential for extensive international cooperation in these areas should be realized, especially with Japan, Europe, and selected developing countries.

- Filling the strategic petroleum reserve at the rate of 500,000 barrels a day, so as to reach the target figure of 1 billion barrels in 1985.

- Conduct energy-related U.S. foreign policy as follows:

  - The United States should continue to oppose, by an enhanced presence in the Middle East, the extension of Soviet influence or control in that area.

  - If and when the USSR becomes dependent on imported supply, accommodation of its needs should be sought within the existing international oil system. Actions by the USSR to obtain supply through direct or indirect intervention should be opposed.

  - The United States and its allies should carefully assess the implications of their growing dependence on imported energy supplies and services, in particular with regard to current and projected Western European dependence upon Soviet gas.

  - The United States should take necessary and appropriate measures, in cooperation with its allies, to enhance the credibility of allied defense commitments, particularly as they relate to both the security of the sea lines of communication upon which oil supply depends and the building of an effective rapid deployment force.

  - The United States should take the lead in establishing an adequate deterrent force as quickly as possible in the Middle East, with the consent and active support of the countries of that region, to deter the Soviet Union from directly or indirectly expanding its influence in the Middle East or obtaining control of access to Middle Eastern oil supplies.

  - NATO stockbuilding should be encouraged, and special wartime energy supply-sharing arrangements should be updated.

  - At Mexico's initiative, the United States should work more closely with Mexico to assure the development and supply of Mexican energy resources in a manner and at a rate that is in Mexico's best interest.

  - The same principle should be applied to Venezuela, as well as to the other nations of the hemisphere.

- The United States and Canada should proceed with cooperative efforts in the area of energy development and infrastructure rationalization, including mutually beneficial planning for
  emergencies and mutually advantageous trade-offs to minimize transportation costs. Such efforts should be pursued
  through the existing "informal" structure of relations, recognizing that considerable effort is required of both countries to
  prevent controversies over U.S. investment in the Canadian
  energy sector from retarding development of Canadian energy
  resources.

- The United States should recognize that the integration of the
  economic and political interests of oil exporters and importers
  is central to the acquisition of secure supplies at predictable
  prices. The major oil-importing countries should not discriminate against OPEC countries' investments as a means of furthering the integration of such interests.

- The United States should exercise a leadership role in assistance to oil-importing developing countries. In particular, the
  United States and other nations should contribute directly to
  the external financing of developing countries' energy development—including previously "marginal" reserves of oil, gas,
  coal, hydroelectric, and biomass energy. This should be done
  to the fullest extent possible with private capital. Additionally,
  enhanced incentives for direct OPEC financial assistance to the
  developing countries should be developed.

- The United States should also support unorthodox funding
  methods to assist developing countries, including private borrowing by the International Monetary Fund (IMF) to fund
  developing countries' energy development; a special "energy
  affiliate" of the World Bank; and special energy program priorities in the ongoing work of the InterAmerican Development
  Bank, the Asian Development Bank, and the African Development Bank.

• Encourage the European Community, Japan, and the United
  States to adopt concerted energy policies as follows:

- The United States, Europe, and Japan should take the necessary steps to assure that the International Energy Agency
  (IEA) emergency oil-sharing plan is credible, realistic, and

workable under emergency conditions. Continued close consultation with the private energy sector in this regard is indispensable.

- The United States, Europe, and Japan should cooperate to assure stronger conservation and efficient energy use policies being placed into effect. Energy pricing should encourage conservation and the development of alternatives to oil.

- Programs of research, development, demonstration, and commercial application of new energy technologies that lend themselves to international cooperation should be carried out aggressively with government and private sector support.

- The United States can and should assist the European countries and Japan in reducing their dependence on oil by becoming a major source of coal for energy purposes. In order to do this, the United States should adopt policies that facilitate the reliable and competitive export of coal, including more certain processes for environmental approvals and policies conducive to the development of the necessary infrastructure such as railroads, slurry pipelines, and port and harbor facilities.

- European and Japanese investment in U.S. coal properties should be continued and further encouraged. The IEA member governments should cooperate to develop a climate conducive to European and Japanese cooperation and investment in the production of synthetic fuels from U.S. coal, shale, etc.

- The United States should resolve the uncertainties created by its nuclear policy in a manner that will facilitate the use of increasing amounts of nuclear power in Europe and Japan as well as in the United States.

- The United States should take the initiative in formulating and carrying out programs with European countries and Japan whereby techniques of plant operation and management accumulated in such countries can be fully utilized to further enhance the safety and reliability of nuclear power generation.

- A regular means of exploring and discussing the entire range of energy issues among the European, Japanese, and U.S. private sectors should be instituted, involving representatives of related fields.

• The United States, Western Europe, and Japan should address the problem of the physical security of energy facilities as well as of supplies, reducing vulnerabilities that pose unacceptable risks to their collective economic viability.

I. INTRODUCTION AND PURPOSE

The world had structured its post–World War II economic development on the premise that oil supply, internationally, would be adequate, economic, and reliable. The world has learned that this premise is incorrect and that there are serious political and economic constraints on that supply. Consequently, the international energy problem today is oil.

Oil is a security problem. The denial of oil could undermine the political stability of nations and threaten the economic survival of the industrialized world. Moreover, there is no "quick fix" to this security problem. Oil importers remain extremely vulnerable to supply interruptions.

Oil is an economic problem. It involves vast transfers of wealth from consumers to producers. This transfer of wealth helps create conditions that make worldwide inflation more likely. Rich and poor nations are burdened, the latter more critically, by constraints on economic growth. Capital is concentrated in nations that until recently played little role in world financial markets.

Importantly, oil is a shared problem. Essentially, all the oil-importing developed and developing nations are vulnerable to supply interruptions and price increases. The developing nations suffer both the direct burdens of oil costs and the indirect effects of the collective vulnerability of more mature economies. Even among producers, oil is a source of internal instability and fears of outside intrusion.

In the end, the interests of all nations converge on resolving the energy, financial, economic, and security problems of dependence on oil. The thesis of the policy paper which forms Chapter I of this book is that the problems must and can be solved and that a high and intensive order of international collaboration and cooperation is essential to a solution.

The preconditions for a solution are clear enough—a credible and determined program to assure a more secure and economic supply of oil while simultaneously developing means to use less oil, develop alternate energy supply and use programs, and reduce vulnerability to oil supply interruptions.

No such program is possible without leadership from the United States. And no U.S. leadership is possible unless the United States has a strong and consistent domestic energy program that complements, and is complemented by, U.S. international policy.

Much of the discussion of energy issues in the United States since 1973 has focused on problems and courses of action within our borders. While there has been growing recognition that the oil problem is the result of foreign developments, there has been until recently little understanding of the international effects of U.S. action or inaction.

Such action—or inaction—will continue to be scrutinized by both consuming and producing countries abroad. To the extent that the United States reduces its imports of oil, it removes some element of uncertainty with respect to the availability of oil to other nations whose energy resource base is not as ample as that of the United States. To the extent that the United States develops and makes available alternative energy supplies and technology, such as coal, nuclear, and synthetic fuels, it provides an alternative to the importation of crude oil by all countries. To the extent that the United States develops and makes available alternate energy end use technologies, it provides broader supply choices. Moreover, such actions by the United States can redound to the advantage of its economy, balance of trade, and private institutions.

Changing the energy supply and use patterns of the United States and of the world is indeed a monumental task. These patterns were established, and can now be developed and changed, only incrementally—one day at a time. Changes are required in energy use in the industrial, commercial, and residential sectors and in the transportation sector—with the latter being the principle factor in creating demand for oil. In the United States, lead times on all major energy supply projects have been allowed to become inordinately long. They could be reduced significantly as a result of changed public policy. However, it takes time to do everything—for example, many years are needed to build nuclear power plants, coal production, transportation, and export facilities and even longer to develop a large synthetic fuels industry, all important alternatives to oil. It may well be that some of the policy initiatives—particularly in the areas of coal and nuclear energy—may not have a major effect on the world energy demand–supply balance in the 1980s because of the long lead times involved. But they can influence the attitudes taken by the oil-exporting countries during this period.

This does not mean that the United States cannot significantly improve its energy supply situation nor that it should seek accommodation with oil exporters or others from a position of weakness. Rather, U.S. energy and foreign policy goals will be served best by embarking decisively and efficiently on the road to enhanced energy supply security. The actions the United States takes—or fails to take—in this decade with respect to energy will have far-reaching effects on itself, on the position of the United States in the world, and on world order. Moreover, they will affect development not only in the industrial democracies that are our allies but in the less-developed Third World countries that are heavily dependent on imported oil as a source of energy.

The purpose of this chapter is to identify issues associated with U.S. international relationships on energy and to recommend actions for the United States and its allies to take in the 1980s. We begin in the following section with a very brief summary perspective on the character and magnitude of historic and prospective world energy production. It serves as a backdrop for the development and discussion of many of the issues that follow.

II. PERSPECTIVE ON FUTURE INTERNATIONAL ENERGY SUPPLY

Today's world energy problem is a political and economic one, not a technical one. However, looking ahead to the 1990s and beyond, adequate resources may not be made available to meet demand at relatively stable prices if steps are not taken now to develop new sources of energy supply. Decisions made in the 1980s will determine what energy will be available in the 1990s and in the early part of the twenty-first century.

There are important changes occurring in the energy demand of the developed and developing countries in response to energy price increases. The developed countries, with their advanced technology and their capital, can create a unit of economic growth with substantially less energy than can the developing countries. A recent World Energy Conference study estimated that the industrialized countries are now using about 60 percent as much energy per unit of economic growth as the developing countries and could further reduce their use of energy per unit of economic growth from 0.8 now to 0.4 by 2020. The study also estimated that the developing countries could reduce their use from the present average of 1.3 units of energy per unit of economic growth to 0.9 by 2020. Even if these levels of energy efficiency are realized, the overall demand for energy will continue to increase as a consequence of economic and population growth.

Table 1-1 shows historic potential world production of primary energy resources—coal, conventional oil, gas, unconventional oil, nuclear, hydro, solar, geothermal, biomass, etc., in quads. The difficulties in balancing demand and supply that result from geographic distribution of energy resources are well known. The production levels indicated in Table 1-1 are what reasonably could be expected, given a sense of urgency and the willingness and ability to produce at these levels. These levels do not provide for contingencies such as concerted supply interruption or wars. Coal and nuclear production and use could be increased if there were to be more favorable politi-

Table 1-1. Potential World Primary Energy Production $(quad^a = 10^{15} BTU)$

Resource	1972	1979	1985	2000	2020
Coal	66	85	106	191	294
Oil	115	145	139	125	106
Gas	46	54	92	157	121
Unconventional oil and gas	0	0	0	9	44
Nuclear	2	7	17	44	157
Hydraulic	14	15	20	33	73
Renewable, solar, geothermal, biomass	26	29	33	56	100
Total	267	335	407	615	895

a. 1 quad $\simeq$ 1 exajoule (10^{18} joules)
  1 trillion cubic feet of natural gas
  34 million tonnes of coal equivalent
  159 million barrels of oil

Source: World Energy Conference.

cal climates than those assumed in making these estimates. Also, the extent of the historic and potential production of renewable sources is noteworthy.

It is also noted that this forecast shows significantly reduced future dependence on conventional oil relative to other energy resources—principally as a function of anticipated depletion of the world's oil resources at competitive prices. Thus, reduced dependence on oil is required in any event as world energy demand increases. Consequently, the United States and other oil-importing countries should steadily seek reduced dependence on oil to ensure that the transition to alternate energy supply and use patterns is accomplished in an orderly and nondisruptive manner.

For some time the energy problem was perceived in the United States as being foreign in its origins but domestic in its solutions. It is now evident that there is essential interdependence for solutions among all the oil-consuming nations.

III. U.S. ENERGY POLICY AND INTERNATIONAL ENERGY RELATIONSHIPS

During the coming decade, countries that do not presently use energy as efficiently as possible or that have highly energy-intensive structural characteristics may well pay a considerable price unless they can improve the efficiency of their energy use. As energy resources become more expensive or if stable supplies of energy are not available, these countries will feel the effects on their economic growth and external balances, and, consequently, on their general economic strength and relative influence at the international level. This clearly applies to the United States.

A. International Impact of U.S. Energy Policy

Both the process of U.S. domestic decisionmaking and the substance of U.S. policy will have major implications for key allies' energy strategies and their confidence in American leadership, particularly since the United States will remain a substantial importer of crude oil through the 1980s. How the United States limits its vulnerability is as important as reducing dependence on petroleum imports from the Persian Gulf. As a result of its huge energy demands, America's choice of fuels, the timing and direction of investments, the extent to which domestic resources are exploited and available for export, the technologies and institutional entities used to carry out policies, and the geographical sources of imported energy—all will have substantial implications for other nations. America's choices will affect international patterns of competition, price relationships, resource development patterns, and relations among other nations.

B. Impact of International Developments on U.S. Energy Policy

U.S. energy policy (and markets) will be influenced by international developments—in particular, the rise of new claimants for oil and increasing uncertainty of access to oil supplies. During the 1970s, oil consumption among developing countries grew at an 8 percent average yearly rate, compared to a world oil consumption growth rate of less than 4 percent. Over the next decade, much of the increased consumption of oil will result from developing countries' and Communist nations' growth requirements.

Some part of the new claims for a greater share of oil in world trade will come from the OPEC oil exporters themselves, whose domestic requirements will grow considerably. Domestic demand of non-OPEC oil exporters (e.g., Mexico, Egypt, and China) also will be increasing significantly. The number of developing countries making sizeable demands upon international oil supply will increase over time to include more than present substantial claimants such as Brazil, India, the Republic of Korea, and Taiwan. (None of these is likely to put great strains upon international supply, with the possible exception of Brazil.) The strategic significance of new claims will most likely come from Soviet and, possibly, Chinese demands. Clearly, U.S. policy on the export of energy production technology could affect the amount of oil available to the world oil market, just as energy supply development anywhere in the world will tend to reduce demand for oil imports and ease pressures on the market. But it should be kept in mind that the internal requirements of a rapidly developing economic infrastructure within OPEC members will probably create added crude oil demands that exceed those of other non-oil-producing developing countries and the Soviet Union combined.

C. Impact of Nonenergy Issues

"Nonenergy" issues and policies may have a significant impact on the international energy situation.

1. *Trade Conflicts.* With regard to Japan, for example, there is a clear danger that an atmosphere of commercial friction may affect the willingness and extent of U.S. and European cooperation with Japan. The potential for this type of problem developing is made clear by juxtaposing Japan's $10 billion 1979 bilateral trade surplus with the United States against its oil-induced trade deficit of about $20 billion with the Middle East during the same year. Under current circumstances, some Japanese contend that there is little alternative but to earn necessary foreign exchange to pay for the oil imports through expanding sales of automobiles, color TVs, electronic products, and other manufactured goods to the United States and Europe.[1] One theoretical alternative would be for Japan to increase its trade in arms and military supplies in order to permit reduced trade in consumer goods—an alternative that neither the Japanese nor the United States finds attractive. No alternative market for consumer goods is in immediate sight, as long as the European markets remain less accessible to Japanese goods than the U.S. market. Resources-rich developing countries' demand for these products is not very large. Consequently, as Japan's reliance on Middle Eastern oil may not decline significantly during the remainder of the century, it does not seem likely that the difficulties of the bilateral trade relationship can be easily resolved. Probably the most significant step that the United States could take to ameliorate the situation would be to collaborate with Japan more fully and effectively in developing alternatives to oil for both nations.

2. *Regional Conflicts.* Significantly, those countries that have the ability to increase oil production substantially are predominantly located in the Middle East, already the source of 58 percent of oil in world trade. Thus, U.S. policy with regard to critical political issues in the Middle East, such as the Arab–Israeli dispute, the resurgence

---

1. One member of the Committee comments: "I do not agree that Japan has 'little alternative' or is limited to the alternative outlined here. It is not necessary for Japan always to be in current account surplus position."

of Islamic radicalism, and disputes between producers, can affect production and prices for much of the oil that will be exported in the 1980s.

3. *Strategic Conflicts.* Some U.S. government experts see the USSR eventually becoming a major oil importer and thus posing a threat because of its consequent larger interest in controlling the Middle East. This is indeed one way the Soviet Union could create dangers for the West. The Soviet Union is about ten years behind the United States in oil exploration and production technology. It is argued that to the extent that relatively early and significant entry of the USSR on the world oil market as a major oil importer is foreseen, it could presumably be useful to modify U.S. legislation to permit the sale and licensing of U.S. oil exploration and production technology to the USSR, thereby enhancing Soviet oil supply self-sufficiency and postponing import needs. Linkages for this change in U.S. policy could be negotiated for modifications of Soviet policy favorable to peace and nonaggressive patterns of conduct conducive to world order.

However, another scenario exists in which the USSR will remain self-sufficient in petroleum but become an even greater than expected supplier of energy to Western Europe. The increased dependency of Europe on the USSR could result from OPEC actions or the actions of certain Arab states. The threat posed by the USSR would then be one of a supplier using economic power to checkmate efforts at mobilizing Western nations on issues affecting Soviet interests. The evolving nature of relations among the United States, Europe, and the Soviet Union will be of importance with regard to West European imports of gas, enrichment services, and electricity from the Soviet Union. In this case, the United States and its allies must seriously weigh the conflicting imperatives of diversifying energy supply and preserving Western security in the longer term.

Strategic relationships in Southeast Asia may also assume an increased importance as relations among China, the USSR, and the United States affect exploration for and trade in petroleum. At present, Indonesia, Brunei, Malaysia, and China make available approximately one and a half million barrels per day (b/d) of crude oil, much of it destined for Japan and essential to the supply security of that country.

4. *Population Growth.* Consideration of the demand side of the energy equation is too often restricted to extrapolations of existing growth rates for various countries or regions or to strategies by which the major fuels might be conserved or demand reduced. Little or no attention is devoted to yet another cause of the increase of future demand—namely, the inexorable increase in human population worldwide. A recent major study[2] by the International Institute for Applied Systems Analysis does conclude, however, that global energy needs can be met over the next fifty years. The study finds that during that period the worldwide population will double to 8 billion, and even with only modest economic growth and extensive conservation, global energy demand is likely to expand to three or four times today's level. The study's not so good news is that to meet the growing worldwide demand, full use of all available energy sources—oil and gas, solar, renewables, and nuclear—will be required. Dirtier and more expensive fossil resources and vast quantities of synfuels will have to be developed, as well as both large-scale solar plants and nuclear breeder reactors. Small-scale solar plants and renewable resources will play a growing role, too, but can only satisfy a modest fraction of the total demand during the next half century.

D. International Energy Supply Security

Since the latter 1960s, when the French called to the attention of the OECD Oil Committee that the United States could no longer be the emergency supplier of crude oil to the allies—as it had been in 1956 and 1967—the question of energy supply security has focused on oil and on international arrangements for sharing available supply. After the 1973–1974 supply emergency, definition of such an arrangement and the commitments to be made regarding stockpiles and standby rationing plans were formulated through the newly

2. The principal goal of the study was to identify strategies for the transition from a globe reliant on oil and gas to one served by sustainable sources of energy. But the original expectation that this could be accomplished within the fifty-year horizon of the study turned out to be too optimistic. Instead, the IIASA group found that there will have to be two transitions. The first, from relatively cheap and clean conventional sources of oil and gas to more expensive and "dirtier" unconventional ones, will continue through 2030. The second, to the essentially infinite supplies of solar, nuclear, and renewable energy, will not be completed until late in the next century. But such a system would be sufficient to sustain the then anticipated global population of about 10 billion persons for many centuries.

founded International Energy Agency (IEA). France, ironically, has elected not to join the IEA. The IEA's emergency plan commits member nations to maintenance of ninety days of imports reserve, a stringent program of reducing consumption, and an IEA-wide plan for allocation of whatever volume of oil is available in the event of an emergency.

In view of the continuing and sometimes rising tensions in the Middle East and in view of the many potential sources of disruption in Middle East oil production, it is exceedingly important that the American and allied dependence on imported oil not cause them to conclude that they must act suddenly with force in the region for reason of a lack of oil reserves or because of public psychological or panic reactions in the event of emergency. It is critical, therefore, that the United States and other of its principal allies have—and soon—oil reserves in addition to IEA commitments.

For example, there are commercially held stocks in the United States and elsewhere that, properly managed, can help buffer an emergency. These stocks are not large enough to accommodate major or extended supply disruptions. The IEA has recently taken action in an attempt to strengthen the cooperative actions among IEA member countries in the use of stocks for disruptions short of an emergency as defined in the International Energy Program established in 1974.

There is, however, some concern about the suggestion that some "mechanism" is needed to manage problems that may arise with respect to shortages of oil before the IEA trigger level of 7 percent has been reached. Carried to an extreme, this proposition would suggest that the international oil market should be managed by some mechanism other than market economics during any period of uncertainty. It is recognized that there is great uncertainty in the international oil market even under what we now call "normal circumstances" with respect to both supply availability and price level. A strong case can be made for avoiding premature intervention by governments in the workings of the market. This is not to suggest that governments do not have both a right and an obligation to inform themselves, through consultations with industry, of trends and events in the international oil market. The market, however, has proved capable in the past of handling supply disruptions that, had governments intervened, might have been worse. Certainly the experience in the United States with respect to allocation and controls is less than convincing evidence of the worth of government intervention. The

oil industry has been, and will continue to be, responsive to governmental concerns with respect to shortfalls of international oil supply,
bearing in mind that continuity of supply is in the industry's interest
as well.

The duration of a cutback is difficult to estimate, though a reasonable maximum limit for a reduction to be considered "short term"
would be sixty to ninety days. This is the period of imports that all
IEA members have targeted their stockpiles to offset. Since cutbacks
are likely to be less than 100 percent, stockpiles of even sixty to
ninety days can, with reduced consumption, provide security for
longer periods.

Moreover, the ability of the major oil exporters to cooperate successfully and sustain a large cutback in their exports is also brought
into question. The consensus that would be necessary in a large cutback is lacking among the member nations of OPEC and OAPEC.
Furthermore, the sharp price rises that importers could cause in their
scramble to obtain supply could be sufficient inducement for some
exporters to break ranks and reduce the severity of the shortfall.
Some major exporting countries have played an important role in
moderating price movements by deliberately producing at levels
higher than justified by their needs for domestic economic development and accumulation of surplus investment funds. This—plus large
inventories and cooperation among importers to draw down stocks—
helped prevent the shutdown of oil production in Iraq and Iran from
leading to runaway prices and a wild scramble for supplies by the
importing countries.

E. U.S. Options in an International Supply Shortage

The United States is the largest oil importer and the only one of the
allies to have global commitments. The United States, therefore, has
particular interest in developing a viable response to short-term supply shortages. While many other industrial nations in Europe, and
Japan, have a higher vulnerability to oil export reductions because of
their proportionately higher imports as a percentage of supply, the
ability of the industrial world as a whole to cope with supply reductions rests to a great extent on the ability of the United States to
cope in a time of shortage.[3] Nevertheless, the United States has failed

---

3. This discussion does not distinguish between types of short-term shortages. One
type of "shortage" can come about as a result of a reduction in oil production such as

conspicuously to develop and prepare agreed upon countermeasures to an oil embargo threat.

Several options do exist to reduce vulnerability to short-term shortages, including (1) accelerated filling of the Strategic Petroleum Reserve (SPR); (2) maintaining a high level of commercial stocks; (3) a combination of (1) and (2); and (4) participating fully in the IEA's oil-sharing program, the International Energy Program (IEP). It should be noted that all four options are mutually compatible.

The one option not considered acceptable is for the United States to continue following its present course—which is only slowly filling the SPR. At the present rate it would take about ten years to reach a security storage level of one billion barrels. It should be recognized that the ability of the United States to absorb a cutback in supplies is, in fact, less than it was five or ten years ago. Our vulnerability has increased rather than decreased and will continue to do so.

The SPR can protect the domestic economy, allow time for any necessary demand management actions to become effective, preserve military strength, and permit greater flexibility in foreign policy options. But the act of creating a Strategic Petroleum Reserve creates its own set of problems and issues. How it is to be paid for is important. Experience over the last several years, combined with the immediate outlook, demonstrate that paying for the SPR is an unusually difficult problem.[4] Also, it cannot be filled at any given time without due consideration being given both to the level of tension created in international oil markets and to the attitudes of major oil-exporting countries. Attempts to fill the reserve at a constant rate would undoubtedly lead to instances where upward price movements might be exacerbated and instances where the more cooperative oil-producing nations might become alienated. On the other hand, trying to fill the SPR at anything other than a constant rate may never get the job done.[5] An acquisition policy for the SPR requires sound and flexible management that works in close consultation and coopera-

---

resulted at the time of the Iranian revolution. Another type of "shortage" can come about as a result of a politically motivated embargo such as that in 1973–74. A third type of "shortage" can come about as a result of war or terrorist activity.

4. One member of the Committee comments: "Since the SPR is part of our national security program, it should be considered like any other national security asset, be that a ballistic missile, aircraft carrier, or submarine. Since the reserve benefits all Americans and contributes to our national security, it should be built and maintained in the same way that we build and maintain other national security systems—through general revenues."

5. One Committee member comments that this sentence should read "will never get the job done."

tion with those exporting nations whose interests are also served by having the United States in a strong leadership position. None of the foregoing should be allowed to hamper positive, strong action on a high fill rate for the SPR.

The United States has additional options:

- Prepare, in concert with its allies, credible means of intervention to protect international lines of supply.

- Reexamine to what extent commercial inventory should be regarded as a reserve beyond that provided by the SPR and what incentives could be provided to increase, maintain, and manage it.

- Review again the elements for an allocation program that could greatly extend the life of an SPR and those commercial inventories that could be regarded as reserves.[6]

- Improve the coordination of the draw-down and build-up of inventories by consuming nations during periods of relatively balanced supply and demand.

IV.   ISSUES FOR THE 1980s

A.   International Security Issues

1. *Imbalance of Dependence and Commitments.*   The United States, Canada, Japan, and Western Europe share a common interest in access to oil, particularly in the Middle East. Not only U.S. interests are at stake. Both Europe and Japan are deeply dependent upon the Persian Gulf region. Yet there has not been an assumption by them of obligations commensurate with the stakes. At present, the United States is bearing virtually all of the responsibilities and burdens. This cannot continue without incurring the risk of alienation within the alliances. Approximately 45 percent of the crude oil exported from the Persian Gulf goes to Europe. In general, European interests in the area have come to be dominated by "economic" considerations, although each of these countries has a particular set of vulnerabilities

---

6. A member of the Committee comments: "We strongly support the concept of a 'white market' coupon-rationing system for gasoline as one means of demand management in an emergency, because we cannot envision an SPR ever being large enough to encompass all contingencies, and we cannot envision an emergency situation ever being so clearly defined as to allow, while it is in effect, a determination of its magnitude and duration.

and concerns. Here again, economic and energy interests have not been matched by political and military commitments. The recent conflict between Iran and Iraq highlights these concerns. The following brief survey illustrates this imbalance.

a. *West Germany.* In 1979, West Germany averaged 1.7 million b/d imports from Mideast producers or 80 percent of its total imports. Germany also plans extensive energy (natural gas) links with the Soviet Union and views this as a necessary and important diversification of its energy sources. Despite recent changes in policy with regard to its naval posture, West Germany's defense concerns continue to focus on Central Europe.

b. *Britain.* Britain continues to limit its role in the gulf region. Its oil interests in the Middle East are rather less than those of most other Western European countries. Its imports from OPEC producers in 1979 were reduced, primarily because of its North Sea oil resources. Britain, however, continues to have an interest in obtaining Middle Eastern oil for its major oil companies' worldwide commitments.

c. *France.* France imported some 2.2 million b/d from the Middle East in 1979, accounting for 87.6 percent of its oil imports. A central aim of French energy policy has been to reduce the role of oil as an energy source from nearly 60 percent of all energy consumed to less than 40 percent by 1990 and possibly 25 percent by 2000. An accelerated nuclear program represents a primary means for achieving this reduction.

France, which is not a member of the IEA, is the only European country that has a forward military and naval presence in the Indian Ocean and operates from bases in Mayotte and Djibouti at the entrance to the Red Sea. In addition, France has pursued a close bilateral relationship with Algeria, Iraq, and Saudi Arabia to assure its own oil supply.

d. *Japan.* Japan is a nation almost totally dependent on imported oil. In 1979, it imported 4.2 million b/d from Mideast producers. Recent Japanese efforts to establish special relationships with producers in the Middle East have been intense but unsuccessful. The high Japanese stake in Middle Eastern oil is not matched by a comparable economic or political presence in the area. Japan has been actively seeking new sources of supply in Southeast Asia and China. There may, therefore, be increasing room to develop concerted U.S.-Japanese policies with regard to economic and security assistance in the Mideast, as well as in the Western Pacific and Southeast Asia.

2. *Supply Security.* Hopes for a coordinated oil importers' strategy to cope with the security dimension of their oil situation have been frustrated by numerous political factors. While it is true that a resolution of certain political problems (e.g., the Arab–Israeli dispute) would not automatically secure supplies of oil at predictable prices, the Arab–Israeli issue does endanger oil supply and interferes with cooperation among the Western allies. U.S.–Soviet competition in the area, coupled with inter-Arab rivalries, further complicate allied cooperation.

The continued dependence of Europe and Japan on the United States for overall strategic deterrence and for a critical role in regional defense remains an important factor. There are, however, fragmentary signs of an emerging division of labor—and, importantly, the requisite political will—among the United States, Britain, France, Germany, and now Japan.[7] This involves allied responses to political and military instabilities in the Persian Gulf, the Mediterranean, and Africa, partly in response to events in Iran and Afghanistan, as well as to concerns about the long-term stability of some of the major oil producers.

It is clear that an expanded role for non-U.S. NATO forces in the Mideast and Indian Ocean regions would go far in demonstrating the oil importers' intentions to reduce the vulnerability surrounding oil for their economies and to reflect a united concern about the need for stability in the region. Short of this, a strengthening of Japanese and NATO Europe defenses would contribute to overall security by allowing an increased commitment of U.S. forces to Mideast defense. Importantly, the concern in Arab states with regard to a unilateral U.S. presence in the area might be allayed with increasing evidence of allied involvement.

B. Bilateral Issues in the Energy Context

1. *Preferential Agreements.* If, as seems likely, uncertainties with regard to oil supply continue and perhaps even multiply through this decade, importers are likely to search for preferential bilateral

---

7. See recent Atlantic Council *Policy Papers* on "The Common Security Interests of Japan, the United States and NATO"; "The Soviet Merchant Marine: Economic and Strategic Challenge to the West"; "Securing the Seas: Soviet Naval Challenge and Western Alliance Options"; and "The Credibility of the NATO Deterrent."

arrangements regarding volumes and prices that cover many areas beyond financial guarantees. Both as a consequence of the diminished role of the international oil companies and of the very complex nature of such arrangements, government-to-government deals may proliferate, although it is unclear whether such deals have resulted in lower prices or better assurance of supplies. There is scarcely a major importer that has not attempted such deals—the United States with the Soviet Union, Saudi Arabia, and Iran; France with Algeria, Iraq, and Saudi Arabia; Italy with Libya; Germany with Iran, Saudi Arabia, and Libya.

It has been the common experience that such arrangements are generally short lived. Moreover, the nonoil "costs" are usually high. The very pursuit of preferential agreements can set ally against ally, corroding security arrangements to their common disadvantage. While it may have been historically inevitable that the United States would be involved in some preferential agreements, the point must be to minimize possible conflict among allies and to recognize that energy supply is only one, albeit important, element in a broad range of bilateral interests. Preferential agreements over the long run are not helpful.

2. *Mexico.* The U.S. approach to energy relations with Mexico is an increasingly important question. The argument for package industrial deals, a quid pro quo based on immigration and trade concessions and massive technology transfer in return for more oil and gas, rests on the questionable assumption that U.S. policy holds the key to Mexican energy development and availability of oil to the United States. The United States has two primary objectives with respect to its energy relations with Mexico:

1. That Mexico maximize its oil exports into international trade in a manner that is consistent with Mexico's national objectives; and

2. That Mexico develop progressively with political and economic stability.

The numerous trade and social issues affecting bilateral relations between Mexico and the United States require more focused attention regardless of energy issues. It is far from evident that explicit bilateral trade-offs are appropriate or effective, particularly in light of Mexican sensitivity in this area. Moreover, it is unclear that such approaches are necessary if Mexican interest alone will lead to higher production.[8] Nevertheless, the feasibility should be explored of U.S. financial and technical support to help Mexico develop its solar, hydropower, and geothermal resources so that exported oil is exchanged for domestic renewable energy production capability.

3. *Venezuela.* The development of Venezuela's Orinoco Tar Belt has attracted considerable attention as a potential means of alleviating oil shortages and enhancing supply security. That Venezuela is a traditional U.S. supplier encourages such thinking within the United States, even though Venezuela has not in the past been accorded more favorable treatment as a "reliable supplier." However, Orinoco development will entail great expense, long lead times, the production of very heavy oil, and the problem of refining the oil in Venezuela.

Interest in oil from the Orinoco is not confined to the United States. Venezuela has signed a number of agreements with foreign countries for technical cooperation in the development of the Orinoco Tar Belt. France and West Germany have entered into agreements for studies on processing the crudes found in the region. Potentially important is a technical assistance agreement with Canada.

The United States and Venezuela have entered into an agreement for R&D and technical exchange, personnel exchanges, equipment testing, and joint technical and research projects in oil and other energy areas. There is considerable pressure in the United States to develop these into a "special relationship" with Venezuela.

Venezuela's view of its national interest appears now to recommend a cautious approach to Orinoco development. U.S. policymakers must ask what benefits would result from pushing for more rapid development in light of long-term mutual interests, including, as in the Mexican case, economic and political stability. The United

---

8. One member of the Committee comments: "This paper realistically recognizes that Mexican energy exports, regardless of destination, benefit both the United States and our OECD allies. However, Mexican energy production policies face and/or worsen a host of economic, social, and political problems of an internal nature for them. Thus, consideration of U.S. policy toward Mexico should be addressed in the broadest possible context, aimed not only at resolving the many outstanding issues (e.g., immigration, water rights, and trade), but also considered in terms of assisting Mexico in overcoming its problems of industrialization and urbanization. Such an approach admittedly would be motivated by concerns broader than energy production. But such cooperation would seem to be prerequisite to Mexico maximizing production."

States should examine the political implications of backing out secure Venezuelan oil from the East Coast. Basic decisions are required on this and the related subject of refinery policy.

One area in which U.S. cooperation with Venezuela—and Mexico—can yield significant mutual benefit is in promoting the development of new oil, gas, coal, and nonconventional energy sources in the hemisphere and in assisting energy-poor countries in Central and South America in paying for imported oil. Venezuelan and Mexican initiatives in these areas may encourage and provide a means for constructive U.S. participation in regional undertakings of this sort.

4. *Canada.* Canadian supply currently offers only modest help to the United States. For some time to come, Canada may continue to have surplus natural gas available for export to the United States in amounts that are of significance to some regional U.S. requirements. In the East, there is the possibility of marginal imports of hydroelectric power from Quebec and Newfoundland, and from New Brunswick and, perhaps, Ontario, some possibility of nuclear-generated electricity imports. In the future, it is possible to conceive of synthetic petroleum from Alberta oil sands plants or liquified natural gas and crude oil from the Beaufort Sea, the Arctic Islands, or offshore East Coast discoveries, should they be large enough. The facts are, however, that Canada's own efforts to build the oil self-sufficiency it should have at this stage make such possibilities remote. The major supply side benefit to the United States of greater Canadian self-sufficiency would be to back out the oil currently imported into eastern Canada into the world market, thus increasing the total supply available to other consumers, including the United States.

On the other hand, there should be real, if not large, possibilities for cooperation in making the most effective use of whatever supplies the two North American neighbors have. Examples lie in the kind of interchange that has, in the recent past, directed Canadian crude oil to the western and north central United States in exchange for supplies to eastern Canada, to the mutual transportation advantage of both countries. Other possibilities lie in joint arrangements and even joint facilities for emergency stockpiles plus agreements ahead of time on the sharing of supplies and facilities to such joint advantage during an emergency supply situation. R&D cooperation on synthetic fuels could build upon complementary needs in this area. In considering and developing such cooperative arrangements, the United States must be careful not to attach the label of "continentalism," a concept strongly opposed in Canada, to what is essentially an incremental and functional approach to cooperation.

There are, of course, other concerns expressed by Canada about U.S. actions. One of these is possible environmental damage by "acid rain" thought to result from emissions from U.S. industrial centers. Cooperative discussions are being held, and the United States has instituted an extensive research program to learn more about acid rain.

Recent efforts by the Canadian federal government to reduce the foreign share in the ownership of Canadian energy companies have generated considerable controversy in U.S.–Canadian relations.[9] Energy-related investment issues may become disruptive. Moreover, the effect of this Canadian policy is to reduce its long-term supply capability by causing a reduction in new investment in resource exploration and development.

Energy issues are part of a broader pattern of U.S.–Canadian relations in which both convergent and divergent interests are present. In light of the prospect of Canada's declining near-term exports and the substantial financial requirements for developing new sources, energy will become a significantly more important issue on the bilateral agenda.

U.S.–Canadian energy relations will face a number of challenges in the 1980s. These include (1) adjusting to supply problems in the oil and gas sectors and the integration of new supply from unconventional and "frontier" sources; (2) taking maximum advantage of the complementary nature of U.S. and Canadian transportation needs; and (3) promoting the efficient utilization of productive capacity.

9. One member of the Committee comments: "In recent months, the Canadian government has proclaimed new energy policies that limit oil prices to levels substantially below world markets; restrict foreign investment in energy; and seriously disadvantage and jeopardize, without compensation, investment previously made by Americans in Canadian energy development. By keeping their domestic oil prices below world levels, Canada is directly subsidizing their exports of energy-intensive products and petrochemicals. This violates the spirit and letter of GATT (General Agreements on Tariffs and Trade) by giving discriminatory promotion to Canadian export goods. The United States had faced similar indictment by the EC, but now has deregulated oil prices. Canada's oil policy is contrary to the International Energy Agreement and OECD investment guidelines, which bind Canada to reducing dependence on foreign oil supplies and to an open investment climate. Furthermore, their retroactive acquisition, without compensation, of a 25 percent interest in oil and gas leases may violate international law.

5. *Japan.* As the two largest industrial democracies, with economies dependent on large amounts of energy, the manner in which
Japan and the United States cope with their changing energy supply
situations will be of great consequence to world structure and order.
Between the two countries there are close economic and strategic
ties, and a commonality of interests in the Pacific region and around
the world.

Assessments of policy must recognize that the energy circumstances of the United States and Japan differ in a number of ways:

- Japan has virtually no domestic oil or gas and very limited coal
  and other energy resources. The United States is rich in domestic
  energy resources, except for oil.

- Oil constitutes a larger proportion of Japan's energy consumption
  than is the case for the United States.

- Industry accounts for almost twice the proportion of energy consumption in Japan as that of the U.S. industrial sector.

- Japan consumes markedly less energy per capita than does the
  United States.

- Japan has a significantly more aggressive policy favoring liquefied
  natural gas (LNG) imports.

- As Japan has essentially no domestic uranium resources, the early
  development of the breeder reactor is of significantly greater
  importance to Japan than it is perceived to be to the United
  States.

Since both countries are large oil importers, there are only limited
steps that either can take on a bilateral basis in the short term to
reduce the vulnerability of the other to the instabilities of the oil
market. Each must aggressively pursue domestic policies and actions
that reduce oil use through conservation and substitution of more
plentiful energy sources. In that process, they will, in effect, help
each other.

A more attractive solution over the longer term requires programs
to facilitate substitutes for oil. In this case, U.S. policies and practices can be helpful to Japan and, at the same time, serve U.S. objectives. As a potential supplier of coal and uranium and related technology products and services, the United States has resources that

Japan needs to reduce its energy vulnerability and that would help preserve a unity of purpose that is in the interest of both countries. For its part, Japan may be able to contribute significantly to R&D on nuclear energy and synthetic fuels and to supply capital inputs for the development of U.S. coal and shipping infrastructure coupled with long-term supply contracts.

Any discussion of relationships with Japan must emphasize Japan's capital and technological base, a base that has permitted outstanding economic growth because it was unencumbered by the needs for investment in defense and energy supply.

6. *U.S. Energy Relations With the Oil-producing States of the Persian Gulf.* The Arab oil-producing states of the Gulf — Saudi Arabia, Iraq, Kuwait, the United Arab Emirates, Bahrain, Qatar, and Oman — produce more than 50 percent of total world oil exports and control about 45 percent of proven world oil reserves. Aside from their role in the international oil markets, the Arab oil-producing states of the gulf are significant to the United States (and other nations of the world) for other important reasons. In the economic realm, they have become major importers of goods and services and major participants in the international financial market. In the strategic realm, the Arab states of the gulf are significant not only because of their oil resources, but also because of their geographic location. In the political realm, the Arab states of the gulf significantly affect U.S. relations with the Soviet Union, Europe, and Israel, as well as with the developing countries generally.

The United States and other industrial countries have been spending political capital in efforts to persuade the Arab oil producers of the gulf to increase their production targets.[10] Such efforts are not likely to have lasting influence on long-run oil price and production levels; moreover, they tend to create the presumption among the producers that a favor is being granted. And even if production levels were increased, they would be of questionable reliability.

Instead, the United States and other industrialized countries should continue to pursue domestic and international energy policies

10. One member of the Committee comments: "I disagree with this. If you mean spend political capital in ad hoc sporadic bursts twice a year that appeal for price moderation without pursuing sound policies toward security in the Middle East and toward energy at home, I agree. But it is definitely in our interest and worth some political capital to make it consistently clear that high oil production is necessary to prevent a third price crisis and to give the cushion to fill the SPR."

that reduce dependence for oil on the gulf producers and foreign security policies that give first priority to reducing the sources of risk that threaten to bring about sudden, sharp reductions in output. In its relations with the oil producers of the gulf, the United States should give primary emphasis to reducing the potential sources of instability. This may mean taking a forward security position in the region. Giving a high priority to risk reduction in the Middle East—in conjuction with reducing reliance on Middle East oil—is likely to be the most effective means of reducing vulnerability during the 1980s.

There may be in the United States an almost discriminatory lack of balance with regard to the legitimate aspirations and concerns of some nations of the Persian Gulf (the paramount example would be Saudi Arabia). Clearly, their future is inseparable from their one asset of real value to the world—oil. They must proceed with plans to evolve into modern industrialized states, and they have a right, if they choose, to make that evolution consistent with their cultural heritage. The social, political, and economic problems of their development, as well as their need to preserve and maintain their independence and security, should be as important as those of the OECD nations and other exporters such as Mexico and Venezuela. Some of these nations are today producing at rates well above those that are in consonance with the long-term objectives of their societies, thereby increasing the risk of social instability, in return for financial assets of somewhat dubious quality, which can only be held in OECD nations and are subject to the erosion of inflation.

The leading nations in the region recognize that their future is tied to the West, and to some extent, they must accommodate their pricing and production decisions with their interest in the political, economic, and security strength of the West. In turn, the West should recognize that these nations welcome the development of alternative energy supplies and conservation, since these would reduce pressure on the oil reserves that are their only real link to the future. Neither the United States nor the other industrialized countries will find a basis for agreement on every political and economic issue with these states, but no one would expect all the members of OECD to agree on every issue. There should be a greater tone of mutual resolution for mutual benefit over a range of issues, rather than speaking in a tone of confrontation over the one issue of oil supply. In the context of Saudi Arabia, the U.S. agenda is broader than simply being involved in a special bilateral relationship for the sake of oil supply to the United States. If, out of such a relationship, a higher level of production emerges, it is not in the context of supply to the United States, but rather in terms of an increment to total world supply.

C. Multilateral Cooperation

The multilateral approach is useful, whether the issue is one of limiting OECD member country oil imports, expanding supply, conservation, diversification, developing alternative energy sources, cooperation among oil companies, or contingency planning for an anticipated or real crisis in the Persian Gulf. In the economic realm, balance of payments, petrodollar recycling, restraint of protection-ist reactions, maintenance of international financial stability, and responses to the energy-related economic problems of the developing countries may all be approached on a multilateral basis. If a multi-lateral approach were to be fully useful, consultation among oil com-panies—now prohibited by U.S. anti-trust laws and the Treaty of Rome—would need to be reinstituted. Consultation among oil com-panies should occur only for a specific, defined, and agreed upon purpose, as is the case, for example, with company advisory groups to the IEA on emergency measures.

However, the prospects for extending the multilateral approach to a potential importer–exporter dialogue are strictly limited. It is important that there be a broad and continuous dialogue with respect to ongoing relations generally, including longer term histori-cal, cultural, and developmental interests, as well as such specific areas of current mutual concern as technology flows, the investment of surplus OPEC funds, and pricing and production policies. It is doubtful, however, that the IEA, OECD, or other "importer" group-ings are cohesive enough to negotiate. It is doubtful, as well, that OPEC represents such a cohesive body (i.e., it does not retain suffi-cient control over price or production). Moreover, if the exporters were to become a more cohesive unit, presumably it would not be in the best interest of the importers.

D. Incentives to Producers

It is often argued that importers should provide incentives to close the gap between producers' preferred production rates and their maximum sustainable capacities, while avoiding the dislocations and potential instability flowing from development at too rapid a pace. It is also useful to encourage "surge," or excess, standby capacities to meet emergencies. OPEC production at levels above that which each member country considers essential to satisfy domestic revenue needs will reflect the responsiveness of the West and Japan to the producers' economic, social, and political objectives.

Unfortunately, however, demands that OPEC members have enunciated cannot be met easily by the industrialized world. For example, "technology transfer" is an insistent and usually oversimplified demand by oil-exporting nations. Four problems can be noted. First is the adaptability of particular technologies to the indigenous needs of the receiving country. Second is the willingness of the receiving countries to accept the presence of foreign managerial talent or the patience to wait to train its own scientists, engineers, and technicians. Third, technology is usually not something a government can give away—it is owned by the private sector and thus cannot be a gift. Fourth, how can the value of transferred "technology" be equated with the price of oil? Japan's and the West's ability to respond to demands for technology transfer is therefore limited (although their arguments are often not accepted by the producers as valid).

Some of the more pressing problems faced by OPEC nations cannot be alleviated by Western and Japanese help. Moreover, ideologically undesirable exposure to Western practices and traditions cannot be avoided if the OPEC countries seek to develop balanced, industrial economies. Industrialization inevitably causes considerable social change and dislocation. The adaptability of political structures to cope with these challenges cannot easily be determined by outsiders.

Over the long term, the essential solution to the problem of obtaining continuous and adequate oil supply at predictable prices lies in the fullest possible integration of the economic and financial interests of oil exporters and importers. This requires an increased sensitivity on both sides to the other's domestic demands and constraints. Interdependence is a fact of the 1980s, yet the need for greater cooperation has not yet been fully accepted.

E. Recycling

There is a growing realization, particularly among Arabian oil producers, that the rate of return on their financial assets has not kept up either with the price increases of their imports or with those of their own exports. A continuation of this trend is thought to be reinforcing the conclusion by some OPEC nations that the long-term economic interests of their countries might be better served through reductions in oil production, with more oil remaining in the ground. This conclusion could be further reinforced if investments in national and international financial markets become subject to greater political risk.

Attractive investment opportunities exist in the long-term sector of the market, and it has been largely due to the oil producers' own high liquidity preference that they have not made full use of these. Increased opportunities for investment in the developing as well as in the industrialized nations will contribute to a fuller integration of the interests of importers and exporters and recycle funds to deficit countries in need and hopefully channel them into productive uses, including alternative energy development. This, in turn, could contribute greatly to overall supply security and political stability.

F. Diversification of Sources

The attempt by individual major oil importers to diversify sources of supply away from the Middle East is of considerable importance, although in the short run, their success could be at the expense of increasing the dependence of other nations on the region. Nevertheless, efforts to increase the number of suppliers is and should continue to be a key ingredient of importing governments' energy policies. The United States and other developed countries, through their private or public oil companies, can further the proliferation of "marginal" producers—particularly the developing countries— through the application of oil and gas exploration and production technology as well as by encouraging private and public investment in the development of new energy resources.

G. Allocation

The importing nations are moving into an uncertain decade in which there will be not only a possibility of sudden cutoffs, but also the possibility of recurring shortages of crude oil. At a minimum, oil-importing nations will have to explore realistically whether it is possible to reach agreement on how to share the given volume of oil available. Arrangements that allow access may prove preferable to attempts to allocate shortages, given the complex set of economic and political variables that must be integrated into the framework of an international sharing program.

The IEA formula for dealing with emergency shortfalls is extremely complex. There has not yet been an emergency that triggered the system. But it may be the most thoroughly tested deterrent mechanism outside the military sphere for coordinating an international response to an emergency. However, there may also be a need for more effective consultation to deal with smaller disruptions short of the trigger.

Apart from the momentary respite of a huge oil buffer in the hands of Western countries (in 1980), there is the continuing change in the terms of crude oil contracts and the structure of the international petroleum logistical system. The proliferation of bilateral oil agreements may be rendering the IEA concept less secure.

This is a key development affecting the workability and credibility of current IEA contingency plans. According to a recent IEA study, as of the end of 1980, some 32 percent of IEA member state crude oil imports were not available to be switched readily in the event of an emergency. This results from contract terms that impose a variety of exporters' restrictions, including destination.

H. Energy in the Developing Countries

The developing countries are facing severe energy supply and payments problems that will seriously threaten their overall development. It is further evident that these problems are of an order of magnitude more serious than those of the developed world. In addition to oil-related problems, the developing countries have large populations that do not have access to conventional energy systems and require development of dispersed energy supply for rural areas. Clearly, it is in the American interest to take action, directly or through multilateral institutions, to assist in solving the energy problems of developing countries—particularly in light of the potentially disastrous implications of severely curtailed development for political stability in these countries. But it is also necessary for the developing countries to take steps. For example, many developing countries encourage energy consumption—and in particular, oil consumption—by maintaining price controls. On the production side, some developing countries with oil potential will not, for ideological reasons, allow foreign oil companies to develop their oil.

In reflecting upon its own energy security needs, the United States must be aware of the reality that over time its most dependable and secure external supplies of energy have come from its nearest neighbors in Latin America and the Caribbean. In times of world crisis, including the 1973 OPEC Arab embargo, OAS member states have kept their energy supplies flowing to the United States. It is therefore important that in establishing its global energy arrangements, the United States recognize the unique linkages that bind it to Latin America and that require that it forge a broad, multilateral policy of hemispheric cooperation not only for energy production but also concerning the development agenda of its neighbors.

Venezuela and Mexico are cooperating to assist oil-short OAS members in Central America and the Caribbean. Trinidad and Tobago are helping their neighbors. A number of major Latin American joint venture hydroelectric facilities are completed or are under construction. The Central American countries are working on interconnection of their national electrical grids and on joint research for development of their geothermal and biomass energy resources. Bolivia's gas and oil pipelines connect with those of Argentina and Brazil. Argentina and Brazil are developing a cooperative nuclear program. The movement toward cooperative energy development in Latin America is gaining momentum.

At the same time, the potential for additional development and cooperation is enormous. Oil exploration in Colombia, Ecuador, and Peru should result in their energy independence. Guatemala has the prospect of being an oil exporter. Brazil can reduce its imports by expanding its alcohol program and is prepared to provide assistance to other Latin American and Caribbean countries in establishing similar programs. With such efforts, imports of Middle East oil to Latin America can be virtually eliminated within the decade, having a substantial effect on world oil markets.

The political stability that will derive from energy security in Central America and the Caribbean also deserves mention. The nations of the Western Hemisphere have been striving to organize these piecemeal efforts to achieve a systematic means of technical and financial cooperation for energy development. It is clearly in the interest of the United States to support these efforts.

The dramatic increase in the cost of energy in recent years provides some possibility for efficient expansion of domestic energy production in other developing countries that are critically dependent upon imported oil. Continued dependence on imports at current levels would enormously compound the difficulty of financing the large external deficits that many developing countries will have. The increase in the real price of oil has created opportunities for the development of reserves of oil, gas, coal, hydroelectric, and agricultural resources previously held to be uneconomical (while threatening the depletion of forest resources in the Third World). By maximizing energy production between now and the end of the decade, the World Bank estimates that developing countries could reduce their oil import bill by $25–30 billion in 1990 (1980 dollars). External capital will obviously be critical to such a program.

It will be important to consider—particularly in the context of what the United States can reasonably expect to influence—that the developing countries would prefer to develop energy industries in as domestically oriented a fashion as possible. The United States can help alleviate the acute manpower and training problems that the developing countries are likely to experience in this area by assisting in providing regional training opportunities. But it is the developing countries themselves that will need to decide the extent to which they develop domestic energy and accept assistance in energy development from abroad.

The financing of these programs is likely to involve the IMF, the World Bank, and other international organizations, as well as the private capital market. The IMF lends to countries faced with balance of payments problems. Some of these countries are oil importers, some are net oil exporters. The World Bank is considering the establishment of an "energy affiliate" to provide additional energy financing for the developing countries. Unusual effort on the part of those institutions will be helpful, but all of the resources they can assemble will meet only a fraction of the capital required by the developing countries for development of their energy resources.

Those countries, and there are a number, that have continued to put forward reasonable terms for foreign investment in resource development have been rewarded by significant private investment in energy resource development. A number of others maintain investment terms that make any investment opportunity unattractive. Still other countries suggest that private investment is denied them on political or financial grounds, when in fact the geological prospects are to begin with not sufficiently attractive to warrant investment. The role for international financial institutions, and for governments generally, is to encourage an environment in which private sector capital can flow into resource development. There is a role for the World Bank with respect to modest participation in specific projects to assure parties on both sides that relationships between the private and public sector will be both reasonable and honored. Such efforts, however, should supplement, not supplant, private investment, which will still have to be attracted by reasonable and appropriate host government financial policies.

If the energy resources of the developing countries are economic to produce and a reasonably stable investment climate is presented, private capital can be expected to flow into energy development. However, there has been limited interest in oil investments in developing countries where production is aimed primarily at import substitution in domestic markets rather than exports[11] and little interest in infrastructure investment to permit exploitation of natural gas, hydro, and coal. The role of multilateral institutions here is therefore straightforward and traditional. They also provide a sound means for

11. One member of the Committee comments: "First, it should be noted that there are very few countries where such a situation might apply. Second, oil consumption in the vast majority of LDCs is relatively small in terms of the economic-sized refinery needed to turn the crude into the products required. Third, where there is an adequate market, it is the inherent nature of the international oil companies to construct refineries and manage an optimized integrated system. Fourth, LDCs require inflows of capital to develop infrastructure for energy and all other economic purposes; crude oil exports, if a surplus becomes available, would be therefore very much to their advantage." Another member of the Committee adds: "Note in particular oil company exploration and development activities in countries such as Brazil, Argentina, India, the Ivory Coast, etc.,"

recycling oil revenues to productive long-term projects. One final point is the objective policy advice that the World Bank traditionally provides to its clients. This is particularly important to a few non-capital-surplus oil exporters such as Mexico, Nigeria, Indonesia, and China.

The World Bank estimates that improved programs of demand management designed to increase the efficiency of energy use could reduce energy consumption in the developing countries by 4 to 5 million barrels of oil equivalent a day by the end of the decade. These potential savings are as important in the overall energy balance as the incremental production that may be stimulated through expanded World Bank lending for energy producton projects. Moreover, the payoff to greater energy efficiency is often immediate, whereas production projects typically have a long gestation.

A fourfold program of complementary IMF, World Bank, and private sector initiatives is therefore needed, with the international institutions acting as a catalyst in eliciting private sector investments:

1. Strong U.S. support of the IMF, which through its lending procedures helps maintain a necessary economic discipline and flexibility in developing economies;

2. Increased World Bank funding of energy investments in the developing countries targeted at import substitution through the development of conventional and renewable sources of energy and intensified advisory work related to management of energy demand and more efficient energy use;

3. Private sector and World Bank support for energy infrastructure in the developing countries to permit exports; and

4. Traditional private sector investment—but on a significantly increased scale—in developing country energy investments aimed primarily at exports.

V. ENERGY POLICY DECISIONMAKING IN THE UNITED STATES

A. Background

There are a number of positive aspects to U.S. energy policy as it has emerged from the 1970s. The United States has accepted the need to reduce oil imports and consumption and has encouraged the production of domestic oil and gas, the increased use of coal, and the development of synthetic oil and gas. The United States has left the door open for more nuclear power, has encouraged conservation and nonconventional energy supply, and has generally accepted that significant changes in energy supply and use patterns will occur in the United States. Encouragement has thus far been given in the form of legislation providing for decontrol of prices on new gas and all oil; substitution of coal for oil in certain uses; development of a synthetic fuels industry; mandatory energy efficiency standards in certain end uses, including automobiles; and a variety of beneficial tax measures related to conservation. As well, provisions had been made for federal funding of solar and other nonconventional forms of energy. Price-induced supply and conservation effects have been proven to be of major significance. In fact, many of the government's actions simply remove impediments from the market or supplement market forces.

Since much of this law and policy is of recent date and is evolving under a new administration, its execution and impacts are still uncertain. For example, the president has proposed (1) reduction or elimination of many of the financial support programs, especially in alternative and renewable sources of energy; (2) slimming down of the Synfuel Corporation and its existing synfuel programs; and (3) eliminating alternative energy programs from DOE and Agriculture and transferring some activities in these fields to a revamped Synfuel Corporation. On the other hand, recent testimony of Secretary Edwards suggests the retention in the DOE of an assistant secretary for conservation and alternative energies responsible for R&D and pilot plants.

Among the negative aspects emerging from the 1970s are allied perceptions that the United States had lost the ability to manage its own domestic energy supply and use programs and to adapt to the changed circumstances of the 1970s. This caused a serious degradation of the ability of U.S. government and industry to continue to influence U.S. international energy relationships constructively. In the 1970s, the United States also lost some of its aura as a reliable supplier and partner in energy programs. This has been the case in oil-, gas-, coal-, and nuclear-related matters.

Additional negative factors have been the lack of harmony in federal and state policies and plans and the lack of trust among the federal and state governments, the energy industries, and the public. There are still serious defects in coherent decisionmaking among private and public institutions responsible for U.S. energy supply and use policy, plans, regulation, financing, schedules, costs, and results. There are continuing major uncertainties with respect to assurance of future supply of gas, synthetic fuels, and electric power and full utilization of domestically available gas, coal, and uranium.

B. Principal Problems Dominating U.S. Government Policy and Decisionmaking

There are now three principal problems that dominate U.S. government energy policy and the decisionmaking process in the United States.

1. *Absence of a Philosophical Framework.* It is important to have a coherent notion of the structure of the energy problem, of its relation to other foreign and domestic issues, and of the government's role in its management. Absent this framework, and quite apart from the content of any specific decision, it is difficult either to select sensible policies or, perhaps more importantly, to build government institutions or employ private institutions that can effectively act to implement them.

The following examples may serve to illustrate this point, as well as to underscore a few of its more serious manifestations:

- The United States remains a significant source of energy for the rest of the world. Coal and uranium are abundant natural resources in the United States, and could help serve the needs of other countries. U.S. technology is also an asset that can help other countries develop their own energy sources. Using these resources to assist other nations with their energy problems and securing both energy and political advantage for the United States thereby could be of considerable significance. But this policy rests, among other things, on the reputation of the United States as a reliable supplier, as indicated in the preceding section of this chapter.

- Energy policy in the United States has been linked more to domestic social policy than to foreign policy. The existing situation does not establish a framework in which domestic energy policy concessions can be made for foreign policy gains.

- The U.S. government has been inattentive to the tasks that only it can perform, while spending considerable time in policy areas where its impact is marginal. Converting electric utilities from oil to coal, for example, has been an area of relentless government activity, but not even those conversions that economics would have dictated in the first place have been achieved. Other governmental activities, such as complex and contradicting environmental standards and coal-leasing policies, have worked in opposition to the fuel conversion policies. Moreover, government has not been aggressive in formulating contingency policies to deal with inevitable oil disruptions—an area of responsibility almost exclusively governmental.

- The striking decrease in oil imports for the OECD in 1980 (perhaps 10 percent for the OECD generally and about 20 percent for the United States) indicates how much might have been accomplished had the United States and others acted earlier to reduce their dependence on oil imports.

2. *Organizational Structure.* The Department of Energy, in which most energy decisions are presumed to originate and where any policy must find fertile ground in which to flourish, is not especially well structured to deal with complicated domestic or international energy policy initiatives.

One problem is that the Department of Energy is a combined regulatory and policy–programmatic agency, as well as being responsible for the production of strategic and tactical nuclear weapons. Putting aside the nuclear weapons responsibility as a historically sound decision, it is believed that in such hybrid agencies, regulation (good or bad) tends to drive out sustained supply policy implementation. Key decisionmakers tend to spend more time on regulation and less on policy and program implementation, especially in such politically unrewarding but important fields as international cooperation.

3. *International Energy Policy Decisionmaking.* Some nations tend to view the United States as insensitive to their interests in its energy policy decisions, but almost all find it difficult to discover who within which U.S. agency is responsible for what facets of U.S. gov-

ernment decisions affecting the supply and use of energy abroad. Viewed from abroad, a few agencies would stand out as having functions that directly relate to international energy policy. In the background are others that may make decisions that can affect the supply and use of energy abroad. Depending upon how they are counted, within the U.S. executive branch there are at least thirteen such departments and agencies, plus the president. The most visible include the Departments of Energy and State, the Nuclear Regulatory Commission, and the Export–Import Bank. The Departments of Commerce, Interior, and Transportation are fairly frequent contributors; and the Departments of Defense, Justice, and Treasury, the Arms Control and Disarmament Agency, the Council on Environmental Quality, and the Environmental Protection Agency have related functions. In dealing with this mélange of agencies, foreign governments are often baffled. They tend to rely on their relationship with the U.S. Department of State as the ordinary instrument for relating to U.S. external concerns. Yet the State Department at present generally lacks the political and technical strength and capacity for responding to their energy concerns.

Within the legislative branch, nine committees of the House of Representatives and eight of the Senate, plus at least one joint committee, have an interest in these agencies and in international energy matters. Among these, the Senate Committee on Energy and Natural Resources, the House Committee on Energy and Commerce, and the Foreign Relations Committees of both bodies have visible, continuing interest.

The interrelationship of these agencies and committees is anything but simple. There is no central department or coordinating body to reconcile or influence domestic decisions of the U.S. government with respect to their potential effects on the supply and use of energy abroad.

Presumably U.S. sensitivity to international energy interests (its own, as well as those of others) would be increased were there a clear responsibility for coordinating within the U.S. government decisions taken in the name of international energy policy or national energy policy that could also assure some consideration of foreign energy interests.

Assuming that it would be good for the United States to be more responsive, there remains the issue of how to achieve this. There does exist an incomplete, sometimes ad hoc and informal, network of arrangements and contacts that assures some coordination, with the coordinative effort depending upon differing perceptions of the urgency and importance of the problem at hand.

At issue is whether something more is needed to make U.S. energy policy decisions more responsive to international considerations— assuming, of course, reciprocal ways to increase the sensitivity of foreign governments to U.S. energy interests. The most acceptable option may well be arrangements to strengthen interagency coordination on energy decisions. Coordination could be achieved by vesting strong authority in a special assistant to the president. An alternative that more closely fits the Reagan administration pattern would be to make the secretary of state a member of the cabinet level Natural Resources Council—President Reagan's senior advisory body on energy policy matters.[12]

C. U.S. Energy Policy and the U.S. Energy Industries

Effective, constructive, U.S. government interaction with U.S. energy industries should include government support of U.S. energy industry performance at home and abroad and energy industry support of U.S. international initiatives. This will contribute to the development of both domestic and external resources. Nonadversarial relations between the two sectors are imperative for the United States and its energy industries to play a key role in international energy developments.

From the perspective of enhancing the ability of the U.S. private sector to make its needed contributions, both domestically and internationally, an effective U.S. energy policy should provide:

* Recognition that energy is not only an important domestic concern of this country, but also a central element of foreign policy.

---

12. One member of the Committee comments: "In view of the current situation—in which Interior chairs a cabinet group on energy and state is angling for authority on all international energy matters—we need to say something more. In particular, I would argue that the new arrangement tends to separate energy and foreign policy even more than it was and so is not a very good idea. Further, by weakening DOE, the new approach weakens the one place where energy and foreign policy can be related at the working level (State doesn't know energy and a cabinet committee is hardly the working staff)."

- Meaningful policies to encourage conservation to reduce energy demand and a sensible emergency response mechanism to handle serious supply disruptions.

- Recognition of the importance of the energy and economic well-being of other industrialized countries to our national security.

- Recognition of the importance of energy for developing countries, for their political stability — and thus to our national security.

- Environmental and safety regulation, tax legislation, public utility regulation (in the regulated electric and gas distribution industries), and a resolution of opposing interests to the end that there is encouragement and support for more intensive development of oil, gas, coal, nuclear, and alternative nonconventional energy sources including synthetic fuels.

- Removal of price controls from new natural gas to encourage conservation and increased production of all domestic energy resources.[13]

- Removal of regulations that severely limit the use of state and federal lands, including the outer continental shelf, in order to stimulate oil, gas, and coal exploration. (Government-owned lands now provide 16 percent of U.S. production of oil and natural gas liquids and 30 percent of natural gas, but some studies indicate that they contain 37 percent of our undiscovered oil reserves and 43 percent of undiscovered natural gas.)

Priority actions that should be supported by U.S. energy policy include:

- Creating a better governmental framework for organizing federal energy activities — both domestic and international.

- Developing an emergency response capability to be used in the event of major supply curtailments that would work more fairly and efficiently than the control schemes implemented by the Fed-

---

13. One member of the Committee comments: "We support the full decontrol of all natural gas and the market-determined use of all fuel sources. We believe that decontrol of only newly discovered natural gas would result in serious political and economic dislocations. It would result in a major transfer of wealth from producing to consuming states."

eral Energy Administration in 1973 and by the Department of Energy in 1979.[14]

- Government taking the lead in reconciling conflicting national priorities and interests and making clear that all viewpoints must be dealt with in a broader context, with trade-offs being made in the interest of meeting U.S. international as well as domestic energy needs.

- Supporting much greater domestic and international use of gas, coal, nuclear power, and energy from renewable sources and providing for significant contributions by the U.S. industries internationally. Environmental, siting, transport, safety, nonproliferation, and nuclear waste disposal issues are a main stumbling block, and policies should be adopted to expedite their solution. Also, in order to assure the most economical supply and use of coal and nuclear power in the United States, the financial viability of the electric utility industry needs to be assured by a more positive approach to rate regulation as well as to planning and financing.

- Applying reasonable tax legislation to the energy industry and to the installation of energy-efficient capital facilities by all industry. Timely development of promising alternative energy sources such as synthetics, geothermal, biomass, and solar may require government financial assistance that goes beyond existing tax and market incentives.[15] Tax policies that would serve as disincentives for investment should be avoided. Continuation of the U.S. foreign tax credit for income taxes paid to foreign governments on foreign earnings of U.S. companies is essential to maintaining the strong position of U.S. companies in the worldwide search for new supplies, as well as in international production and distribution.

14. For an examination of this issue, see the recently completed study undertaken by the National Petroleum Council's Emergency Preparedness Committee at the request of the U.S. Department of Energy.

15. One Committee member comments: "My own view is that there have been too many goodies for synfuels and alternative energies. On synfuels I believe the Committee for Economic Development report, "Helping Insure Our Energy Future—A Program for Developing Synthetic Fuel Plants Now" [July 1979] went far enough in recommending support—with a lot of emphasis on assured outlets—for a limited number of medium- to full-scale "pilot" plants. Something parallel is justified for the alternative energies. The details of investment credits and other tax arrangements become very technical and some anomalies should be corrected. Time periods should be extended. Area limitations should be raised or eliminated to facilitate economic operations."

VI. GENERAL OBSERVATIONS
AND CONCLUSIONS

A. Throughout this decade, oil will remain the single most important commercial fuel, while such other primary and secondary energy sources as natural gas, coal, nuclear power, electricity, and energy from renewable sources must be relied upon increasingly. Conservation of energy will continue to moderate the rate of increase in demand, especially as prices of all energy sources rise. Reducing demand for energy and securing access to oil while developing other sources will continue to be the major energy preoccupation of the United States and other governments.

B. There will be no significant short-term relief for the United States from dependence upon oil imports, given the lead times required to develop existing resources and alternative energy sources on a sufficient scale, achieve significant conservation, and generally alter the pattern of energy end uses. The strategic implications of this continuing dependence will bear increasingly on U.S. leadership of the alliances. By 1990, however, if the United States pursues more reasonable policies toward energy markets, U.S. dependence on foreign oil can be significantly reduced.

C. Until the United States can clearly demonstrate both the capability and the will to fully develop alternatives to oil, as well as its remaining oil resources, and thus reduce the leverage of the exporters, it is probable that oil exporters will continue to employ oil as a means to achieve political as well as economic objectives.

D. Further reduction of U.S. imports relative to the volume of discretionary OPEC exports can be achieved to a significant extent by increased production of alternative domestic energy forms and through continuing improvements in energy conservation. Such a move on the part of the United States is of crucial importance, both in moderating future OPEC price increases and in stretching out the availability of future OPEC supplies to those of the OECD nations and the developing countries who do not have indigenous energy resources and are critically dependent on OPEC oil.

E. The United States needs to move urgently to develop its alternate energy forms, especially synthetic fuels. The time lags required to achieve meaningful increases in production mean that we must get moving now to begin to achieve changes in U.S. energy supply and use patterns by the end of the 1980s.

F. Increasing domestic energy production and decreasing U.S. imports will have a significant economic advantage to the United States. It will keep jobs and tax revenues here in the United States rather than exporting them to OPEC countries, will moderate U.S. inflation, and will strengthen the U.S. economy. The implications of this in regard to U.S. foreign policy and military strength are fundamental and significant.

G. While the possible emergence of the Soviet Union as a net oil importer of increasing consequence may be a source of some concern, the increasing dependence of Western Europe on the Soviet Union for energy supply will also become worrisome if the trend continues.

H. There have been serious deficiencies in U.S. energy policy decisionmaking and in the pattern of interaction of the U.S. government with the private sector. If energy policy in the United States is quickly characterized by better decisions with respect to all domestic sources, there is a good chance that the vulnerability of the United States and its allies can be reduced significantly by 1990.

I. While improvements in energy efficiency will moderate the increases in demand for energy, including oil, key oil-exporting countries could also lower supply—and sustain price. Moreover, new claimants for a share of oil in trade—the developing countries generally and perhaps the Soviet Union—will put greater pressure on world supply. And the internal requirements of a rapidly developing economic infrastructure within OPEC members will probably create added crude oil demands that exceed those of other non-oil-producing developing countries and the Soviet Union combined.

J. The prospects for an importer–exporter dialogue are severely limited. There are conflicting priorities among the exporters as well as disparate vulnerabilities among the importers. The social, political, and economic problems of the oil-exporting countries of the Persian Gulf in the course of their development, as well as their need to preserve their independence and security, should be regarded as being as important as those of the OECD nations and other exporters such as Mexico and Venezuela.

K. There will be no significant short-term relief for our European and Japanese allies from their dependence on oil imports. Differing vulnerabilities and perspectives among the United States and its allies may complicate attempts to develop a consensus on how to deal with common energy concerns in a coordinated and concerted manner.

L. The actions on energy matters that the United States, Canada, Japan, and the nations of Western Europe take individually and together will constitute a major element in their future relationships and future world order. The United States, Canada, Japan, and Western Europe need to provide a political climate suitable for concerted action and to contribute to a credible strategic position as well as to assure compatible international economic policies.

M. The severe and growing energy problems of the non-oil-producing developing countries, with the associated risk of political instability, will require special efforts, particularly in domestic energy development in these countries. The big problem will center around the capacity of the developing countries to pay for their oil imports without a serious disruption of the world financial and economic structure. New methods must be found, in collaboration with the developing countries, the oil-exporting nations, and the developed world, to finance these transactions. Means must also be found for providing the developing countries with the technologies they require for energy resources exploration and development.

N. U.S. energy relationships with Latin America on a multinational basis can be effective, both politically and in terms of cost effectiveness. Germany, France, the United Kingdom, and Japan are active in cooperative energy activities in Latin America. The Soviet Union is developing close commercial ties with several Latin American countries, notably Brazil and Argentina. Both U.S. cooperation and competition are suggested.

O. A fundamental element of U.S. policy for Central America should be assistance for oil exploration and for the development of hydropower, geothermal, and biomass energy resources.

P. Several Latin American countries have excellent potential for increasing domestic energy production (Brazil—alcohol; Colombia, Ecuador, Peru—oil; Argentina, Brazil—nuclear; etc.). Investment in development of this potential could substantially reduce demand for Middle East oil.

Q. Fuels from biomass, particularly in Latin America, ethanol from crops, and methanol from wood will be a factor in reducing demand for oil in the 1980s and may become a new element in international energy commerce.

VII. POLICY RECOMMENDATIONS

A. A Strategy for the 1980s

A strategy composed of the following elements is recommended:

1. Strengthen the capability of the United States to provide international leadership by:

    a. Assuring that U.S. energy policy fully reflects the interaction of domestic and international energy interests;

    b. Organizing to administer that policy consistently;

    c. Integrating the administration of foreign policy and energy policy;

    d. Relying more fully on market processes and the private sector for efficient policy implementation, both domestically and in international programs; and

    e. Allowing U.S. energy producers to respond to higher world energy prices to develop domestic resources and thereby establish a course that has the potential to reduce U.S. imports substantially by 1990.

2. Conduct U.S. foreign and domestic policy to:

    a. Secure access to world oil supply;

    b. Strengthen the oil importers' bargaining position vis-à-vis exporting countries;

    c. Reduce the risk of exporters acting to cut off supplies;

    d. Create incentives for exporters to understand the commonality of interest all share in solving the problem of oil; and

    e. Help to alleviate the special burdens of non-oil-producing developing countries or those who depend substantially on imports of energy.

3. Encourage the European Community, Japan, and the United States to adopt concerted energy policies to:

    a. Reduce demand for oil;

    b. Cooperate multilaterally to secure access to energy supplies in addition to allocating shortages—and instead of competing for scarce energy resources;

c. Promptly develop other fuels as alternates to oil;

d. Carry out cooperative research and development and demonstration programs on conservation and alternate supplies; and

e. Reduce vulnerability to oil price increases and supply interruptions.

B. Strengthening the Capability of the United States to Provide International Leadership in Energy

1. *U.S. International Energy Policy Decisionmaking.* A Council on International Energy Policy, reporting to the National Security Council and with commensurate authority, should be established to provide for coordination of domestic and foreign policy on energy and energy supply security.

2. *Political Strategy.* The United States should strive to deal with those aspects of the energy problem that are within its control. U.S. government and energy industry strategy should focus on reducing demand growth; increasing domestic and international supply; developing alternatives such as domestic and imported (non–Middle East) gas, coal, nuclear, and synthetic fuels and fuels from renewable resources; cooperating with other consuming nations on research, development, and demonstration of energy technology; diversifying sources and helping developing countries to improve their energy security. This strategy requires a recommitment on the part of Congress as well as the administration to the emergency oil-sharing contingency plans of the International Energy Agency. It also requires stable and consistent market-oriented policy by the federal government, the ability to act on the part of the energy industries, supportive regulation, and the development of public understanding.[16]

3. *U.S. Government Energy Organization.* The Department of Energy (DOE) should be reorganized to be responsible for energy supply and use policy, planning, and programs. DOE would be responsi-

---

16. It may not be possible to overemphasize the importance — to the U.S.'s own well-being as well as to its capacity for international leadership — that the United States get its own energy supply and use system in good order. Recent views of the U.S. National Committee of the World Energy Conference on dealing with U.S. domestic energy problems are presented in summary form in the Appendix.

ble for U.S. government research, development, and demonstration (RD&D) programs related to conservation, the supply and use of oil, gas, electric power, coal, nuclear, and non-conventional technologies, emergency planning and preparedness for imported oil supply cutbacks or shortages, and management of federally owned energy resources and supply activities. The U.S. government should undertake no energy RD&D or supply activities in competition with the private sector. However, it should be prepared to support such activities where national security and foreign policy interests are served. This suggests a more robust DOE role in some energy RD&D than apparently now contemplated by the Administration. Moreover, this rationalization of functions would permit a leaner, cheaper, and better organization of the U.S. government to deal with energy.

4. *Conservation.* The relative price of energy in final use may not generate investment in conservation to the degree that would seem justified by the energy outlook in the medium and long term. Cost-effective conservation measures should be spurred by market pricing of energy combined with selective energy efficiency goals.

5. *Coal Use and Export.* The development and use of U.S. coal resources should be vigorously pursued by U.S. industry and utilities and strongly supported by government policies to streamline coal leasing, mining, and use. Worldwide U.S. coal exports should be encouraged, along with the development of improved domestic transportation facilities, port and harbor facilities, and export-related transportation techniques and systems.

6. *Oil Use and Pricing.* Industry, utilities, and households should continue to be encouraged by price signals to substitute other energy sources for oil.

7. *Gas Use and Pricing.* The use of gas should be encouraged in recognition of its growing supply potential. Gas prices should continue to increase to competitive fuel levels. The environmental and other advantages of continuing the use of natural gas in existing facilities should be recognized and legislation prohibiting such use should be repealed.[17] The government should encourage the development of all

___

17. A member of the Committee comments: "Natural gas is a premium fuel because of its clean-burning characteristics and thus is particularly important to small consumers who

gas supplies on a price-competitive basis and in line with security and other broad national interests.

8. *Nuclear Power Development.* The U.S. government should (1) improve the nuclear regulation process to focus on overall safety and efficient and timely licensing; (2) standardize safety evaluation procedures; (3) together with industry, assure the safety and encourage the public acceptance of nuclear power; (4) demonstrate safe radioactive waste disposal and the feasibility of the breeder reactor; (5) assure the orderly and timely completion and operation of the 178 plants completed, under construction, and planned, and the planning and completion by the year 2000 of an additional major increment of nuclear power.[18]

9. *U.S. Electric Utility Industry Viability.* The president should establish a task force to examine and recommend specific measures affecting the U.S. electric utility industry to the end that its structural and financial viability is assured and that it can play a large and active role in energy conservation; the fullest practical use of U.S. coal and nuclear energy resources; the rapid deployment of innovative technologies and approaches to electric generation; and overall, the assurance of future national supplies of electricity that are adequate to support the nation's needs as well as resuming the position of international leadership the industry once enjoyed.

10. *Alternative Energy Sources.* Alternative energy sources—synthetic fuels, biomass, solar, geothermal, etc.—while of limited significance for the energy situation in the short term, should nevertheless be developed in as rapid a manner as is economically efficient. The emphasis here should be upon reducing the lead times associated with these alternatives by creating incentives for development; mechanisms for risk sharing by the U.S. government and industry; not

---

do not have an alternative means of minimizing air pollution. Also, natural gas is a finite resource. Thus, there would appear to be some need to direct natural gas away from consumers who have better alternatives in the context of energy and environmental policy. In addition, there is little prospect in the near term for total deregulation of all natural gas supplies, and therefore, erroneous price signals are transmitted that encourage less than optimal allocation of gas consumption."

18. A member of the Committee dissents as follows: "This is not a matter of public sector determination in the manner implied, and the intervention by the government to assure such a development, without qualifying resources to the full cost of that power (unsubsidized) and to public attitudes toward it is unacceptable."

allowing regulatory developments to unduly impede progress; and providing for state industry mechanisms to resolve state and local impact issues.[19] The incentives should provide for speeding the process of developing technology and environmental accommodation. The potential for extensive international cooperation in these areas should be realized, especially with Japan, Europe, and selected LDCs.

11. *Strategic Petroleum Reserve.* The filling of the Strategic Petroleum Reserve should be regarded as essential for the United States to cope with interruptions in supply of imported oil. The accelerated filling of the reserve should be efficiently pursued, at the average rate of 500,000 barrels a day, so as to reach the target figure of 1 billion barrels in 1985. Flexibility and consultation are essential in meeting this goal.

C. International Energy Relations

12. *Soviet Intervention.* The United States should continue to oppose, by an enhanced presence in the Middle East, the extension of Soviet influence or control in that area. This effort is all the more important in the wake of Soviet aggression in Afghanistan and some possibility that the Soviet Union may emerge as a net oil importer of some consequence. If and when the USSR becomes dependent on imported supply, accommodation of its needs should be sought within the existing international oil system; actions to obtain supply through direct or indirect intervention should be opposed.

13. *Supply Dependence upon the Soviet Union.* The United States and its allies should carefully assess the implications of their growing dependence on imported energy supplies and services. Strategic assessment is needed, in particular, with regard to current and projected Western European dependence upon Soviet gas, nuclear fuel enrichment services, and electricity.

14. *Supply Security.* The United States should take necessary and appropriate measures, in cooperation with its allies, to enhance the credibility of the Western defense commitment, particularly as it

---

19. One member of the Committee comments: "I have no dissent on returning regulatory responsibility to the states, at least without qualification."

relates to the security of the sea lines of communication upon which United States and allied oil supply depends. Specifically, greater European and Japanese contributions to overall defense efforts will allow the requisite U.S. forces to be committed to Middle East defense. The building of an effective rapid deployment force should be actively pursued in close consultation with U.S. allies, with adequate manpower in the United States and equipment stockpiled in prospective deployment areas.

15. *Establishing a Credible Middle East Deterrent.* To deter the Soviet Union from directly or indirectly expanding its influence in the Middle East or obtaining control of access to Middle Eastern oil supplies, an adequate deterrent force should be established as quickly as possible in that area, with the consent and active support of the countries of the region. The United States is the only country capable of taking the lead in this operation. Other NATO nations and Japan should undertake agreed assignments within the region. Their role would be to maintain freedom of navigation for all nations. A second role would be to be responsive to the regimes of the region and their desire to protect themselves against external influences that are undesirable as they perceive them. These roles are dependent upon the Middle East countries affected and in no way imply – or should imply – military leverage over the production and pricing policies of oil-producing countries in the Middle East.

• France, the Federal Republic of Germany, the United Kingdom, and Canada should provide appropriate military assets to the Middle East–Persian Gulf area to enhance allied capability and to demonstrate allied solidarity.

• Other NATO/Europe nations and Japan should apply their own civil assets, including airlift and sealift, to support this allied presence in the Middle East–Persian Gulf area. Countries with past operational experience in the Middle East region could provide valuable intelligence and training support for forces in or being deployed to the area.

16. *NATO Stockbuilding for Defense.* From a defensive point of view, NATO stockbuilding should be encouraged, particularly where protected or dispersed storage can be made available. Special wartime sharing arrangements should be updated, taking into account

NATO's considerable dependence on non-NATO sources of oil supplies and on the vulnerability of production, refining, and transport facilities in NATO countries.

17. *U.S. Energy Relationships with Western Europe and Japan.* To provide for a mutually beneficial future, the following recommendations are offered:

a. The United States, Europe, and Japan should take the necessary steps to assure that the IEA emergency oil-sharing plan is credible, realistic, and workable under emergency conditions. Furthermore, they should cooperate so that IEA plans and procedures are continually coordinated on a regular basis, in order to assure that the disparate needs and capabilities of all IEA members under potentially differing emergency conditions are fully taken into account. Continued close consultation with the private energy sector in this regard is indispensable.

b. The United States, the European Community, and Japan should adopt policies that reduce pressures on the oil markets in the longer term as well as the near term:

   • Stronger conservation and efficient energy use policies should be placed into effect;

   • Energy pricing should encourage conservation and the development of alternatives to oil; and

   • IEA member countries should strengthen other policies and programs that facilitate supply alternatives.

c. Programs of research, development, demonstration, and commercial application of new energy technologies that lend themselves to international cooperation should continue and should be carried out aggressively under bilateral and multilateral arrangements. Such arrangements are proposed for both government and private sector support. Worthy of particular emphasis are projects in:

   · Conservation techniques
   · Coal combustion and transportation
   · Shale oil and tar sand development
   · Coal liquefaction
   · Coal gasification
   · Nuclear reactor safety

- Nuclear-reactor-related technologies, including the breeder reactor
- Solar energy
- Hydropower
- Methanol production
- Geothermal energy
- Biomass
- Fusion.

d. The United States can and should assist the European countries and Japan in reducing their dependence on oil by becoming a major source of coal for energy purposes. In order to do so, the United States should adopt policies that facilitate the reliable and competitive export of coal, including more certain processes for environmental approvals and policies conducive to the development of the necessary infrastructure such as railroads, slurry pipelines, and port and harbor facilities.

e. European and Japanese investment in U.S. coal properties should be continued and further encouraged for the benefit of all concerned, as this would secure a stable source of supply for Europe and Japan and would provide stable demand for the United States. Large-scale transactions in U.S. coal will assist in redressing recurrent balance of payment problems. European and Japanese cooperation and investment in the production of synthetic fuels from U.S. coal, shale, etc., will further enhance the longer term prospects of energy supply security.[20] The IEA member governments should cooperate to develop a climate conducive to such investment.

f. It is of interest to the United States that Western Europe and Japan make full use of nuclear power to reduce their use of oil.

---

20. A Committee member comments: "The question of synthetic fuels export from the United States should be approached with caution, lest it create a counterproductive domestic political issue where none now exists. There is little likelihood of significant synfuels output in this decade. Difficult domestic issues of environmental protection, water allocation, and the creation of massive intrusions into sparsely populated areas will have to be reconciled if a synthetic fuels industry is to develop rapidly in the 1990s. To achieve this reconciliation will require what will be perceived as sacrifices by many interests in the United States. Direct export of coal would not be encumbered by these difficulties. Foreign investment in synfuels research, development, and demonstration would serve the same objectives for those investors, even if the synthetic fuels were consumed in the United States, since it would help lessen U.S. demands on world oil supplies."

The United States should resolve the uncertainties created by its nuclear policy in a manner that will facilitate the use of increasing amounts of nuclear power in Europe and Japan, as well as in the United States. In this regard, the United States must fully recognize the needs of its allies for establishing their own nuclear fuel cycles under appropriate international safeguards.[21] In this regard, the United States should seek greater Japanese and European cooperation and coordination in support of the enhancement of safeguarding of the entire fuel cycle and preventing nuclear weapons proliferation.

g. The United States should take the initiative in formulating and carrying out programs with European countries and Japan whereby techniques of plant operation and management developed in such countries can be fully utilized to further enhance the safety and reliability of nuclear power generation. Also, the United States, in its move to amend the siting regulations of nuclear power plants, should take into consideration that these regulations will have substantial influence on the nuclear power programs of Japan and Western European countries and, in light of the present level of and possible future progress in nuclear safety technologies, make such regulations models that will facilitate and encourage the expanded use of nuclear power safety.

h. A regular means of exploring and discussing the entire range of energy issues among the European, Japanese, and U.S. private sectors should be instituted, involving representatives of related fields. Among the first items on the agenda of such a continuing dialogue should be the means of expanding U.S.–Japan and U.S.–Europe energy trade, which will contribute substantially to the security of Japanese and European energy supplies, the creation of additional jobs in the United States, and the improvement of U.S. economic conditions and will enhance the U.S. trade position.

---

21. One member of the Committee registered dissent to this sentence, offering as alternative language: "In this regard, the United States should recognize the needs of its allies to establish their own nuclear fuel cycles, consistent with growth in their nuclear power programs and as needed to support breeder reactor development and deployment schedules. The establishment of nuclear fuel cycle facilities should be in a manner consistent with the Treaty on the Non-Proliferation of Nuclear Weapons and under appropriate international safeguards. Any separated plutonium in excess of immediate needs for breeder reactors should be deposited under international custody."

i. The United States, Western Europe, and Japan should address the problem of the physical security of energy facilities as well as of supplies, reducing vulnerabilities that pose unacceptable risks to their collective economic viability.

18. *U.S.-Mexican Energy Relationships.* As the economic development and political stability of Mexico are more important to U.S. national interest than marginal increases in Mexican energy exports, the "leverage" approach by the United States to bring about Mexican production increases is inappropriate. Instead, and at Mexico's initiative, the United States should work more closely with Mexico to assure the development and supply of Mexican energy resources in a manner and at a rate that is in Mexico's best interest.

19. *U.S.-Venezuelan Energy Relationships.* With regard to Venezuela, the same principle should be applied. For example, the United States should consider very carefully what the benefits of pushing for more rapid development of the Orinoco region would be, particularly in light of such longer term interests as political stability. The United States should be responsive to Venezuela's decisions and ready to assist further, if asked. U.S. willingness to work with and support Venezuelan initiatives for regional energy development and financial help to energy-poor countries in the hemisphere could yield substantial gains.

20. *U.S.-Canadian Energy Relationships.* The United States and Canada should proceed with cooperative efforts in the area of energy development and infrastructure rationalization, including mutually beneficial planning for emergencies and mutually advantageous trade-offs to minimize transportation costs. Such efforts should be pursued through the existing "informal" structure of relations. Bilateral relations in the energy area, in harmony with and supplementary to IEA arrangements, should concentrate on, where feasible:

• Agreeing on longer term availability and pricing of gas exports from Canada;

• Facilitating the adjustment to supply problems in the oil and gas sectors and the integration of new supply from unconventional sources and frontier sources, such as the McKenzie Delta and the Arctic Ocean;

- Taking maximum advantage of the complementarity of energy transport needs of both countries by joint Canadian and U.S. governmental and private sector support of efficient common use projects;

- Promoting the efficient utilization of productive capacity;

- Undertaking joint arrangements and even joint facilities for emergency stockpiles; and

- Reaching agreements on the sharing of supplies and facilities in emergency supply situations, including the availability of natural gas to displace oil.

Considerable effort is required of both countries to prevent controversies over U.S. investment in the Canadian energy sector from retarding development of Canadian energy resources.

21. *Integration of Oil Exporter–Importer Interests.* The United States should recognize that the integration of the economic and political interests of oil exporters and importers is central to the acquisition of secure supplies at predictable prices. The major oil-importing countries should not discriminate against OPEC countries' investments as a means of furthering the integration of such interests.

22. *Energy Development in the Developing Countries.* The United States should exercise a leadership role in assistance to oil-importing developing countries. In particular, the United States and other nations should contribute directly to the external financing of developing countries' energy development—including previously "marginal" reserves of oil, gas, coal, hydroelectric, and biomass energy. This should be done to the fullest extent possible with private capital—including that made available through the international banking community. Additionally, enhanced incentives for direct OPEC financial assistance to the developing countries should be developed, while continuing to make available attractive investment opportunities in the industrialized countries. Unorthodox funding methods should also be considered for U.S. support, including private borrowing by the IMF to fund developing countries' energy development, a special "energy affiliate" of the World Bank, and special energy program priorities in the ongoing work of the Inter American Development Bank, the Asian Development Bank, and the African Development Bank.

A fourfold program of complementary IMF, World Bank, and private sector initiatives is therefore needed, with the international institutions acting as a catalyst in eliciting private sector investments as well as indigenous energy policies designed to promote energy development in the developing countries now heavily dependent on oil imports:

1. Strong U.S. support of the IMF, which through its lending procedures helps maintain a necessary economic discipline and flexibility in developing economies;

2. Increased World Bank funding of developing countries' energy investments targeted at import substitution and intensified advisory work related to management of energy demand and more efficient energy use;

3. Private sector and World Bank support for developing countries' energy infrastructure to permit exports; and

4. Traditional private sector investment—but on a significantly increased scale—in energy investments aimed primarily at energy exports from the developing countries.

INTERNATIONAL ENERGY IN THE 1980s

Melvin A. Conant

I. INTRODUCTION

The central purpose of this chapter is to describe the key factors and forces affecting energy—especially access to oil in international trade. The industrial world's (and LDC's) continuing dependence upon imports is at the core of our difficulties.

This chapter focuses on the present decade and on the geopolitics of supply. Policy options for the longer term must be examined and key ones chosen and implemented during this period if we are to find our energy prospects improved in the future. The following propositions define the likely energy situation of the 1980s:

1. Throughout this decade (and for much longer) oil will remain the primary commercial fuel. Other energy sources—such as gas, coal, and nuclear—will be relied upon increasingly but cannot possibly displace oil. Secure access to other peoples' oil will continue to be a major energy preoccupation of governments and companies. To the extent that efforts to exploit energy alternatives prove unsuccessful or inadequate, oil will have to make up the difference.

2. There will probably be no significant relief for the United States from dependence upon oil imports, given the long lead times

required to develop alternative energy sources on a sufficient scale, to achieve significant conservation, and generally to alter the pattern of energy end uses. The strategic implications of this continuing need for imports will bear ever more heavily on U.S. leadership of the alliances, as it will on the considerations of our allies, most of whom share, to an even greater degree, energy vulnerabilities of their own.

3. The energy situation faced by each of our allies differs from that of the United States in their resource base and therefore in their options; different perspectives of oil-importing allies will continue to frustrate attempts to develop a consensus on how to deal with common energy concerns in a coordinated and concerted manner.

4. While lower rates of economic growth and improvements in energy efficiency will reduce the demand for energy, including oil, the adoption by all key oil-exporting countries of production rates significantly below capacity will also lower supply (and sustain price). Thus, we cannot expect that lower demand will in and of itself improve upon the leverage of oil-importing nations.

5. Moreover, new claimants for a share of oil in trade—most importantly the USSR and LDCs generally—will put pressure upon exporters to increase supply at a time when some key producers prefer to husband their resources; competition will stiffen for the barrel placed in international trade.

6. The possible emergence of the USSR as a claimant for some of the international barrel is already having its effect upon free world alliances and on Middle East events. This unprecedented change in Soviet strategic interests and vulnerabilities will be a source of continuing concern depending upon the mix of options chosen by the Kremlin to obtain oil. By all accounts, however, the greater Soviet concern will not be for imports to meet domestic needs but to meet the needs of Eastern Europe.

7. The energy policy options that can be considered for the 1980s are severely limited. In essence, energy supply until at least 1985 has been predetermined and can only be influenced by conservation or lower levels of economic growth. Specific options, then, must include improving the allied capability to withstand contrived shortages. Particular attention should also

be given to the means by which key oil exporters can be encouraged to produce above their present "preferred production rates," which are designed in part to keep supply and demand on "knife edge." The risk that miscalculation can lead to a supply emergency, and even to war, will be—or ought to be—a constant worry.

It is crucial to the longer run that energy policies lead now to energy investments on a scale that offers the prospect of reducing oil imports by bringing alternative sources to market. Unless these investments are made in the first half of this decade, the 1990s will be a repeat of all our energy concerns—but magnified, as economic growth generally will bear ever more heavily on whatever volume of oil producers decide should be exported.

8. Until alternatives to oil are available, it is highly probable that Middle East and North African oil exporters generally will continue to employ oil as a means to achieve political objectives, as well as economic and financial goals. When these objectives involve matters likely to divide allies, sudden strains will be placed upon the fabric of our relationships.

9. This greater politicization of oil will be facilitated by the changing logistics of international oil trade. The role of the international oil companies (IOCs) is likely to be even more restricted, and the international oil system—its efficiency and security—will be still further impaired as governments of both exporting and importing nations increasingly intervene in supply. The erosion in the role of IOCs in meeting demand from a multiplicity of sources has become a major cause of apprehension for governments concerned about how their needs may be met. Government involvement insures the politics of oil.

10. The financial implications of ever higher prices loom as never before; the resilience displayed by the international financial system after 1973 is unlikely to be repeated time and again. Institutional arrangements for coping with sudden strains and for a prolonged period of very large OPEC surpluses still urgently need to be strengthened. Yet debates on how these may be devised continue without resolution. "Ad hoc" rescue attempts are more likely to be our lot, not far-reaching agreements as to how developing importing nations can cope with sudden surges in demand for foreign exchange when traditional

trade and investment is so inadequate to meet current and foreseen import bills.

11. The process involved in a dialogue between oil exporters and importers must begin; dependable understandings with respect to prices and volumes are now vital to importers if not yet regarded as such by exporters, at least to the same degree.

The paradox is that despite all these concerns, both oil importers and oil exporters wish to prolong the oil era. The former need to prolong the transition from oil to gain more time to develop energy alternatives. The latter need to prolong the transition from oil to lay the basis for their own economic well-being when oil revenues will no longer be the mainstay of their societies. Can these objectives be reconciled? Can the industrialized world secure an agreement on stable supplies at predictable prices in exchange for the long-term development guarantees that OPEC nations demand?

Five basic questions must be asked about domestic and international energy strategies as they relate to dependence upon foreign oil:

1. Does the strategy include commitments to conservation and the acquiring of alternatives to oil?

2. Does the strategy promote diversification of sources?

3. Does the strategy have as one of its objectives an increase in the volume of oil placed in world trade in order to lessen the risk of too small a margin between supply and demand, as well as to reduce over time the importance of the Middle Ease as the principal supplier?

4. Does the strategy more fully integrate the economic interests of oil exporters and importers?

5. Does the strategy strengthen the community of free nations? In time of emergency as well?

II. WORLD ENERGY TRADE

In terms of aggregate figures of energy in world trade, oil dwarfs all other commercial fuels. However important coal or gas is to certain regions (Algerian LNG to Europe; Netherlands supplies to Western Europe; USSR gas to Central Europe; and so forth), there is simply no comparison to the overall role of oil. Somewhere between a half and two-thirds of the oil consumed worldwide may still come from foreign sources by the end of the decade. Nor is it likely over this decade that the proportionate shares in national energy budgets taken by oil, gas, coal, or nuclear will vary significantly. An estimate of OECD energy demand and supply is given in Table 2-1.

Obviously, anticipations of energy demand rest very largely on one's expectation of annual average OECD economic growth rates (see Table 2-2). We have an imperfect understanding of the relation-

Table 2-1. Summer 1980 Estimates of OECD Energy Balances, 1985-1990 (*in mbd*)

OECD Energy Consumption[a]	1979 Actual	1985	1990
Oil	41.8	39.7	39.6
Natural gas	15.0	16.2	18.0
Coal	13.9	17.7	21.0
Nuclear	2.6	5.6	7.8
Hydro	4.7	5.8	6.5
Total primary energy	78.0	85.0	92.9
OECD oil production	15.3	14.7	14.2
Required imports	27.4[b]	25.0	25.4

a. Figures do not necessarily add due to rounding.

b. Includes 0.9 mbd stock build-up.

Table 2-2. Total Estimated Free World Oil Production, 1985-1990 (*in mbd*)

	1979	1985	1990
OECD[a]	15.3	14.7	14.2
Non-OPEC developing countries	5.3	8.8	10.9
Desired OPEC production	31.3	34.4	35.9
Total	51.9	57.9	61.0

a. Includes 0.5 mbd processing gain in the United States.

ship between these two factors. Depending upon one's selection of a particular growth rate, one can begin to trace the consequences upon the mix of energies likely to be required. Once again, for the 1980s, it is unlikely that there will be an appreciable shift in the primary commercial fuels.

Current projections for OECD general economic growth range from 1.5 to 3.5 percent; some have forecast a 1 to 2.5 percent growth rate for the industrial world as a whole and also for the key economies of Germany and the United States. Projections of improved efficiency in the use of energy indicate that a GNP–energy growth rate of something near to 0.8 may be feasible (and some believe it can be less). No consensus is available as to what these lower GNP projections (or improved efficiencies in the use of energy) mean to the pursuit of substitutes for oil.

To a great extent, the world's energy future to 1985, and in some cases beyond to 1990, has already been determined by the actions taken—or more accurately, not taken—over recent years. Any further changes in energy planning cannot be significant much before 1990. Existing energy sources in industrial and developing countries create patterns of consumption and supply that cannot be altered to significantly reduce the need for oil imports except over many years.

Of course, this "unalterable" near-term energy future is alterable— for the worse. Underlying all discussions on energy trade from the Western point of view is the uneasy feeling that what supply is available can be reduced or cut off very largely by producers' decisions. Thus, since it is largely beyond the importers' power to change their energy situation in the nearer term, their vulnerability remains undiminished.

Still, certain measures taken now can demonstrably reduce their vulnerability in the 1990s. No one fuel or technology, however, can be relied on alone; instead, it is becoming apparent that a number of alternative energy supplies will have to be developed. Oil cannot be replaced in the next ten to twenty years, but its dominance can be proportionately reduced by changing the basic energy supply mix of importers. All oil will probably still be between 45 and 50 percent of energy supply in 1990; today it is slightly more than 50 percent.

The industrial world's vulnerability is at a maximum now because of its singular dependence on oil—especially Middle East oil—for the largest portion of imported energy supply (see Tables 2–3 and 2–4). Thus, the risks associated with oil dependency have vital con-

Table 2-3. Fall 1980 Estimates of Demand for OPEC and Gulf Oil
(*in mbd*)

	1979 Actual	1985	1990
OECD	27.4	25.0	25.4
Non-OECD industrial countries	0.3	0.4	0.5
Non-OPEC developing world	2.2	1.5	2.0
OPEC	2.3	3.5	6.0
Net CPE imports (exports)	(0.8)	1.0	2.0
Demand for OPEC oil	31.4	34.4	35.9
Foreign demand for OPEC gulf oil	20.3	23.0	23.5
Non-OPEC gulf	0.4	0.5	0.5
Total foreign demand for gulf oil	20.7	23.5	24.0
Gulf oil as percentage of world oil trade (percent)	62	73	72

Table 2-4. Hypothetical Level of OPEC Oil and LNG Production
(*in mbd*) to Meet Estimated Free World Demand

	1979	1985	1990
Saudi Arabia	9.6	13.3	14.5
Iran	3.0	3.5	3.5
Iraq	3.4	4.0	4.5
Kuwait	2.5	1.6	1.6
United Arab Emirates	1.8	1.9	2.0
Libya	2.0	2.1	2.0
Nigeria	2.3	2.2	2.2
Venezuela	2.3	2.1	2.1
Indonesia	1.6	1.6	1.6
Algeria	1.2	1.1	1.0
Ecuador	0.2	0.2	0.2
Gabon	0.2	0.2	0.2
Qatar	0.5	0.6	0.5
Total oil and LNG	31.4	34.4	35.9
More likely production		30.2-32.0	30.6-32.0

sequences on international relationships. Different fuel sources, however, predominate in different geopolitical areas and carry different risks than those of oil. Coal is an example. A mix of fuel sources, then, allows different portions of total supply to be exempt from the risks associated with other portions. Their risks are "complementary." Diversification in types of energy and in their sources is a common objective of allies, and it is entirely attainable with the requisite commitment by governments and companies to the opportunity.

Furthermore, the geographical weight of oil sources shows few signs of changing. Those countries that have the ability to increase oil production because of a large reserve base (see Table 2-5)—and "the ability" should not be confused with "the will"—are predominantly located in the Middle East, already the source of some 58 percent of oil in world trade. Despite attention now being given such largely unexplored areas as the Arctic and offshore regions, increased vol-

Table 2-5. Countries Possessing the Oil Reserve Base to Expand Oil Production in the Near Term (to 1985)[a]

Country	1979 Production[b] (mm b/d)	Percent of World	Reserves-to- Production Ratio
Saudi Arabia	9.5	14.5	55:1
Iran	3.1	4.8	32:1
Iraq	3.4	5.3	34:1
Kuwait	2.2	3.5	95:1
United Arab Emirates	1.9	2.8	48:1
Mexico	1.6	2.5	50:1 (low estimate)
North Sea	1.9	2.0	
England	1.6	2.4	40:1
Norway	0.3	0.6	40:1
World	65.7	100	

Note: Iran's production has since fallen to less than 1 mbd even before the Iraqi-Iranian war. Apparent inattention to field and well maintenance probably placed the near-term ceiling on Iran's oil production at a level no higher than 2-3 mbd, though continued negligence in the production facilities could rapidly lower this capacity, as could an inability to repair war damage. Iraqi damage is considerable and likely to be repeated.

a. John Sawhill, deputy secretary, Department of Energy, Testimony before the U.S. Senate Foreign Relations Committee, February 20, 1980.

b. BP Statistical Review, 1979.

umes of oil in world trade during the balance of this century are likely to come from already established producing areas—from extensions and the application of improved recovery techniques.

Neither China nor Mexico—to select two exporters that some anticipate could be important sources of additional supply—are likely to be such. At least over the next decade or two, their rising internal demands and need for foreign exchange will conflict with the desire to husband oil reserves. While the Mexican petroleum resource approaches that of some Middle East fields, it is probably not another Saudi Arabia and will likely constrain oil development and production for export to that volume that meets development objectives generally, not in response to higher demands from importers. The calculation that had exporters simply meeting importer demand is gone forever. We do not know the Chinese potential, but it seems reasonable and prudent to think of the huge population base and the nation's industrial program and then of that meager 2 mbd that presently is consumed. China may, in time, be a large importer of oil. The geopolitical implications of this are awesome.

The alternatives to oil—gas, coal, and nuclear—are not available in sufficient volume to displace oil. How quickly they may begin to replace oil in those end uses (heating, petrochemicals, and electric power generation) for which they can be substitutes depends very largely on public attitudes toward their exploitation and the policies of governments as to their availability, plus long lead times. There appears to be little doubt as to the ample resource base; finance is not listed generally as a principal barrier, and technology is developed or developing.

The case for gas rests on the reserves already found in enormous volume, especially within the Middle East and the USSR. The USSR and Iran together account for nearly two-thirds of the gas available for export. Over the long run, it is likely that large producing areas proximate to Europe or in the United States—not to mention the hoped for resources of the Arctic—will be major suppliers, although the evidence is scarcely in. The extent to which gas is exploited rests on exporting government policies (as to export volume and price parity with oil) and on importing nations' energy priorities. The logistics of gas may be the largest issue of all, with pipeline gas strongly favored over LNG. Gas is not expected to be a substitute for oil in world trade for many years to come, but its resource base is at least equivalent to that of oil (see Table 2–6).

Table 2-6. Natural Gas: Market Status of Proved Reserves
(*billion barrels oil equivalent*)

	Proved Reserves	Available for Export	Export Committee	Surplus Available for Export
OECD	82	12	9	3
Sino-Soviet	167	80	3	77
OPEC	170	64	14	50
Other non-OPEC	33	12	1	11
World Total	453	170	26	144

Source: As of December 31, 1978. Jensen & Associates, Middle East Economic Survey
(MEES), January 28, 1980.

world trade for many years to come, but its resource base is at least
equivalent to that of oil (see Table 2-6).

In 1978, international gas trade was 2.9 million barrels of oil
equivalent per day, of which only 470 thousand boe/d was LNG.
By 1990 the major potential gas exporters are likely to be Mexico
(0.3 mbd equivalent); Algeria (1.3); USSR (to the West only, 1);
Norway (0.5); Iran (0.5); Abu Dhabi and Qatar (0.24); the Far East,
including Australia (0.7); the Netherlands (0.5); and Canada (0.5).
By 2000, new entrants could be Nigeria (0.5); and Saudi Arabia
(0.6). (At century's end, the Netherlands will probably no longer be
a gas exporter.) The total of all these sources' supply in 1990 might
be 6 mbd and by 2000, 8.3 mbd.

We need to assume that there is no likely reversal of U.S. and
USSR declines in oil production. If the United States reduces its oil
imports, it will probably be for reasons other than very large additions to domestic reserves. If the USSR forestalls the time at which it
may be an importer for its own or, more likely, Eastern Europe's
needs, it will probably be due to the rapid expansion of gas and
nuclear sources. The importance of the Middle East reserves is so
great that the region is certain to remain the principal supplier to the
world.

Thus far the discussion has focused on the centerpiece of energy
supply—conventional oil. In the longer term, however, the "unconventional" oils—tar sands, shale, and heavier oils obtained through
improved extraction techniques—may become the principal means of

prolonging the oil era. There is no doubt that the resource base for such oil is immense, exceeding that of the conventional oils. Also, the geographical distribution of unconventional resources, with large deposits in the United States, Canada, and Venezuela, is far different from that of the conventional oils, pointing to an eventual shift of imports from Middle East and North African supply. Nevertheless, the uncertainties in some of the technologies involved for recovery and processing, environmental considerations, and vacillating government policies restrict current projections of the unconventional contribution to from 1 to 2 mbd by 2000. Still, it is entirely possible that a concerted multilateral effort on the part of importers could raise the actual level of production two or three times by 2000 and possibly even more. Obviously, this implies a level of effort not currently anticipated.

The case for coal has been developed in two recent public studies, each of which concludes that very large opportunities exist to increase domestic production both in certain highly endowed areas (the United States, the USSR, China, Australia, South Africa, and so forth) and also more generally than may have been previously thought. The more conservative case for coal, represented in Table 2-7, shows a threefold increase in its international trade by the century's end. Even then, it could conceivably be no more than 15 percent of the oil then in trade (assuming preferred production rates are no higher than the 30 mbd in 1979). One of the interesting aspects of coal versus oil is its geography: OPEC nations are not known to possess significant amounts of coal.

Table 2-7. International Coal Trade, 1960-2000

Year	Imports/Exports (mmboe/d)
1960	0.7
1970	1.6
1978	1.7
1985	2.3
1990	3.4
2000	5.4

Source: Petro-Canada, 1980.

Table 2-8. Outlook for OECD Coal Production: Demand and Imports

	1976	1977	1985	1990	2000
			Production (mtce)		
WOCOL[a]	NA	964	NA	NA	2813
OECD[b]	953	NA	1329	1569	1743-1928
			Demand (mtce)		
WOCOL[a]	NA	990	1235-1370	NA	2000-3025
OECD[b]	986	NA	1388	1667	1854-2081
			Imports (mtce)[c]		
WOCOL[a]	NA	145	200-230	NA	355-620
OECD[b]	33	A	59	98	112-154

Percent Growth per Annum 1976/77-2000

	Production	Demand	Imports
WOCOL[a]	4.8	3.1-5.0	4.0-6.5
OECD[b]	2.5-3.0	1.7-3.2	5.2-6.6

a. Carroll Wilson, *Coal: Bridge to the Future* (1980)

b. OECD/IEA, *Steam Coal: Prospects to 2000* (1978).

c. WOCOL's figures are total imports; OECD's are net imports.

The larger case for coal is put by the OECD/IEA[1] and especially by Professor Carroll Wilson of MIT,[2] whose study outdistances the OECD targets by a considerable margin (Table 2-8). Whichever may prove to be more accurate, and clearly the OECD targets are attainable, the central point is that coal is still a largely unrealized option. While not likely to be significant in world trade generally within this decade, coal's importance could lift by the 1990s.

The nuclear option is very generally discounted for all the environmental and safety reasons plus sharply rising costs of construction, reduced electricity demand, and so forth. The reduction in nuclear projections for 1985, while a revealing portrayal of postponed hopes

1. OECD/IEA, *Steam Coal: Prospects to 2000 (1978)*.

2. Caroll Wilson, *Coal: Bridge to the Future (1980)*.

Table 2-9. OECD Nuclear Power Projections *(capacity in gigawatts)*

Estimator	(year)	1978	1979	1980	1985	1990
OECD	(1970)				562.6	
	(1973)				542.3	
	(1974)				513.0	
	(1975)				486.4	
	(1975)				464.9	
	(1976)				399.8	
	(1976)				330.6	
	(1977)				318.6	
	(1977)				258.8	
	(1978)				213.9	
International Consultative Group on Nuclear Energy	(1979)		109.2		237	310.5
CIA	(1979)	95.3		130.6	213.9	
DOE/Sawhill	(1980)	97			195-242	

(Table 2-9), does not make clear the present nuclear role—in the United States, for example, some 13 percent of all power generation. As an alternative to oil (or coal) for power generation, nuclear energy already performs an important role. Currently, we are understandably impressed more by the man-created barriers to its further use. But it is at least possible that these will be progressively dismantled; nuclear energy is not ruled out in the Soviet bloc nor in China, Japan, France, or in many developing nations. The uranium resource base is now presumed adequate through this century. Enrichment facilities built and committed for will also be sufficient (and the geography of uranium and of enrichment involves countries other than OPEC).

However, no matter how pronuclear the world might become in the coming years, it is already nearing the horizon of 1990 as determined by nuclear power plant lead times. The nuclear debate will have to hinge on post-1990 scenarios.

What is needed—and is not available—is a ready alternative to oil as the world's most important commercial fuel. Such an alternative would be a marginal energy source found in sufficient quantities, geographically dispersed, easily transportable, able to be produced and deployed rapidly to meet variations in levels of demand, and available at a price level determined by the marginal cost of its production rather than by its scarcity. Oil once met these requirements.

Certain substitutes could, over time, promise to satisfy most, if not all, of these criteria. Conventional coal and gas are all found in sufficient quantities to be exploitable within this decade. Both can be exploited with presently available technology, and each is economic. The range of incentives necessary to maximize these options is still not yet encompassed by public policy. Environmental and labor obstacles, plus concern about the durability of fuel-switching regulations, are among the more critical questions not yet addressed.

The price of future energy from unconventional sources—coal gasification and, in the 1990s, oil from shale or the Orinoco Belt or Canadian tar sands, methanol from coal, and the like—is estimated to be within the range of $35 to $40 per barrel or per barrel of oil equivalent (1980 prices). This is clearly within economically feasible ranges, but again, actual availability even under the present synfuels schedule and other programs is not likely for many years to come.

In developing these energy alternatives, there may be scope for more than just a national effort. Multilateral participation may be a wise tactic within the alliances and may be the more acceptable route with host countries.

If, then, a greater emphasis is not placed on the development of substitute conventional supplies (gas, coal, nuclear, the "unconventional" oils), conventional oil will remain the prime energy source in world trade. A dramatic reduction in oil use and hence a reduction in dependence upon oil imports may occur in the next twenty years as a consequence of lower OECD economic growth rates and increasing efficiency of energy use (conservation). Nevertheless, both effects are more likely to be responses to producer government restrictions in the supply of oil rather than results of concerted importer efforts to lessen their vulnerability as oil-importing societies.

In further consideration of energy in the 1980s, one can choose to concentrate on the oil factor, on the more rapid development of energy alternatives, and/or on conservation. These latter pursuits have their appeal in that they flow from being oil import dependent. But it is oil that presents the grave strategic risks and oil that can corrode alliances; it is therefore oil on which the balance of this chapter concentrates.

III. CONSIDERATIONS AFFECTING
OIL SUPPLY IN THE 1980s

Throughout this decade, most of the industrial nations and much of the developing world will remain significantly dependent upon imported oil. Canada, Norway, and possibly the United Kingdom are the exceptions, yet even these countries will be unable to insulate themselves from the world energy situation. Problems of short or unreliable supply will affect all nations. Furthermore, the major source for oil in world trade will continue to be the Middle East. The region's contribution of almost two-thirds of today's international supply is not likely to be challenged by oil from other sources.

At the end of 1979, the Middle East accounted for 56 percent, or 361 billion barrels of total world "proved" reserves. This compares with U.S. "proved" reserves of some 26.5 billion barrels, or 4.1 percent of the world total, and Western Europe's of 23.7 billion barrels, or 3.6 percent. In a global perspective, as of January 1, 1980, total "proved" oil reserves amounted to 641 billion barrels. Petroleum reserves are believed to be adequate to meet moderate increases in demand. In the 1980s there will be no physical limit to oil supplies. This does not guarantee, however, that the volume of oil to be placed in world trade will be sufficient to meet demand.

Crude oil supply increased at a rate of 5.5 percent per year from 1923 through 1973. This period of increasing availability of oil may be approaching its plateau. Some assert that world production will peak in this decade; others think it is unlikely to do so much before century's end. In either case, oil-importing nations may have to adjust to a period during which supplies could remain at present levels or even decrease, but for essentially nontechnical causes. Instead, for political, economic, and financial reasons, the volume of oil likely to be available in world trade through the 1980s may be in the lower range of 30 to 35 mbd—although it could fluctuate at short notice and as the interests of key exporters dictate. This quantity may come close to that which is required to preserve national economies. Regardless of cost, these volumes must be obtained. If one chooses to assume that the volume of oil in world trade be half again as much, then one must also assume no limits on production except those of technical origin (field characteristics and the like), which would be imprudent.

Price

Owing to the necessity of obtaining a minimal level of oil supplies, it is unlikely that even increasing prices could significantly reduce demand below a critical volume (26 mbd in international trade). Market forces will prove inadequate in allocating what are generally anticipated to be tighter supplies of this strategic commodity. In a reasonably orderly market and with moderate OECD growth, an annual 7 percent increase in the real price of oil over the next decade should be anticipated. This is a far higher rate than that currently suggested by the World Bank's director of policy planning when he wrote that "most present forecasts indicate a real increase in prices (by 3-5 percent a year) over the 1980's"[3] or by an internal IEA paper that asserts most public and private energy forecasts assume that the real price will grow by about 2-3 percent annually. No economic or financial forecast can persuade a reader which of these three projections will prove to be more nearly correct. An orderly world trade system for oil is not probable, however, for reasons that are found in the subsequent discussion of the international oil system. The far higher real increase per year of 7 percent is not, we argue, improbable — especially as key exporters have the capability to set price and volume in light of their own concerns, which need not match those of industrial importers.

Prices will be set to reflect (1) the presumed price of available or prospective alternatives to oil; (2) the revenue needs of the producers (itself a complex mix of domestic and foreign objectives); (3) the rising costs of producers' imports; (4) the deemed value of a finite, diminishing resource; (5) the ability of the importing nations to pay, and (6) the producers' anticipation of the appreciated value of their overseas investments of revenues surplus to their immediate needs. The relationship between price and all these factors can never be constant; rather, it will be shifting. Moreover, the most important factor may be domestic and foreign objectives, not the pressure of what is euphemistically called the "market."

Present and future OPEC pricing policies will also be influenced by the perceptions of oil exporters as to when alternatives and substitutes for oil will make a significant impact on the world oil market.

3. *Foreign Affairs* 59, no. 2 (Winter 1980-81): 407.

These policies will be shaped by the industrialized nations' success in developing substitutes and alternatives. In this regard the U.S. synfuels program (reflecting private and government initiatives) may yet be an important consideration for producers' long-range planning.

Oil-importing nations may no longer look so surely to Saudi Arabia to be the key price moderator in OPEC. The Saudis' failure in 1976–1977 to maintain a strategy based on a two-tier pricing system as a means of forcing prices to the lower range, coupled with their current aim not to increase capacity over the present perhaps 12.5 mbd installed but only 9.5 mbd "sustainable," leaves Saudi Arabia less able to increase production substantially in support of a lower price. Saudi influence today—and for the foreseeable future—is based more on its ability to continue to meet its revenue needs through a significant reduction in exports—perhaps by 3.5 mbd—thus sustaining, not lowering, price.

Rumors that Saudi Arabia plans to increase sustainable capacity to at least 12 mbd do not alter these conclusions. Increased capacity will give the Saudis increased flexibility, but not to the extent that it could singly acquire control over OPEC pricing policies. (Incidentally, note the relatively modest Saudi increase now being mentioned—compared with the West's projection of only a few years ago that there would be a Saudi capacity increase to 20 mbd sustainable in order to meet future world oil demand.)

The abandonment of the Saudi marker crude in OPEC pricing and continuing pressure of the spot market—previously entered only by marginal suppliers—led in 1979 to price "leap frogging" on an unprecedented scale. While oil exporters and importers continue to talk about the need for an orderly pricing process—most recently in the report of the OPEC Long-Range Strategy Committee—there is little evidence of any intention or even willingness, not to mention ability, to reestablish price discipline. OPEC's continuing inability to create and abide by production-prorationing schemes plus difficulties in reconciling price splits make future monolithic OPEC actions improbable; there is nothing to prevent individual oil exporters in (and outside) OPEC from making their own pricing decisions.

Preferred Production Rates (PPRs)

The role of oil-exporting governments in defining the terms of supply has shifted from focusing largely on price determination to include the setting of export limits through PPRs. Depletion policies or limits have been set for a variety of technical, economic, and political reasons by almost all oil exporters (OPEC members, Canada, Norway, Mexico, and the United Kingdom).

Future export levels of OPEC members will not be set simply to meet incremental world demand, nor is it likely they will be set by OPEC as a whole. Rather, individual oil-producing nations will limit their oil exports in order to serve a wide range of national needs and interests. More and more, these national concerns are seen as best served by lower production rates.

Crude oil production of OPEC members averaged 30.7 mbd in 1979, and exports were 28.3 mbd. In the summer of 1980, OPEC production fell to about 27.5 mbd, while the crude oil productive capacity (sustainable) of OPEC members (including Iran, still rated at 5.5 mbd) was approximately 35 mbd. Installed capacity is approximately 41 mbd. Thus, a gap between maximum sustainable capacity and production and export levels exists—yet if one subtracts the Iranian capacity of 5.5 mbd from the total maximum sustainable capacity, the margin is 2.5 mbd.

Preferred production rates may be set for a number of reasons that in the view of the oil producers are more valid than the customary meeting of incremental world demand. First among these is the maintaining of prudent production rates in order to avoid technical problems inherent in too rapid depletion. Second is the desire to conserve a resource that is finite. For some nations, it is their key revenue-producing asset. Hence, the idea of slowing production to await future price increases and/or to have more time to build a diversified economy is compelling. Third, for some producers, increased production means generation of excess revenues that cannot be used effectively for domestic economic growth. A major concern is the need for some form of guarantee for the value of their overseas investments—investments made necessary by higher exports of oil. If there is no guarantee that the real value of these investments will increase so that they assure the producer of sufficient income against future needs, and that they are secure, then there is little incentive to continue generating excess income. Fourth, a PPR may reflect a producer's desire to reduce the pace of development, so that the disruptive effects of too rapid change can be avoided. Among these concerns is increasing uneasiness in the Middle East over the continuing necessity for foreign workers and skills.

Reducing the pace of development is not as simple as reducing the rate of oil production. Domestic political imperatives and pressures from foreign states often make the development and industrialization process self-propelling. The internal tensions that result from unrestrained modernization have been seen in almost every developing country—to date most dramatically in the Iranian example. Yet some of the more vulnerable countries, most particularly Saudi Arabia, are continuing with expansive development programs. Might the ramifications of slowing the process be more severe than the tensions generated by its continuation? Saudi officials content that these internal tensions will be placated by the benefits—material wealth—deriving from modernization.

For oil producers generally to obtain the same income in 1980 as was earned in 1978, they need to export only 46 percent of the amount then supplied. The supply curve of oil could continue to be "backward sloping"; the higher the price, the less producers are likely to supply.

Fifth, decreased production may also be seen as (1) a way to force oil-importing nations to limit consumption and thereby moderate pressures upon the producers to export at present or even higher levels or (2) necessary to establish or maintain influence in OPEC (essentially to support price) and (3) as a way to obtain foreign political objectives through the withholding or granting of supply.

Further, and sixth, the PPRs of oil-exporting nations will be defined also by the responsiveness of the industrial world to their insistence upon (1) more "liberal" transfer of technology and (2) trade concessions from the industrialized world (the elimination of import duties and nontariff barriers, for example). Can these be reconciled with the concerns and objectives of the importing nations?

The risks in limiting production are considerable. If OPEC were to produce only 46 percent of the 1978 level, damage to the world community would be incalculable. One danger is the possibility of a price spiral resulting from either real or anticipated supply shortages. Another hazard is that the requisite investments to increase capacity against future needs will not be made in time. There would be the risk of a military reaction from the industrialized world as the volume of oil in world trade is reduced below that critical minimum level where national survival is deemed to be at stake. That level, in aggregate, is probably in the range of 25–27 mbd, or an export volume only some 3 mbd below present supply. Another Iran would suffice to make real these apprehensions, as would a Saudi decision to drop exports by that amount. The precariousness of the present situation is clear.

Finally, the danger exists that the industrialized world will not respond in a coordinated manner to this matter of maintaining supply levels but that individual nations would seek various forms of preferential access to help insure that their needs, at least, are met. More on this later.

Owing primarily to these PPRs, it is possible that OPEC production will not exceed 30 mbd in the foreseeable future, and it is conceivable that it will even fall below that level. We are being warned repeatedly that this will be the case. The hypothetical level of OPEC exports listed in Table 2-4 still assumes a range of exports higher than 30 mbd—and note the gap that by 1985 cannot probably be covered by other sources of energy. 1990 is even more grim unless the commitments are made now to alternatives. Moreover, future crude supply will likely be tied evermore closely to the exporters' objectives of processing more of their own crude and limiting sales of lighter crudes to a proportion of heavier oils. Finally, given the continuing importance of Middle East producers in determining volumes and prices, terms for supply may be those that nations in this volatile region of immense strategic importance choose to define.

The establishment of PPRs will be partially affected by regional politics. The Middle East has been an area of chronic instability since World War I, and political factors and forces will continue to destabilize the region throughout the 1980s. Among these are (1) the Arab–Israeli dispute; (2) inter-Arab disputes (many of which predate oil by a thousand years); and (3) radical internal changes in regional states. If the U.S.–initiated Camp David peace process, particularly the Palestinian autonomy talks, remains at an impasse, the failure could be reflected in OAPEC PPRs and the designation of export destinations. U.S. involvement in the problem presented Arabs by the existence of Israel keeps the United States a likely target for Arab retaliatory moves. U.S. allies in Europe and Japan regard themselves as inextricably involved in this situation—and quite possibly as an indirect path for Arabs to influence the United States.

All of these reasons for setting PPRs have a compelling logic from the producers' viewpoint. This does not mean that the actual levels set will be the result of prudent calculation. The chance the opposite will occur heightens importers' concerns.

Importers' Perspectives[4]

The four basic concerns of oil-importing nations are (1) the continuous supply of oil, (2) in adequate volumes, (3) at prices within their capacity to pay, and (4) preservation of the international financial system to help obtain the funds to pay for oil imports, assuming, as seems necessary, that the traditional process of trade and investment are not available.

In 1979, 46 percent of the oil consumed in the United States was imported, while 90 percent of Europe's oil consumption and almost 100 percent of Japan's were met by imports. Recalling the propositions at the beginning of this chapter, the interests of importers center upon obtaining oil in volumes set not by exporters' PPRs but at levels nearer to their maximum sustainable capacity (35 mbd). How can importers obtain this supply until substitutes or alternatives are in place?

Recycling

The ability of OECD members to bear the burden of new price increases, as in the past, will be reduced because (1) their net import bills will be larger in absolute terms and (2) a smaller fraction of OPEC's increased revenue earnings will immediately be respent because OPEC imports of goods and services are already at high levels and cannot continue to increase almost endlessly.

The IMF estimates that the OPEC surplus will reach $120 billion in 1980. A major concern of the industrialized world is whether this surplus can be recycled in a way that will preserve national economies and the international financial system. A central complaint of the oil-producing countries has been the lack of stable and secure investment outlets for surplus revenues in order to guarantee future income. The oil-importing countries must attract OPEC funds for investments in productive sectors of their economy. Although these may be complementary objectives, their achievement is often hindered by nonfinancial considerations. For example, some key OPEC

4. These are also the interests of oil exporters and offer hope for a dialogue. How each side defines "adequate" and a price within one's "capacity" to pay is key; assurance of "continuous" supply may be even more difficult to obtain.

members do not place a high level of trust in the industrial world's banking system. The freezing of Iranian assets in the United States reinforced their doubts.

Conversely, public opinion in some of the oil-importing nations is suspicious of huge OPEC investments in their own national economies. In the United States in particular, public and congressional concern surrounding OPEC and Arab investments has often been highly emotional, going beyond those steps taken by many governments to limit foreign investments in sensitive industries. A recent report by the U.S. comptroller general concludes that OPEC's assets in the United States, which totaled approximately $44.4 billion in 1978, do not pose a threat to the present or future stability of the U.S. economy. Nevertheless, there has been no appreciable shift in U.S. public opinion, and there are almost always bills before Congress to limit the scope and level of OPEC nations' investments in America. There has been scant recognition of the point that these investments, especially in longer term holdings, should be particularly welcome.

To date, the OPEC surplus has been recycled through the Eurobanking system, commercial banks, portfolio and foreign direct investment in foreign countries, the gold market, and world financial institutions. OPEC's own facilities—the Arab Monetary Fund and the Special Fund—have played a small role. Yet all of these combined may be unable to handle an OPEC surplus of the magnitude anticipated through the 1980s. New methods of dealing with this massive transfer of resources on a multilateral basis must be devised. Otherwise, a proliferation of barter arrangements and bilateral deals—including guaranteed oil supply in exchange for guaranteed real rates of return on investments—should be expected.

Preferential Agreements

If, as seems likely, uncertainties about supply continue and perhaps even multiply through this decade, understandings between importers to mitigate the consequences of competition for what is likely to be limited or, even worse, uncertain supply may not be any more timely and successful than those of the past. Importers are likely to search for preferential arrangements regarding volumes and prices that cover many areas beyond financial guarantees. As a consequence both of the diminished role of international oil companies and of the very complex nature of such arrangements, government-to-government deals will proliferate, although it is not yet certain that these deals have resulted in lower prices or better assurance of supplies. There is scarcely a major importer who has not attempted such deals—the United States with Saudi Arabia and Iran; France with Algeria, Saudi Arabia, and Iraq; Italy with Libya; Germany with Iran, Saudi Arabia and Libya; and so forth. The common experience is that these arrangements are generally short lived. Moreover, the non-oil "costs" involved are usually high. The very pursuit of preferential arrangements can set ally against ally, thus corroding security arrangements to their common and possibly grave disadvantage.

Diversification

Similarly, the attempt by one or two major importers to diversify their sources of supply away from the Middle East might succeed, but in the short run their success could have the effect of increasing the dependence of other oil-dependent nations on the region. Moreover, the potential for a major importer of Middle East oil to diversify its sources of supply is limited. Nevertheless, efforts to increase the number of suppliers is a key ingredient in most importing governments' energy policies.

The Western Hemisphere energy "system" is one frequently mentioned example of energy diversification, owing primarily to the immense reserves of unconventional oil located in Canada, the United States, and Venezuela. The enthusiastic planners often ignore, however, the barriers of extremely long lead times needed for bringing these reserves on stream, as well as the very considerable and perhaps intractable political obstacles involved in such an undertaking. Furthermore, the United States especially must take into account how such an action will appear to its allies, who might still find themselves hugely dependent upon Middle East oil. A scheme that infers that supply would be dedicated to a particular market would precipitate similar efforts elsewhere and be the source of unending competition between governments.

Imbalance of Interests and Presence

The United States, Japan, and Western Europe have a common interest in access to oil, particularly Middle Eastern oil. It is not U.S.

interests alone that are at stake; both Europe and Japan are deeply dependent upon the gulf. Yet there has not yet been an assumption of obligations by the latter two commensurate with their stakes. For the time being, the United States is largely "going it alone," and this situation cannot continue without running risks of alienation within the alliance. Attitudes between allies over such matters will inevitably affect the character of the policies pursued to obtain oil, possibly to our common disadvantage, in time of emergency shortfalls and over the longer run when generally tighter supply is anticipated.

Although the interests of Western Europe, Japan, and the United States in the Middle East coincide in that each is concerned with securing oil and the recycling of petrodollars (preferably through their own national economies), the United States alone has a role within the region and around it, reflecting its special responsibility in the strategic balance it must maintain with the USSR. These are also the particular concerns of Japan, a nation almost totally dependent on imported oil. In 1979, it imported 4.2 mbd from OPEC producers. Recent Japanese efforts to establish special relationships with producer nations in the region have been intense but unsuccessful. Their high stake in Middle East oil is not matched yet by a comparable economic or political presence in the area. Japan has been actively seeking new sources of supply in Southeast Asia and China, again without notable success.

Meanwhile, approximately 45 percent of the crude oil exported from the Persian Gulf goes to Europe. In general, European interests in the area have come to be dominated by economic considerations, although each of these countries has a particular set of vulnerabilities and concerns. Here again, economic and energy interests are not matched by a commensurate political (or military) presence in or near the region.

In 1979 West Germany averaged 1.7 mbd imports from OPEC producers, or 80 percent of its total imports. Germany also has extensive energy (natural gas) links with the Soviet Union and views this as a necessary and important diversification of energy sources. But West Germany's major defense role will continue to focus on Central Europe rather than the gulf.

The United Kingdom continues working to redefine its role in the gulf. Its direct oil interests in the Middle East are less than those of most of the rest of Europe—imports from OPEC producers in 1979 were only 821,000 b/d or 68 percent of total imports—primarily because of North Sea oil. However, the United Kingdom continues to have an interest in obtaining Middle East oil for BP's and Shell's worldwide commitments.

France imported some 2.2 mbd from OPEC members in 1979, which accounted for 90 percent of crude imports. A central aim of French energy policy is to reduce the role of oil as a primary energy source from nearly 60 percent of all energy consumed to less than 40 percent by 1990 and possibly 25 percent by 2000. France is the only European country that has a forward military and naval presence in the Persian Gulf region, maintaining a squadron in the Indian Ocean and operating from bases in Mayotte, the easternmost of the Comoro Islands, and Djibouti at the entrance to the Red Sea.

Need for Consensus

Hopes for a coordinated oil importers' strategy to cope with the uncertainties of their oil situation have been frustrated by a myriad of political factors. Despite strong evidence to the contrary, U.S. policy, after the 1973–1974 oil embargo and quadrupling of oil prices, was that oil and politics could be separated. While it is probable that a resolution of political problems, most particularly the Arab–Israeli dispute, would not in and by itself secure supplies of oil at predictable prices, neither does the Arab–Israeli issue facilitate oil supply or cooperation among allies. U.S.–Soviet competition in the area, which has come to involve historic inter-Arab rivalries, radical versus royalist state confrontations, and the Arab–Israeli conflict, make a common stand among allies on any oil issue even more difficult.

Since the Suez crisis of 1956, there has been no common, allied front on the Arab–Israeli issue. Lebanon in 1958, the Six-Day War in 1967, and especially the Yom Kippur War in 1973 all evoked fragmented allied responses. Europe's refusal during the 1973 war to let U.S. cargo planes land en route to Israel was perhaps the most vivid demonstration of a disunited NATO.

To date, the United States has seemed to discount the possibility of a multinational approach—political, economic, and strategic—for dealing with common concerns surrounding access to oil. Yet such an approach toward the issues of supply security, oil prices and ability to pay, international financial problems, and a military presence in the Middle East would go far to demonstrate the oil importers' intentions to reduce the uncertainties surrounding oil for their economies and would reflect a united concern about the need for stability in the region. Growing sensitivities in Arab states regarding a unilateral U.S. presence in the area might be better contained with increasing evidence of European involvement. As importantly, would successful cooperative efforts among oil importers create a more effective basis for the oil producers–oil consumers dialogue?

The International Energy Agency, the obvious vehicle for cooperation on energy issues, will need an agreed upon definition of a larger role to confront the supply problems and persistent shortages of the 1980s. IEA planning for emergencies and registering of oil sales has been extensive. But IEA attempts to deal with less than emergency situations—namely, setting import ceilings and worldwide allocations systems (which are activated with less than the presently required 7 percent) or a common stock policy—have fallen short; the necessary broad consensus among its members has been lacking.

Strategic Petroleum Reserves (SPR)

At the very least, creation and maintenance of Strategic Petroleum Reserves (SPR) is essential if the oil-importing nations are to cope with shortages. It is all the more vital that the United States possess this reserve if it is to have the option for waiting out a shortfall rather than finding itself compelled to act for reasons of vulnerability to interrupted or substantially reduced supply. The IEA commitments for stocks and standby rationing have been met by a number of members, but not by the United States. At present, the United States has what is termed a "strategic reserve" of some 90 million barrels, which is equivalent to only about ten days of imports. This volume is wholly inadequate. Since 1974, the obtaining of this reserve has been frustrated by government inattention and incompetence, by concerns about cost, and by Saudi Arabia's warnings not to proceed. Yet there is probably no other course of action (along with stringent conservation) that is more essential through this decade for America's energy security and its capability to act in a decisive manner.

There is still no hard definition of what constitutes "strategic" stocks (those under government control); confusion continues as to whether commercial inventories should be counted within the SPR.

If one does, the United States is well off without making any further effort. If one does not include commercial inventory—as the industry recommends—then the United States is critically vulnerable.

Allocation System

The importing nations are moving into a decade in which there may not only be a possibility for sudden cut-offs but also persistent shortages of crude of one characteristic or another due mainly to the PPRs of oil exporters. At a minimum, oil-importing nations will have to reach a consensus on what needs have to be met and how, assuming a particular volume of oil will be available. A standby allocation system with the necessary complexity may be required.

The IEA formula for dealing with emergency shortfalls, caused by producer actions aimed at one or more importers, is extremely complex. Because the international oil companies no longer control the amount of oil they did when the original IEA formula was developed, the IEA allocation system must be revised to accommodate this change, at the very least, if means can be found for doing so.

While the need for an allocation scheme to deal with the implications of PPRs is now more widely acknowledged, there is nothing in the EC, IEA, or OECD record that leads one to think allocation is possible, short of war. There is very little in the events of recent years to cause one to think that the requisite political will exists to act in unison.

Incentives

There is a critical need on the part of key importers to find incentives that will close the gap between producers' preferred production rates and their maximum sustainable capacities. As noted earlier, OPEC production at levels above that which each member country considers essential to satisfy domestic revenue needs will partially reflect the responsiveness of the West and Japan to producers' economic, social, and political objectives. If these are not met, then the supply–demand balance could be kept on a "knife edge" by the decisions of no more than a few exporters acting independently or in "conscious parallelism." Unfortunately, the demands that OPEC members have enunciated cannot be easily met by the industrialized world.

For example, "technology transfer" is an insistent and usually oversimplified demand of oil-exporting nations. It presents three serious problems. First is the question of whether a particular technology can be readily adapted to meet the indigenous needs of the receiving country without, second, the willingness to accept the presence of foreign managerial talent—or the patience to wait for sufficient numbers of its own population to be adequately trained. Third, technology is usually not the government's to give away, but has been developed by the private sector; it cannot be a gift. And by what measurement can "technology" be equated with the cost of oil? Thus, Japan and the West's ability to respond to demands for technology transfer is limited, although their arguments are not accepted by the producers as valid. Indexing oil prices to inflation and open market access are also considered vital to oil-producing countries, yet these are also difficult for oil importers to provide on a preferential basis.

Some of the more pressing political and social problems faced by OPEC nations cannot be alleviated by Western and Japanese help. Exposure to Western practices cannot be avoided if these countries seek to develop more balanced economies, regardless of the pace of that development. Industrialization implies social change and dislocation; the adaptability of political structures to cope with these challenges cannot be determined by outsiders.

The essence of the challenge with regard to obtaining continuous and adequate supply, at predictable prices, lies in the fullest possible integration of the economic and financial interests of oil exporters and importers. This means an increased sensitivity, on both sides, to domestic demands and constraints. Interdependence is a fact of the 1980s, yet its acknowledgement and therefore the need for cooperation have not yet been recognized.

In summary, there is no limit on the physical availability of oil through the 1980s. Oil will be limited in world trade essentially for nontechnical reasons, making its supply seem more of a diplomatic than a logistical problem. Furthermore, the ability of the oil-importing nations to influence the level of oil produced is limited. The balance between demand and available supply will remain precarious and will be maintained very largely by the oil exporters, throughout this decade at least. Demand will ultimately balance with supply;

however, this balance could be struck at a level that the industrialized world may find very difficult to accept. The risk of confrontation grows and, with it, the danger of war to obtain supply.

IV. THE INTERNATIONAL OIL SYSTEM

Until the early 1970s, the supply of international oil by the "majors" was the outstanding characteristic of the system. In balancing supply (which they developed out of vast reserves chiefly in the United States, Venezuela, and the Middle East) with demand (which they created out of the lower cost, cleanliness, and superbly efficient logistics arrangements of oil), these seven companies dominated all industry functions. They were pre-eminent in exploration and development, in refining, in transportation and delivery. They were foremost in research and the introduction of new technology. Possessing very large cash reserves, the majors were, by and large, self-financing.

They operated in, almost literally, a world of their own. While headquartered in Britain and in the United States, they operated worldwide on a scale that placed them, in the views of others, "beyond the effective reach of government." Their calculations as to their commercial and financial interests dominated other considerations, and they succeeded in fashioning a remarkably successful provisioning of a resource that they were instrumental in making available (and eventually vital) to the industrial and developing world.

Two factors eroded their role and their power: (1) Their very achievement turned oil from a commercial commodity into a strategic interest, causing the inevitable involvement of governments themselves both in the terms by which oil was supplied and in the security of its flow; and (2) apart from the earlier discoveries in the USSR and the United States, which for some years were the major sources of oil in world trade, the subsequent vast discoveries, all in the countries of the "colonial belt," guaranteed that oil would figure very greatly in the post–World War II movement toward national independence. Oil became the symbol of political and economic nationalism. The role of the foreigner and his disproportionate share in the return on its sale became the objects of great attention and were often the instruments by which the challenge to the West was fashioned.

While oil-importing governments (France, the United Kingdom) had some oversight over the actions of oil companies, the latter were generally left to their own devices. But with national independence, producer governments moved to enlarge upon their own role. By the early 1970s, the hitherto key role of the private international oil companies had been drastically cut. Price, share of profits, taxes, determination of volumes, and often of destinations were now the province of governments, acting individually, but sometimes in an agreed way through OPEC and OAPEC. Several decades earlier, this surrender to producing governments by the oil companies would not have occurred without a military response. It is worth noting (by producer governments especially) that the transition occurred without French or British or American gunboats; for various reasons, the one time centers of European empires were both unable and unwilling to employ force to reassert control, and the United States would not help provide the means to do so. In effect, they chose to adapt to changing circumstances and attempted to accommodate the new interests within the international system. The battle cry of the IOCs was simply "force majeure"; there was no alternative.

As control passed to producer governments, nearly every importing government—except the United States—created a national oil authority or a national oil company. These actions were taken in an effort both to acquire some measure of influence over imports and to match the producer governments' oil entities and thus be responsive to the producers' expressed intention to bypass the "majors."

The speed with which the position of the majors in world oil trade has altered is astonishing, given the absolute requirement of societies to have oil supplied in adequate volume and in continuous supply. At the beginning of the 1970s, the international oil companies owned or managed most of the oil in world trade. They carried much of it in their own or chartered tankers, and they distributed it through their own affiliates and third-party sales. So large was their share that the IOCs dominated oil traffic. No other company or group of companies could challenge their role. No nation or group of importing nation could do so until the producer governments supported each other's initiatives.

By 1979, nearly half of all oil in world trade was supplied directly by the governments of the oil-producing nations. These sales included both bilateral state-to-state deals and strictly commercial transactions. For all practical purposes, however, all oil put into world trade was there as a consequence of producer government decisions. By making highly uncertain how much supply would be available, for how long, and at what price (and when it would be changed and whether the changes would be retroactive), the producer governments were instrumental in further compelling the IOCs to relinquish their third-party sales, curtailing still further their traditional supply role. Third-party sales by IOCs were cut at least in half, leaving importing nations no alternative to the spot market for immediate supplies. For longer term supplies, companies continued their search for bilateral deals with producing governments. Japan was particularly hard hit by the shifting logistics of international oil trade, losing access to nearly 2 mbd. As OPEC and OAPEC strategies have matured, the transfer of IOC power has been almost complete.

In turn, the seven major IOCs are becoming increasingly vulnerable to world oil market fluctuations (i.e., dependent on expensive or unreliable crude oil and product sources of supply). As can be seen in Table 2-10, the degree of vulnerability or open market dependence varies substantially among the seven, with the four U.S. partners of ARAMCO—Exxon, Mobil, Socal, and Texaco—in a somewhat better position than the other three. If and when the preferential lifting of Saudi oil is removed from these companies, some 7 mbd will be managed otherwise, and the percentages indicated of reliance upon the "open" or "spot" market will increase greatly.

As of September 1980, however, though their supply role had diminished greatly, the technological assets mustered by the IOCs continue to be important—indeed, irreplaceable. The producers' need for their skills remains strong. The IOC experience in managing field development and production is a necessity for nearly all producers, as is the IOC competence in organizing very large industrial projects. Moreover, their very considerable cash reserves make them factors still in "downstream" investments. Above all, IOC management of the international logistics system is vital to all parties. The IOCs are of great importance in the complex process of sorting and delivering crudes worldwide. Their owned or chartered tankers are still principal instruments for moving oil, and there is no substitute yet available for their involvement.

The increased role of producer government oil entities (and of the importing government's own instruments to help obtain supply) has not improved upon the efficiency of supply; rather, the opposite has occurred. The claim that the use of government-to-government chan-

Table 2-10. Estimated Current Supply Positions of the Seven Major International Oil Firms (*in 1000 barrels daily*)

	British Petroleum	Gulf Oil	Shell Group	Exxon	Mobil	Socal	Texaco	Total
Open market dependency	600	175	400	330	30	0	0	1535
Basic demand	3100	1500	4600	2300	3100	3300	3300	22,700
Percent of dependency	19	12	9	7	1	0	0	7

Source: Petroleum Intelligency Weekly (PIW), April 14, 1980, p. 2.

nels offers greater assurance of supply and may even result in better terms has not been convincingly demonstrated anywhere. To the contrary, these channels have injected uncertainty into all aspects of oil.

The IOCs' role as international managers is urgently needed today and in the anticipated tighter oil market of the decade ahead. The proliferation of government-to-government deals increases the obvious dangers of still further politicization of oil trade. Moreover, there is a need for the IOCs' expertise in advance planning, for capacity investments, and for exploration in high risk areas to assure that sufficient supply, or at the very least surge capacity, will be available if needed.

While single nations can help preserve the oil logistics system, generally by doing nothing further to impair it, actions undertaken on a broad international front by nations acting in concert would be more successful. But as in other aspects of oil imports, the need is not matched by political will.

V. PROSPECTS FOR THE WORLD OIL MARKET—THE 1980s

Throughout the 1980s, there will be no substitute for oil—and for Middle East oil in particular. Despite what may yet be major commitments to develop alternative energy sources and to diversify supply away from Middle East sources, neither will materially alter the basic condition of import dependence within this decade. A difficult transition through the remaining oil era is unavoidable. By 1990, synthetic energy sources will be making only a small contribution, while the outlook for renewable energy is even more uncertain—technology for "large-scale" solar installations, for example, has not yet been invented. In short, access to sources of conventional oil will remain the main objective.

As stated in the original propositions, however, petroleum reserves are adequate to meet moderate average increases in demand. We assume only moderate increases in the volumetric requirements of industrial states for imported oil. We expect large (7–10 percent) increases in annual oil consumption by OPEC members and by a few LDCs (Korea, Brazil, India); the USSR and China may also enter the world oil trade as new claimants. Over the 1980s, the critical issue will not be the size of the reserves but the volumes of oil placed in world trade.

It is projected, then, that general tight supply, punctuated by occasional brief periods of "surplus," will be our lot. These conditions may include periodic instances of spot, or even chronic, shortages. Moreover, the supply of light crudes specifically will be very tight, even with a markedly worsening (below 3 percent) average OECD growth rate.

There will be no dependability in the terms of oil. Price changes, altered volumes, and different proportionate liftings of light and heavy crudes will be common. At the same time, there will be no non-OPEC producers able to bring world prices into some kind of regime or even hold them constant. Rather, it is more likely that their own production policies will follow those of OPEC members— the gradual exploitation of resources so as to stretch out the oil era.

OPEC's position as the supporter of world oil price is not likely to become stronger. Although OPEC-wide price floors are discussed as a way to prevent consumer countries from forcing prices to decrease (and ceilings to assure that OPEC price moderates), it is clear that the key oil exporters can achieve desired price supports through individual action. Moreover, if OPEC's interest in an automatic price-fixing system is renewed during a world recession, such a system would probably lack durability. Current failures to maintain a unified price system will likely be repeated as ever-increasing scarcities of light and low sulphur crudes and ever-tightening market conditions complicate such efforts on the part of producers with different needs and objectives.

With the loss of the effect of market conditions upon the production of oil, it appears that both within OPEC and without, difficult economic decisions about oil will acquire political aspects. These oil-related decisions are bound to create tensions between exporters and importers and between importers and other importers, all for different reasons and needs.

Five more precisely defined developments add to future supply uncertainty by reflecting the extent to which oil exporters (1) intend to process more of their crude than is now done (OPEC refining is about 6 percent of OECD refining) and tie oil sales to the utilization of refining capacity in the Middle East and elsewhere; (2) choose to limit sales of their increasingly desirable lighter crudes to a proportion taken of their heavier oils or other export products (this trend will become stronger as competition intensifies for the lighter end of the barrel); (3) increasingly practice selectivity in determining export destinations, both to favor developing countries and to promote political objectives; (4) become directly involved in sales as a matter of long-held policy—now made more significant as the majors pull back or cancel supply commitments particularly, but not exclusively, on third-party sales (this withdrawal may now amount to some 4–5 mbd—transferred, as it were, to government account; nor should one dismiss the high probability that the 7+ mbd of Saudi crude in the U.S. oil companies' lifting commitments will end and that this extraordinary volume will also be added to the government trading account)—giving rise to the question of who will obtain this oil; and (5) alter production levels as a consequence of cutbacks in the pace of national development plans.

As supply certainty remains insecure, diversification efforts may take the form of regional commitments. The following are examples of attempts to decrease the growing energy dependence on the Middle East—Andean Pact coordination; a "Western Hemisphere Energy Program"; a Central American League (Venezuela); Japanese attempts to form a "Pacific Basin Economic Zone" (which may include the USSR once the BAM railway is completed); expansion of EC–North Africa–Middle East interrelationships, including economic, financial, political, and military components; and increased U.S.–Canadian energy coordination.

Until the recent events in Iran and Iraq, the IOCs provided their own and others' refineries with a universal pool of spare capacity from which to secure supplies at reasonably competitive terms. This systemic flexibility rested upon the IOCs' multiple sources of supply. Individually held stocks and added national storage facilities will now be necessary, which will further strain the market.

OECD/IEA supply forecasting will remain difficult at best. It is made ever more so by OPEC country delays in signing supply contracts pending the outcome of their semiannual meetings and by individual producers running up contract prices in relation to rising spot market prices. The lack of durability in supply agreements will continue to remain an incendiary factor in the world oil market.

Yet the IEA's ability to monitor crude oil deals should improve in the future, since oil transactions and selling prices must now be registered in compliance with the Tokyo Summit agreement. IEA will soon have a better idea of price spreads and general market conditions than present data can provide; oil companies usually make no distinction between equity oil and supplies made available to them under "special lifting arrangements." Furthermore, no one presently knows what state and company storage capacity actually is, making it difficult for IEA to estimate how much spare capacity is available for whatever purposes. A current objective of IEA is the better coordination of stockbuilding policies and practice.

There is a recurring suspicion within the oil industry that warns of the possibility of a group such as IEA that might manipulate stocks to produce a particular result in the international oil market. Opinion is divided on this prospect, with some recognizing that key importers may need some mechanism of their own to counter oil producer actions.

Will the decade of the 1990s be different from the situation projected for the 1980s? Not unless oil importers diversify sources of supply, develop alternative forms of energy—especially gas, coal, and nuclear power—and conserve. Every failure to make significant progress on substitutes for oil places an ever heavier burden on oil itself—the very circumstance to be avoided.

VI. NEW CLAIMANTS FOR OIL

It is generally agreed that over the next decade, much of the increased consumption of oil will more likely be a result of LDC and Communist nations' growing requirements, not of substantial increases in consumption by the industrial nations of the free world. During the 1970s, oil consumption amongst LDCs grew at an 8 percent average yearly rate, compared to a world oil consumption average yearly growth of less than 4 percent. In nearly every case, the growth in the LDCs' oil consumption exceeded that of their growth in energy consumption generally—and by two percentage points.

It is not likely that we shall experience a general lessening in the dependence of any category of nations upon a significant volume of imports. Some nations—perhaps Canada, for example—ought to be self-sufficient or even exporters of petroleum, but these will be relatively isolated examples of no major importance to our general anticipation of governments competing for supply. If one accepts that the high range of supply will be available during the next decade, LDCs (non-OPEC and excluding Mexico) may not provide more than

10 percent of world oil production—greater than the present share of about 6 percent, but still representing volumetrically what could be considered "marginal" supply.

Some part of the new claims for a share of oil in world trade will come from the OPEC oil exporters themselves, whose domestic requirements will be growing. Domestic demands of non-OPEC oil exporters will also be increasing—for example, Mexico, Egypt, and China. The number of LDCs that will make the larger demands upon international oil is small and may not include more than the following—Brazil, India, South Korea, and Taiwan. The strategically significant new claims will most likely be those from Russian and possibly Chinese demands.

The Soviet Union

The future energy situation of the USSR is the subject of continuing debate: Will it be able to maintain its energy self-sufficiency and continue to supply Eastern Europe, even if it loses its ability to export to Western Europe? Or will Russia have to obtain foreign supply for itself and for Eastern Europe?

It seems prudent to assume the latter, for it is through an anticipated or actual oil deficiency on the part of the USSR and/or its European satellites that issues of great strategic consequence could be posed to the United States and NATO. Specifically, the USSR anticipates a stake in Middle East oil because of (1) a decline in the growth of its own domestic production, which will lead eventually to the CEMA (Eastern European) nations becoming importers of oil; (2) the need for Eastern Europe to buy oil; and (3) the need to increase Soviet abilities to manipulate and profit from the West's and Japan's great dependence upon imported oil.

Overall, we shall be involved in a general situation in which the superpowers will overlap in their interests increasingly and compete for advantage. The USSR intends to keep the United States from regaining its global influence and power; the United States wants to keep the USSR from acquiring such influence and power. Thus, it is a "game" of "mutual encirclement."

Oil is more likely to be a pressing problem for the USSR because of the Soviet resolve to continue as a major energy supplier to Eastern Europe. The USSR itself is likely to remain largely energy independent for the next decade and perhaps for the following one as well. It has very large energy resources and options as to its domestic efforts and international maneuvers that offer the Soviet Union a greater choice than is often assumed to be the case. Both gas and nuclear — and possibly coal — could save the USSR from becoming oil import dependent. The costs to the USSR of oil imports for Eastern Europe's account — or for its own — could be exceedingly high. We believe that earnings obtained by the USSR on its oil exports account for half of its foreign exchange — urgently needed for imports, often including food. Could the USSR meet Eastern Europe's bill? The strategic implications of such an accomplishment would be of great importance: Contrast it with the prospect of continuing U.S. dependence on overseas oil sources.

By 1985, Eastern Europe may require an additional 1 mbd a year. The USSR, however, may have no surplus for export or may be compelled to dispose of it — not to Eastern Europe, but elsewhere for foreign exchange. From 1985 on, economic growth will be severely limited if there is no increased amount of oil available. After 1990, the nuclear option may be the most significant. If additional oil cannot be found nor the nuclear prospect be realized, despite its very great priority, then the question will loom ever larger: What will be the political consequences of economic hardship on the Soviet political system?

Whatever confidence the Soviets may have in their ability in the medium term to continue to meet their oil needs from domestic production, the Eastern European states will have the most pressing requirements, yet may lack the means to pay for oil. Moreover, they may be unable to obtain concessionary terms from oil exporters. If these states cannot obtain oil, then the USSR might well consider deeper involvement in the Middle East. The crisis is known to be coming, but it is not immediately at hand. The USSR is thus given the chance of moving more cautiously than might otherwise be the case. (Kuwait's current purchase of Soviet military items, which is said to be paid for in oil, is an example. Similarly, recurring indications that the Saudis are considering commitments to sell as much as 300,000 b/d to the USSR is another signal that Middle East producers may accommodate the Soviets' need for Eastern European supply or, in an exchange, help meet Soviet Far Eastern requirements.) In the longer run, the Soviets may be more likely to exploit domestic political instabilities in the region, offering aid and advice to dissidents—perhaps in Iran, Iraq, Libya—in order to have special influence at the time supply from the region will have become truly essential to themselves.

At no time will the Soviets ignore the West's and Japan's vulnerability to oil supply interruptions. The Soviets will seek to be in a position to exert great leverage.

In summary, it is a prudent assumption that, for the first time, the USSR must look to foreign supply. Next, were it not for its extraordinary emphasis upon a "secure" Eastern Europe, the USSR might choose to postpone for many years its becoming significantly dependent on foreign oil. We believe the USSR will exert every conceivable effort to keep its hegemony in that region; hence, the USSR will seek oil not so much for its direct use but to keep energy control over Eastern Europe.

Soviet moves in Afghanistan and elsewhere in the gulf region (South Yemen [PDRY] and Ethiopia) may not be necessarily part of a direct global extension of its power, customarily defined. Rather, these may be somewhat more limited moves aimed at acquiring a means to disrupt supply to the West and also assure supply for itself from the Middle East. In fact, however, such a vantage point could imperil the industrialized world.

In light of the likely decline in Soviet oil production over the next decade, is it desirable for the United States to cut off Soviet access to high technology drilling equipment? The crucial question that must be answered by the U.S. government is whether it is in its best national interest to increase world oil supply, regardless of the source, and perhaps to decrease Soviet incentives for meddling in the Middle East. Or is it preferable not to assist the Soviet Union's efforts to increase production, thereby possibly forcing them to divert funds from military spending to the energy sector. There is no conclusion to this debate in the United States, while European allies show every intention of strengthening their energy links with the USSR.

The People's Republic of China

Similarly, it seems imprudent to believe that China will continue through the balance of this century to be an exporter of oil. Estimates of China's reserves and the ease with which they can be exploited are at present purely conjectural. As its own development gains momentum, it is nearly impossible that the nation will escape the petroleum era; rising transport demand alone could consume Chinese production and, in time, far exceed any likely to be incremental domestic production during the 1980s and 1990s. China may continue to export to its client states and Japan for political reasons, but these amounts are not likely to be significant. Hence, China may be in a situation comparable to that of the USSR—it loses its export capability. Nations that have imported Chinese oil will have to find other suppliers, and then China may well become a net importer. It is by no means inconceivable that the effect of a Chinese loss of energy self-sufficiency would result in a total additional demand upon oil in world trade of something in the league of 3 mbd well before this century is over.

Thus, by the end of the 1980s, the Soviet and Chinese impact upon available international oil could be in the order of an increased demand of possibly some 5 mbd or an amount approximately equal to all gulf production save only that from Saudi Arabia. Such a demand—which could only be met from Middle East reserves—conveys its message loud and clear: The Middle East acquires even greater importance.

Brazil

In the case of Brazil, we have another example of a significant additional demand for a share of oil in world trade, assuming its efforts at exploration do not do more than decrease by 50 percent what would otherwise be imported. Brazil could still have an import requirement by the end of the decade for 2 mbd.

From these claimants alone—the USSR, China, and Brazil—could come a demand for imports in the order of nearly one-fourth of today's supply of oil in world trade. If one adds to this an anticipated increase in the OPEC states' own energy requirements, we are looking at a situation in which new claims by the end of the 1980s could total one-half of today's international supply. Quite clearly, such demand cannot be met if current preferred production rates of oil exporters are maintained.

VII. DEBT FINANCING OF ENERGY-IMPORTING DEVELOPING COUNTRIES

The nonoil developing countries have been—again—particularly hard hit by the sharp increase in oil prices. As can be seen in Table 2-11, the combined current account deficits of these countries rose from $6 billion in 1973 to $47 billion in 1979. The cumulative debt from 1974-1978 totals $148 billion. By 1985, it is estimated (conservatively) that their cumulative debt will be near $650 billion. How these debts will be financed is now a matter of acute concern to the international financial community.

Following the 1973-1974 quadrupling of oil prices, most international financial analysts were optimistic. On the whole, they felt that the international financial system would be capable of responding to the needs of the developing countries, and initially it was. By 1979, however, this general optimism had faded into pessimism.

The post-1973 recycling process was carried out largely by commercial banks, which loaned funds to developing countries. These private sources accounted for almost 60 percent of funds used to finance deficits. Table 2-12 shows the amounts of financing and the major means used. Moreover, in 1974, the IMF created a special oil facility, which offered medium-term financing to developing countries. Drawings from this fund dropped off sharply after 1976, while suppliers' credits were also only a minor addition to the overall financing picture.

In the past, OPEC deposits in these banks were sufficient to cover such loans. As the debt of developing countries continues to grow, however, commercial banks will be unable to meet the demand for funds. The tendency of nonoil developing countries to choose private over official channels is attributable primarily to their desire to avoid the conditions, often severe, that accompany IMF or World Bank loans. But the crucial point is that there is no prospect that with ever higher oil prices, developing countries (and some industrial societies) can expect to earn the foreign exchange to meet their bills. Nor is there any early relief to be found in steering energy policies and commitments of LDCs away from oil. However desirable a development, it is likely that the burden on them of oil payments will remain an acute and very destabilizing burden throughout this decade.

Table 2-11. Current Balances of Major Country Groups ($ billion)

	1973	1974	1975	1976	1977	1978	1979	1980
OPEC	8	60	27	37	29	7	65	76
OECD	10	-27	-0.5	-18	-25	9	-30	-32
Nonoil developing countries	-6	-24	-38	-26	-24	-36	-47	-60
Other non-OECD countries[a]	-4	-10	-18	-13	-9	-10	-11	-12
Total (discrepancy, net)	8	-0.5	-29	-20	-29	-30	-23	-28

a. USSR, Albania, Bulgaria, Czechoslovakia, East Germany, Hungary, Poland, Romania, Peoples Republic of China, North Korea, Cambodia, Laos, Vietnam, Gibralter, Malta, South Africa, and Yugoslavia (also includes trade not specified as to origin or destination).

Note: Minor inconsistencies result from rounding.

Source: OECD, Economic Outlook, December 26, 1979, p. 65.

Table 2-12. Non-OPEC Developing Countries: Financing of Balance of Payments Deficits, 1974–1978 ($ billion)

	1974	1975	1976	1977	1978	Total
Current account before official transfers	-29.1	-36.9	-25.9	-23.1	-30.5	-145.5
Financing unrelated to external debt	8.3	7.4	6.0	9.3	9.1	40.1
Official transfers	5.4	5.9	5.2	5.7	6.8	29.0
Direct investment, net	3.7	4.4	4.2	4.0	4.8	21.1
Other	-0.8	-2.9	-3.4	-0.4	-2.5	-10.0
Change in gross international reserves (- = increase)	-2.5	2.0	-11.2	-11.1	-14.2	-37.0
Net amount to be financed	23.3	27.5	31.2	24.9	35.6	142.5 = 100%
Financing						
Official sources	8.3	10.2	8.7	10.0	11.0	48.2 = 34%
IMF, etc.	1.4	1.6	3.1	-0.8	-0.3	5.0 = 4%
Suppliers' credits	0.5	0.8	1.3	1.2	1.5	5.3 = 4%
Commercial banks, etc.	13.1	14.9	18.0	14.5	23.4	83.9 = 59%
Memo: BIS-reported bank claims on non-OPEC LDCs, end year	33.5	60.0	78.8	98.7	121.7	
Change from previous year		26.5	18.8	19.9	23.0	

Notes: Minor inconsistencies result from rounding. Data does not reflect 1979 doubling of oil prices.

Source: Morgan Guaranty Trust Co., World Financial Markets, December 1979, p. 3.

This heavy reliance on commercial lending has thus led to huge accumulations of medium- and short-term debt and debt servicing. Debt service for these developing countries has been increasing faster than the debt itself. In 1973, the percentage of developing countries' exports needed to finance interest and amortization payments was about 9 percent; it increased to about 17.5 percent in 1979. It is estimated that by 1985, half of all these nations' income will have to go into servicing that debt—a trend that is unsustainable.

Debt is a normal consequence of development, but when the funds borrowed are not available for productive capital investments that will serve to generate income to service that debt, obvious problems develop. While the economies of most of these nonoil developing countries have been functioning, they are not creating sufficient new productive capacities. Modifications of growth plans are underway, but some level of economic growth must be sustained. If exports diminish or export markets are closed off because of rising protectionism in the industrialized world, financing of the debt will be impossible.

At present there may be no aggregate Third World debt problem, but there are problems with individual countries unable to secure adequate funds and meet debt service payments. The heavy concentration of borrowing by a small number of leading countries is the most dangerous aspect of the growing Third World debt. During 1979, Brazil, South Korea, Mexico, and Argentina were the largest borrowers in the Euromarkets. The problems that these nations, often considered to be on the "threshold" of development, are facing with financing are severe and are creating extreme difficulties for the less well off nonoil LDCs, which are also seeking funds.

During 1974–1978, fifteen countries were added to the previous list of three that were unable to repay their debt obligations and had to work out multilateral debt renegotiations. Their problems were caused by a combination of both high debt burdens and poor management of their economies. If one or more of these countries were to default, the borrowing prospects of all developing countries will be quickly and adversely affected. As the debts of these nonoil countries continue to accumulate with no signs of relief, the consequences upon their economies could be profound. Political stability would be an early casualty. Are there any options?

An integral part of the developing countries' demand for a new international economic order (NIEO) is the insistent call for generalized debt relief. They view this as necessary to help them cope with a deteriorating world economy caused, many contend, by the conspicuous consumption patterns of the industrialized world and by the price actions of oil exporters. To date, the industrialized world has responded that there is no generalized debt problem, and therefore, cases are best dealt with on a country-by-country basis.

General Observations

1. The present need is for more medium-term lending. This would most likely continue to come from the commercial banks, as the IMF is basically available for short-term loans and the World Bank for long-term loans. If present apprehensions over excessive debts and servicing obligations persist, some form of official guarantees may be required by the banks to convince them to continue performing this recycling role. The IMF has stated that there is presently no need for a new facility; it is, however, developing contingency plans.

2. Such an approach would require close coordination in international lending between public and private sources and also between various public institutions. Commercial banks would have to stiffen their own conditions and ask developing countries requesting funds to make adjustments in their economies. The IMF must never abandon its own conditionality. These steps will often mean exceptional difficulties for the country involved, but are absolutely essential if the deficit problem is to be successfully addressed over the long term.

3. As outlined most recently in the Brandt Commission report, there is also the need in nonoil developing countries for loans exceeding the amount required for immediate debt financing. The additional funds are essential in order to permit these countries to build viable, productive economies.

4. OPEC countries must be directly involved in coordinating with industrial countries their otherwise perhaps separate efforts to solve the growing problem of Third World debt.

5. Finally, there may now be a need for a formal institutional mechanism for renegotiating private debts.

VIII. THE PERSPECTIVE FROM THE
UNITED STATES IN THE 1980s

The nation's interests in international energy trade will be based on a number of factors:

1. The United States will continue to be dependent upon oil imports. Even if one assumes that the objective of a 50 percent reduction from the 1979 level (to about 4 mbd) can be realized by the middle of the decade, that level will still represent too great a vulnerability in the absence, at least, of standby rationing and a sufficient SPR.

2. Natural gas imports (pipelines and LNG) from Mexico, Canada, and overseas may continue to increase and be of particular importance to regions of the country, but will not represent a larger share of the national gas budget, most probably not more than a total of 2 trillion cubic feet (tcf), or less than 1 percent of total gas consumed.

3. With forecasts of declining U.S. oil (and gas) production, the efforts now only beginning to develop alternatives to oil (coal gasification, solar sources, and so forth) are not likely to produce significant results in terms of lowered oil imports within this decade. (The single possible exception could be coal.) The nuclear option will still be available.

4. The principal causes for whatever reduction in oil imports occurs will most likely be (a) a low economic growth rate and (b) continuing improvements through "conservation," achieved through higher prices and greater efficiency in the use of energy.

The sum of these warn of continuing energy vulnerability through the 1980s. The significance of this lies in the risks run by the United States directly to its own economy and the constraints import dependence places on the nation's worldwide strategic role.

In the context of that role, the United States will have to consider:

1. That most allies generally do not have energy options comparable to those of the United States. They have to rely upon oil and gas imports to an even greater extent. Their coal reserves will

not sustain a large increase in production. Their nuclear options can probably be pursued more effectively than it will be in the United States. Allies' vulnerability to shortfalls, contrived or otherwise, puts an additional challenge to the international economic, financial and security systems, and imposes continuing demands for consensus and leadership,

2. That the anticipated emergence of the Soviet bloc as a net importer of oil raises unprecedented concerns as to the actions Moscow may take to obtain supply. The question is not only one of Soviet actions and U.S. response, but also of the extent to which European and Japanese dependence upon oil imports and gas leads them to give higher priority to accommodation with the USSR on these matters than the United States, with its global role and interests, may think prudent.

3. The likelihood of NATO and Japan accepting greater security commitments in the Middle East and along the sea lanes more nearly commensurate with their stakes in international oil. What consequences might flow from their not doing so?

The United States remains the one country best able to influence energy supply. As the leader in the free world alliance and as the world's largest single importer of oil, a potential leader in developing substitutes and alternatives for petroleum and in support of conservation, and the single most influential financial center, the energy actions of the United States will continue to receive closest attention.

It is not bromidic to continue to insist that the United States develop a comprehensive national energy policy that would, at the very least, provide a general sense of long-term direction and give coherence to short-term measures nationally and internationally. Every incentive to increase self-sufficiency and to decrease imports must be encouraged ever more urgently. Federal lands, particularly in the frontier areas of Alaska, both on- and offshore, must be made available for exploration; the cumbersome regulatory process must be streamlined; and a careful reassessment of the regulations of the Environmental Protection Agency and other instruments of government must be undertaken.

The adversary relationship between government and the oil industry, and between sectors of the public and industry, may be the most important barriers to the achievement of U.S. energy objectives. It both affects performance domestically and diminishes the role of the companies internationally. Presently, there is no accommodation in sight nor any particular effort underway to moderate the pervasive mistrust between them. The national interest is injured, and hence the international energy situations of allies are worsened as well.

The success of U.S. domestic actions constraining oil use and limiting imports will have global repercussions—as would their failure. Though it is unlikely that conservation or the development of substitutes and alternatives to oil will have a major impact on reducing U.S. imports through the 1980s, such actions will alter the perceptions of allies as to the U.S. capability to lead and of producers regarding their own policies and actions.

A point basic to the eventual obtaining of secure supply relates to the need of addressing the producers' argument that increasing production levels is not, presently, in the best national interest of most of them. The United States in concert with allies must still find the economic and financial incentives and provide the technology and training needed for development to lift production above preferred production rates and thus be better assured of adequate and continuous supply at manageable prices.

III U.S. ENERGY RELATIONS WITH THE ARAB OIL-PRODUCING STATES OF THE GULF

Richard D. Erb

INTRODUCTION

The Arab oil-producing states of the Persian Gulf—Saudi Arabia, Iraq, Kuwait, the United Arab Emirates, Bahrain, Qatar, and Oman— produce over 50 percent of total world oil exports and control about 45 percent of the world's proven oil reserves. Of the seven, Saudi Arabia is by far the most significant producer, not only because it is the largest crude oil producer, with a preferred production level of 8.5 mbd, but also because over the short run it can vary production by 1 to 1.5 mbd around that level. More importantly, a decision made by the Saudi government to increase or decrease its preferred production level by 50 percent would have a significant impact on the world price of oil over the next decade.

Among the other Arab producers of the gulf, Iraq is not only the second largest producer, with a prewar production level of 3.4 mbd, but also the only Arab producer likely to increase its preferred production level over the next decade. Kuwait and the United Arab Emirates, each producing in the range of 1.5 to 2.2 mbd, are not insignificant producers, but production increases in the future are not very likely. Bahrain, Qatar, and Oman are relatively minor producers, with production in all three amounting to less than 1 mbd.

Their importance, however, stems from their geographical and political relationships with the other Arab producers of the gulf.

U.S. Dependence on Oil in the Region

The United States imported 1.5 mbd of crude oil in 1980 from the Arab oil-producing states of the gulf, or 28 percent of total U.S. imports and 9 percent of total U.S. consumption. Of the 1.5 mbd total, 1.2 mbd came from Saudi Arabia. But even if the United States imported no oil directly from the region, it would remain indirectly dependent in three important ways. First, since the world oil markets are integrated, U.S. suppliers outside the region shift their prices and redirect their exports in response to developments in the region. Thus, all U.S. oil imports are indirectly affected.[1]

Second, oil price and production shifts in the region affect the economies of countries with whom the United States has extensive trade and financial relations. Thus, when a sudden cut in oil production in the region curtails economic growth in Japan, Europe, and elsewhere, U.S. export growth is depressed. In addition, many countries that are in debt to the U.S. government and the U.S. private sector find it increasingly difficult to meet their principal and interest payments when they are hit by oil price increases and production cuts.

Third, even if the United States and its economic partners imported no oil from the region, the United States would find its economic situation and its security influenced by developments in the region. For example, should the Soviets or some other power move into the region under such circumstances, it would suddenly have access to vast oil reserves that can be tapped with relatively low cost methods of production. Cheap oil in turn would give the Soviets a competitive economic advantage and could fuel a larger military machine.

---

1. Production data used in this report were obtained from the *International Energy Statistical Review* (various issues), published by the U.S. National Foreign Assessment Center.

Other U.S. Interests in the Region

Aside from their role in the international oil markets, the Arab oil-producing states of the gulf are significant to the United States (and other nations of the world) for other important reasons. In the economic realm, they have also become major importers of goods and services and major participants in the international financial system. In 1980, their total imports of goods and services amounted to almost $100 billion. At the end of 1980 their external financial assets had accumulated to $210 billion, and by the end of 1981 they are likely to exceed $300 billion.

In the strategic realm, the Arab states of the gulf are significant not only because of their resources, but also because of their geographic location. Even if there were no oil reserves, control of the region would give the Soviet Union something it has sought for centuries—a warm water port. In the political realm, the Arab states of the gulf affect U.S. interests in a number of areas, including, among others, U.S. relations with Israel, U.S. relations with other industrialized countries, and U.S. relations with developing countries.

In the first section below, the factors that led to the oil price shocks of 1973–1974 and 1979–1980 and the critical roles played by the Arab oil producers of the gulf are reviewed. In section II, the economic, political, and security factors that appear to influence the oil price and production decisions of the Arab producers are examined. Section III concludes with a review of the array of U.S. interests at stake in the region and a set of policy recommendations.

I. POSTWAR TRENDS AND EVENTS IN THE 1970s

Although OPEC is usually perceived as the culprit, oil price increases during the 1970s cannot be attributed to any single event or institution. Instead, a number of political, economic, and security developments evolved during the two and a half decades of the postwar period and laid the basis for the oil price increases of the 1970s. By the late 1960s, conditions were very different from those of the earlier postwar period, when the foundations were laid for the future growth of world dependence on oil production in the region. The oil price shock of 1973-1974 was the outcome of a revolution in the structure of the market, while the oil price increases of 1979-1980 were the outcome of a different kind of revolution.

A Time of Foreign Hegemony

During the early years of the postwar period, the major industrialized nations dominated the Middle East region in a number of ways:

1. Most governments in the region were subject to Western domination or had not yet established independence from Western colonial rulers;

2. Europe and the United States were able and willing to influence domestic political developments within the region;

3. Europe and the United States had a strong military presence in the region;

4. The Texas gulf region was the largest oil-producing region in the world and the Texas Railroad Commission controlled oil prices by controlling oil production; and

5. The United States possessed sufficient excess production capacity to meet sudden increases in demand or sudden cuts in foreign production.

In the early postwar period, much of the Middle East region, including North Africa, was dominated by Western powers. Some of the territories had not yet achieved independence. For example, independence did not come until 1951 in Libya, 1961 in Kuwait, 1962 in Algeria, and 1971 in Qatar, Bahrain, and the United Arab Emirates. In some states that enjoyed an independent status—for example, Iran and Iraq—the governments owed their authority to outside powers because they were put in place by the departing governments.

At times, outside powers came to the rescue of fledgling governments. One of the most controversial interventions came in the early 1950s, when the Iranian government, under Muhammed Mossadegh, nationalized the oil industry. As a consequence, production was shut down for more than two years. With support from the U.S. Central

Intelligence Agency, Mossadegh was overthrown, and the shah was returned to power.

U.S. and British military presence also served as a credible deterrent to outside intervention as well as to intraregional military incursions. In 1948, President Truman threatened the USSR with retaliation should it invade Iran or Iraq. Iraq's expansionist tendencies, evidenced by frequent border conflicts with neighbors, were checked by the threat of U.S.-British military intervention and by indirect military assistance to Iraq's adversaries—for example, the Kurds. U.S. intervention in Lebanon in 1958 also was motivated in part by a desire to send a message to the new Baathist regime in Iraq.

At the beginning of the postwar period, the world oil markets were controlled by two dominant power structures. One power structure was the system of production regulation by state authorities in the United States. The most famous of these authorities was the Texas Railroad Commission. The other dominant power structure rested with the major international oil companies operating in the Middle East—sometimes called the "seven sisters." Both power structures were able to assert a great deal of influence over oil price developments because of their ability to influence total production.

In the Middle East, the major oil companies were able to manage the growth of oil production over time in a way that prevented sudden sharp price declines. In the United States, the system of government regulation was run in such a way that a high level of excess productive capacity was normal. Thus, throughout much of the postwar period, surge capacity in the United States was sufficient to moderate price increases when there were sudden production cuts—as occurred during the Suez invasion of 1956 and the Arab-Israeli War of 1967.

Declining Hegemony. During the postwar period, a number of political, economic, and security developments altered the ability and willingness of the major industrialized countries to influence events in the Middle East. As a result of internal revolutions and in some cases peaceful changes in leadership, governments increasingly asserted their political independence from the nations of Europe and the United States. Within individual nations, governing institutions were established and expanded. Governments also were strengthened by growing numbers of citizens with the education and technical skills necessary to run modern bureaucracies. Oil ministries in particular were able to attract the cream of the crop of those who had acquired business training abroad.

On the security front, European military presence in the region declined when British forces were gradually removed during the 1960s. A U.S. military presence was not substituted because of the Vietnam War and because of shifts in domestic attitudes toward defense spending and military intervention abroad. The interest and ability of the United States to influence domestic developments within the region also declined—in particular, because of a preoccupation with the Vietnam War.

Dramatic changes also took place in the international oil markets. As new oil was discovered in the larger Middle East region, governments invited new oil companies and also established national oil companies to develop and market those resources. Old and new companies were pressed by governments to develop new fields as rapidly as possible and to increase production. Given the pricing systems then in place, production increases provided the only method by which governments could increase their oil revenues. As a result, the international oil markets became more competitive, production grew rapidly, and the effective international price of oil declined during the 1960s. In turn, the decline in oil prices triggered an acceleration in the growth of world oil demand.

The growth in the demand for oil in the United States also began to outpace the growth in U.S. production capacity, especially during the 1960s. As a consequence, domestic political groups sought to reduce U.S. government restrictions on oil imports. More importantly, excess production capacity began to decline, thus reducing the ability of the United States to offset production declines elsewhere.

In sum, by the late 1960s, the world economy had become hooked on cheap Middle East oil. At the same time, the ability and the willingness of the major oil-consuming nations to influence political and security developments in the region had been sharply eroded. The stage was set for the oil market revolution of the early 1970s.

The 1970-1974 Oil Market Revolution.   By the early 1970s, governments in the region had little reason to fear the political or security consequences of asserting national sovereignty over their oil resources. Although public attention focused on the so-called OPEC cartel revolution, OPEC had been around for a decade. The real revolution took place when individual governments seized control over oil production (and prices) from foreign oil companies. Libya tested the water in 1970, and the others quickly followed.

At the same time, the governments began to take the initiative on oil prices. Although the oil-producing governments had planned to raise the price of oil, by 1973 two developments were to propel them faster and further down that path than many had anticipated. First, on top of an already rapidly growing demand for oil in response to the decline in oil prices during the 1960s, a world economic boom further stimulated the demand for oil. In 1972 and 1973, respectively, world oil demand grew by 7.1 percent and 8 percent. In the face of this growing market demand, the producers doubled their prices in September 1973.

Second, the Arab-Israeli War of October 1973 led some of the Arab oil producers to impose an embargo and reduce production. Although the production cuts were modest, the United States lacked the surge capacity to soften the consequences on spot market prices. In an environment of sharply rising spot market prices—with some spot market quotes piercing the then unheard of range of $16 to $20 per barrel—the major oil producers met in December 1973 and again raised the price of oil. When the dust finally settled, the oil-importing nations paid an average $10.50 a barrel to the oil exporters in 1974, over four times the average price per barrel at the beginning of the decade. Although the Arab-Israeli War of 1973 accelerated the transition to a higher price level, that transition probably would have occurred anyway.

During the 1970–1974 period, the international oil market was transformed from a highly competitive market to one that was dominated by relatively few producers. Although public attention initially concentrated on the OPEC cartel, the most critical price-production decisions were made by the Persian Gulf producers—in particular, Kuwait and Saudi Arabia.

Prior to 1974, production in these two countries had been growing, especially in Saudi Arabia. Between 1970 and 1973, average daily oil consumption outside of China and the Soviet bloc increased by 8.3 mbd. Of that total, production increases in Saudi Arabia alone accounted for 3.8 mbd, or 46 percent of the total increase.

In 1974, Kuwait established a preferred annual production level of 2 mbd, a cut of about 1 mbd from its pre-embargo production level.

Saudi Arabia, meanwhile, established a preferred annual production target of 8.5 mbd—a level close to its pre-embargo production level. These decisions were significant because Kuwait and Saudi Arabia had been expected, prior to 1973, to be the primary sources of new oil during the 1970s.

Given the size of Kuwait's and Saudi Arabia's oil resource bases and the development plans of the major international oil companies, many oil market forecasters had expected production levels around 5 mbd in Kuwait and around 18 mbd in Saudi Arabia by the early 1980s. Such expectations, for example, lay behind early 1970s forecasts of stable oil prices for the 1970s. Without Kuwait's decision to cut its production level and Saudi Arabia's decision to hold production in the range of 8.5 mbd, oil prices after 1974 no doubt would have dropped sharply. To put this another way, the durability of the 1973–1974 oil price increases rested primarily on decisions by Kuwait and Saudi Arabia not to develop their full production potential.

Among the other Arab producers of the gulf, the availability of oil resources imposed limits on production increases in the Emirates, Qatar, Bahrain, and Oman. After 1973, Iraq was the only Arab producer of the gulf capable and willing to increase its production, but management and political problems limited the potential increase in Iraq's production level. Among the other OPEC members, there were none capable of making up Kuwait's cut in planned future production, let alone Saudi Arabia's.

During the period from 1974 to the end of 1978, Saudi Arabia also enjoyed a considerable amount of market power to influence short-term price developments. During the soft oil market of 1975, for example, Saudi Arabia cut its production by almost 1.5 mbd. During 1977 and 1978, Saudi Arabia used its excess production capacity to counter pressures from other OPEC producers for larger oil price increases. Primarily as a result of Saudi Arabia's policy of oil price moderation after 1974, oil price increases between 1974 and the end of 1978 did not keep up with world inflation. Depending on which inflation index is used, the inflation-adjusted price declined in the range of 20 to 30 percent during that period.

The Second Oil Shock. Lulled into a false sense of confidence by price moderation and perceptions of an oil glut in 1977–1978, the world economy was suddenly surprised by the 1979–1980 oil price shock. The 1979–1980 oil price shock, however, was different in character from the 1973–1974 price increase. Whereas the earlier price increase occurred because of a shift in the structure of the market from one that was increasingly competitive to a market dominated by a few producers, the 1979–1980 oil price shock was the indirect consequence of a domestic political revolution affecting a major oil producer.

In late 1978, prior to the revolution, Iran's oil production had almost returned to its sustained production potential of 6 mbd. Technical considerations had limited Iran's ability to increase its production significantly above 6 mbd, while domestic revenue requirements encouraged the government to produce as close to 6 mbd as possible.

During the revolution, Iran's production was shut down for a couple of months, but once the new government was in place, production was increased. Statements by officials in the new government, however, indicated that in the future, Iran's preferred production level would be around 3.5 to 4 mbd, about 2 mbd less than the pre-revolutionary preferred production level. Since no other OPEC producer was willing, and in most cases able, to increase its preferred production level to offset the decrease in Iran's, world oil prices needed to rise in order to adjust non-OPEC supply and demand to Iran's lower production level.

The adjustment in world oil prices was complicated by a number of factors. Management and production problems in Iran led to output of only around 3 mbd after the revolution. Perceptions that the gulf region was significantly more unstable led many oil users to increase their desired oil stock levels as insurance against future shutdowns. Since non-OPEC oil supply and final consumption demand adjust to price changes over a period of time and not immediately, prices in the short run rose sharply.

World oil price increases were moderated somewhat by production increases among the OPEC members. Compared with their preferred production levels, production was increased by 0.8 mbd in Saudi Arabia and 0.2 mbd in Kuwait. In addition, Iraq increased production by almost 1 mbd, while other OPEC members increased production by 0.5 mbd. Almost all producers took advantage of the tight markets to charge whatever price the marker would bear. A major exception was Saudi Arabia. Although it too raised the price of oil, during 1979 Saudi Arabia maintained its price level below the prices charged by other OPEC and non-OPEC producers.

During the first half of 1980, the oil markets began to soften. Kuwait cut production and announced a new preferred production level of 1.5 mbd, while cuts also were made in the production levels of other countries. In an effort to achieve a unified OPEC price at a level below the price then being charged by many other OPEC members, Saudi Arabia produced about 1 mbd above its preferred production level. At a time when Saudi Arabia's strategy seemed to be having some success, the Iran–Iraq War broke out and brought exports from those countries to a halt. As a consequence, the international oil markets tightened. At the time this book was going to press, exports from Iran and Iraq had resumed, the oil markets were softening, and Saudi Arabia again was taking the initiative to achieve a unified OPEC price level. In addition, Saudi Arabia was seeking agreement among the OPEC members for a pricing formula that would increase the OPEC price level in parallel with world inflation and world economic growth.

II. FACTORS INFLUENCING THE OIL PRICE AND PRODUCTION DECISIONS OF THE ARAB PRODUCERS OF THE GULF

There has been more than a little debate about what factors influence oil price and production decisions of the major Arab producers and in particular Saudi Arabia. In the latter case, some observers give primary emphasis to economic factors, while others focus on noneconomic factors. In addition, some observers believe that the major producers explicitly coordinate their oil price and production decisions within the context of OPEC, while others believe that decisions are made independently.[2]

Is OPEC A Cartel?

The experience since 1973 suggests that OPEC is significantly less than a cartel. The members have not been able to agree on a long-term production allocation scheme nor on how to manage their pro-

2. For a more in-depth analysis of these issues, see Richard D. Erb, ed., "The Arab Oil-Producing States of the Gulf," *The AEI Foreign Policy and Defense Review* 2, nos. 3 and 4 (1980).

duction levels in response to short-term fluctuations in the demand for OPEC oil. Since early 1979, the members have even failed to agree on a unified price.

Although the members do not behave as a cartel, the OPEC organization has played three important roles. First, it provided a politically visible forum within which members could reinforce their individual nationalization programs. For example, it is unlikely that, standing alone, Saudi Arabia or Kuwait would have nationalized their oil production facilities as early as they did.

Second, the OPEC organization also provided a politically visible forum within which the members could stand up to the all powerful, ex-colonialist, Western industrial countries. Thus, even though other developing countries were hurt by the OPEC price increases, they ported the OPEC countries politically.

Third, although each member may independently set its own production and pricing policies based on an assessment of its own national interests, the OPEC discussions provide an opportunity for members to exert influence on each others' policies. Although such pressures may not result in a coordinated production program, individual members may be less likely to engage in flagrant beggar thy OPEC neighbor policies during soft market periods. For example, Iraq was subject to criticism and pressures from other OPEC members in 1975 when it shaved prices and increased oil production while other members were cutting production in response to soft markets. More importantly, OPEC meetings have enabled those producers with little or no individual market power to press Saudi Arabia regarding its price and production policies. Most OPEC members want Saudi Arabia to lower its preferred production level in order to bring about an even higher price level.

In the remainder of this section, the economic and noneconomic factors influencing the oil price and production of the major Arab producers of the gulf are assessed, with special emphasis on Saudi Arabia.

Economic Motives and Production Strategies

There exist two different perspectives regarding the economic motives underlying preferred production levels of individual oil producers. One is often called the "oil in the ground" perspective, while the other is usually referred to as the "maximum revenue" perspective. Both look beyond short-term fluctuations in a country's production level, and both recognize that a number of years are required before final demand and energy supplies from other sources respond significantly to price changes.

Under a "maximum revenue" strategy, a producer will seek to maximize the flow of oil revenues over some near-term period—a period perhaps as long as fifteen years. Under an "oil in the ground" strategy, oil will be retained in the ground for the distant future even if lower levels of production result in lower revenues over the near future. In other words, while revenues may be lower over some near-term horizon because of lower production, the oil held in the ground will generate revenues in the long run.

From an economic perspective, a "maximum revenue" strategy makes sense if a country has better investment alternatives than holding oil in the ground. An "oil in the ground" strategy makes sense if the alternatives are considered too wasteful or too risky. From the point of view of an oil-producing government, there are two fundamental alternatives to holding oil in the ground—additional domestic development expenditures and additional foreign financial investments.

As discussed below, the governments of Kuwait and the United Arab Emirates are following an oil in the ground strategy, while the government of Iraq is pursuing a maximum revenue strategy. Noneconomic considerations seem to have little or no direct influence on oil price and production decisions in those countries. The strategy of Saudi Arabia is a subject of much debate, however, and a source of uncertainty for the future.

Kuwait. Although Kuwait possesses sufficient reserves to enable it to more than double production if desired, the government has been reducing its preferred production level from 3 mbd in 1972 to its current level of 1.5 mbd. At 1.5 mbd, a modest increase in Kuwait's production over the near term would have a minimal downward impact on the international price of oil. Thus, Kuwait would be able to increase its revenues over the near term if it increased production. However, the Kuwait government believes that keeping oil in the ground for the distant future makes sense, given the investment alternatives.

On the domestic front, Kuwait's population of around 1.3 million limits the amount that can be spent each year on consumption and productive investments. Since more than half of the population is non-Kuwaiti, the government is reluctant for social and political reasons to expand its domestic investments by encouraging more foreign labor to enter the country.

As of the beginning of 1981, Kuwait held foreign financial assets amounting to over $60 billion—or almost $50,000 per capita. Although Kuwait's investment income is not reported, 10 percent or $6 billion a year is a reasonable estimate. Modest additions to that amount each year are more than sufficient to diversify Kuwait's economic wealth while at the same time maintaining Kuwait's low profile in foreign financial markets.

The United Arab Emirates. Although total UAE production is the outcome of independent decisions within each emirate, production decisions in the emirate of Abu Dhabi dominate total output. In 1980, Abu Dhabi produced 1.35 mbd of crude oil, while the other emirates taken together produced only 0.36 mbd. Although each of the other emirates would like to increase production and revenues in order to meet their own consumption and development needs and to gain greater independence from Abu Dhabi, limited oil resources prevent production increases. Abu Dhabi meanwhile generates more than enough resenues to meet expenditure requirements within the emirate and to provide funds for the other emirates through the federal government. At 750,000, the total population of the United Arab Emirates is even less than that of Kuwait. In addition, more than half is made up of foreigners, and there is a reluctance to import more labor for social, political, and security reasons.

Thus, Abu Dhabi is in a position similar to Kuwait—it does not need the revenues. As a consequence, Abu Dhabi has been gradually reducing its preferred production to its current level of 1.25 mbd, and further cuts in Abu Dhabi's output from a 1980 average of 1.35 mbd are in store.

Iraq. With a relatively large population of thirteen million, Iraq has domestic investment opportunities capable of productively absorbing revenues generated in the oil sector. In addition, Iraq maintains a large and expensive military organization. As a consequence, and in contrast to the other Arab producers of the gulf, Iraq has increased oil production in order to increase revenues.

As mentioned above, Iraq's efforts to increase production created conflicts at times with other producers. In effect, other producers were reluctant to cut their preferred production levels in order to offset the depressing impact of Iraq's production increases on international oil prices. During and after the Iranian revolution, when oil markets were tight, the Iraqi government rapidly increased its production from 2 mbd to almost 3.5 mbd. Public statements by officials prior to the Iraq-Iran War indicated a clear desire to increase production further in order to finance domestic expenditure requirements.

Although the war has resulted in a cut in Iraq's production, Iraq will probably attempt a rapid increase in production to its former level. If anything, expenditures to war-related damage and to rebuild its military will stimulate the leadership to produce at even higher levels. In short, Iraq remains a revenue maximizer.

Saudi Arabia. There exists a range of views regarding the factors that influence Saudi Arabia's oil price and production decisions. Statements by Saudi officials more often than not provide a confusing and sometimes conflicting picture about what factors influence their oil decisions. For example, at times official statements suggest that their oil price and production decisions are based primarily on economic interests, while at other times, official Saudi statements suggest that their economic interests are being sacrificed for political and humanitarian reasons.

Within Saudi Arabia, many believe that a preferred production level of 8.5 mbd is too high and that Saudi Arabia is sacrificing its economic interests. A cut in production is advocated—even if such a cut results in lower revenues over the near term. By keeping oil in the ground, it is argued, production will last longer into the next century. Producing too much oil over the near term generates too much revenue, which in turn encourages an overly ambitious and wasteful domestic development program and also results in excessive accumulation of high risk, low return foreign financial assets.

A number of observers believe, however, that Saudi Arabia has maintained a high preferred production level and behaved as a price moderate since 1974 in order to maximize its revenues over the near term. It is argued that Saudi Arabia seeks to maximize revenues in order to fund government transfers, an ambitious domestic development program, foreign assistance, and an expanded military capability. Those who hold this perspective believe that statements of Saudi officials that Saudi Arabia is sacrificing its economic self-interest for moral, political, and other considerations are self-serving. As a *Wall Street Journal* editorial claimed: "In fact, the Saudis have consistently priced their oil to maximize their own revenue. . . . Of course, they also claim all political benefits of appearing to be moderates when profit maximization dictates a higher production, lower price scenario."[3]

While it is difficult to assess the motives behind anyone's behavior, it is especially difficult to make judgments about the factors that influence Saudi Arabia's oil price and production decisions. In part, this stems from the fact that the economics of Saudi Arabia's decisions per se are complex and require judgments about long-run energy supply and demand developments as well as on long-run domestic economic developments and long-run international financial developments. In addition, economic factors have an impact on social, political, and security developments, which in turn have an impact on economic developments. Finally, like any government, decisions in the Saudi government are a result of a collective decisionmaking process. Thus, a variety of individuals and groups, with different values, backgrounds, knowledge, and judgments influence oil price and production decisions.

From a purely economic perspective, Saudi Arabia's oil price and production decisions are complex in part because of Saudi Arabia's large oil base and significant market power. Thus, a change in Saudi Arabia's preferred production can have a significant impact not only on oil prices in the short run, but also on the behavior of prices over an extended period of time. Because of this monopoly power, up to a given price level, reductions in Saudi production are consistent with higher near-term revenues because the higher prices earned on the reduced production offset the loss in revenues due to the production cut. Beyond that price level, however, the production cuts necessary to sustain higher prices will reduce near-term Saudi revenues.

Let us suppose for a moment that the Saudis are in fact seeking to maximize their revenues over the near term, as suggested by the *Wall Street Journal* editorial. The technical economic problem is

---

3. *Wall Street Journal*, November 15, 1979.

finding the right combination of Saudi production and price that will maximize its revenue over some near-term horizon. Such a decision requires forecasts about the future supply and demand for Saudi oil at different price and production levels. Short-run energy forecasts are difficult enough, let alone forecasts for ten to fifteen years in the future. Since energy supply and demand respond to current price developments with a long lag, it would be a high risk strategy to extrapolate short-run supply and demand responses over the long term. If current prices are allowed to rise too high, future demand might drop off more sharply than expected once the world has adjusted to the higher price.

Some of those in Saudi Arabia who argue for a cut in preferred production believe that such a cut would in fact increase current and near-term Saudi revenues. In effect, they are making an implicit judgment that future world supply and demand responses to a higher price will not result in a further drop in the demand for Saudi oil over the near term.

Others, however, who argue for higher prices and a cut in Saudi Arabia's preferred production, are willing to accept the prospects of lower revenues in the near term because they believe that excess revenues in turn lead to excessive and wasteful domestic expenditures. Those concerned about the negative social and political impact of Saudi Arabia's ambitious domestic development program also argue in favor of cutting production.

Those favoring a cut in Saudi Arabia's production also argue that the government's foreign financial holdings are politically risky and earn too low a rate of return. At the beginning of 1981, private and public foreign financial investments probably amounted to over $100 billion or around $15,000 per capita.

In the judgment of this observer, Saudi Arabia's production and price behavior cannot be explained by either the oil in the ground theory or the maximize revenue theory. As with many government decisions, it would be a mistake to underestimate the role of chance and the sequential nature of decisions in the Saudi government. For example, in 1974 the Saudi government had considerable economic latitude to gradually lower its preferred production level in accordance with an oil in the ground strategy. It could have cut production and revenues instead of increasing government expenditures. However, the Saudi government embarked on an ambitious domestic development program. In my opinion, the decision not to cut production probably was influenced by broader political and security considerations. For example, the Saudis were concerned about the impact of such a cut on the world political situation and were concerned about possible military intervention if they squeezed too hard.

Once the economic program was underway, there were domestic, social, and political risks as well as domestic economic costs associated with a sharp cut in the plan. Thus, by 1977 the Saudi government may have become more concerned about future revenue prospects and thus more careful that the price of oil did not rise to a level that would eventually force it to sharply cut production and thus revenues (or seek an explicit production-cutting agreement with other OPEC members).

Looking to the future, the Saudi government continues to follow an ambitious domestic development plan. In addition, events following the Iranian revolution have encouraged the government to expand military expenditures even more rapidly. Thus, it is not unreasonable to expect that the current Saudi leaders will continue to be price moderates and that they will not cut their preferred production level from 8.5 mbd. As in the past, the latter does not preclude periods of production below 8.5 mbd if oil markets should become especially soft.

Although the experience of the last decade suggests it might be wishful thinking, it is not unreasonable to ask how Saudi Arabia might react if world supply and demand adjusted more sharply to the recent price increases than is conventionally forecast. In that circumstance, a temporary reduction in Saudi Arabia's production would probably become a permanent reduction. In addition, domestic expenditures would have to be curtailed or foreign financial assets drawn down or some combination of both.

III. U.S. INTERESTS AND POLICY
RECOMMENDATIONS

Prior to 1974, relations between the U.S. government and the Arab governments of the gulf were relatively limited. Embassy staffs on both sides were small, and direct meetings between U.S. government officials and their counterparts in the Arab governments of the gulf were infrequent. Meetings between officials with economic or financial responsibilities in particular were a rare occurrence. On the U.S. side, relations with the Arab nations were handled primarily by regional specialists.

Following the oil price increases of 1973–1974, the U.S. government moved quickly to develop more extensive ties with governments in the region. These expanded ties included not only security and political matters, but also economic and financial subjects. Among the Arab producers of the gulf, the United States concentrated its efforts on Saudi Arabia, but not to the exclusion of Kuwait and the United Arab Emirates. The absence of formal relations with Iraq, however, limited communication.

Post–1974 U.S. Policy Objectives

During the period following 1973, successive U.S. administrations pursued a variety of policy objectives when dealing with the Arab producers of the gulf. From the Nixon administration to the Carter administration, there was a high degree of continuity in the policy objectives pursued vis-à-vis the Arab producers of the gulf.

On oil matters, the U.S. government expended a good deal of effort to persuade the Arab oil producers to increase their production levels and to moderate price increases if not lower prices. In addition, the oil governments were encouraged to expand their production capacity in order to permit production increases in the future and to provide excess production capacity so that surges in oil demand could be met without sharp price increases. Not surprisingly, the most intense efforts were focused on Saudi Arabia.

The U.S. government also pursued other economic objectives. The producer governments were encouraged to establish ambitious domestic expenditure programs in order that their imports of goods and services would grow rapidly. Higher imports were desired not only to reduce the current account surpluses of the producers and thus reduce the likelihood of international financial problems that might be associated with the surpluses, but also to stimulate export growth in the industrial countries. Although the U.S. government encouraged import growth in general, it also encouraged the oil producers to buy as much as possible from the United States and to utilize the services of U.S. corporations and government agencies in their domestic development programs.

With respect to their foreign financial investments, official U.S. rhetoric encouraged the surplus oil producers to invest their financial assets in dollar-denominated assets. During periods of falling dollar exchange rates, more intense efforts were made to persuade investment managers in the region that the long-term prospects for the dollar were favorable. The U.S. government also encouraged the oil producers to manage their assets in a conservative manner and not to switch from currency to currency or from one asset market to another in response to short-term market developments or for political reasons. On the international financial front, the United States also encouraged the producers to lend to the International Monetary Fund.

The United States also pressed for larger development assistance flows (beyond that being given to Arab nations). These included requests for larger grants to the International Development Association, the soft lending arm of the World Bank, as well as special capital contributions to the World Bank. The oil producers also were encouraged to provide more bilateral assistance to governments faced with serious balance of payments problems.

The United States also has sought political support from the Arab producers for the principles and institutions of the postwar international economic system (IMF, the development banks, General Agreements on Tariffs and Trade [GATT]) and less support for the rhetoric and proposals of the New International Economic Order.

In the security realm, the United States has attempted to maintain its role as a major supplier of arms to the region for military as well as economic reasons. More recently, the United States also has sought support for a land-based military presence in the region, in particular in Oman and Saudi Arabia. The United States has also attempted to discourage countries from using military force in dealing with intra-regional conflicts.

In the political realm, the United States has pressed Arab leaders in the region to support the Camp David agreements and to support and participate in a continuation of the Camp David process. The United States also has sought political and diplomatic support for U.S. policies and actions concerning the Soviet Union. Such efforts intensified following the Soviet invasion of Afghanistan.

U.S. Interests: Conflicts and Interrelations

The U.S. diplomatic initiatives cited above illustrate the ways in which successive U.S. administrations since the early 1970s perceived and pursued broad categories of U.S. interests vis-à-vis the Arab producers in the region. It is not possible within the context of this brief overview to analyze those policies and evaluate whether previous administrations correctly perceived U.S. interests and pursued the appropriate policies. Looking to the future, developments in recent years indicate that more public attention needs to be focused on the interrelations, and in some cases conflicts, among the major U.S. interests in the region. This is particularly true of U.S. interests involving oil, as outlined below.

Dependence versus Price and Production. One of the policy dilemmas confronting the United States stems from the relation between the price of oil and dependence on the Arab producers of the gulf — and in particular dependence on Saudi Arabia. It is not possible to become less dependent on the region without lower levels of production in the region. Lower levels of production, however, result in higher oil prices than would otherwise exist. Thus, less dependence on the region means lower production and higher prices.

In the past, U.S. government policies have opted for lower prices rather than less dependence. Indeed, efforts to persuade the Saudis and other producers to increase their production revealed a U.S. willingness to become more dependent on the region for oil in return for the benefits of lower oil prices. Although the economic, social, and political costs of higher oil prices may justify the costs and risks inherent in becoming more dependent on the region, the trade-off between the two has received little public attention and discussion within the United States.

At any given level of dependence, the degree to which the United States is vulnerable depends on many other conditions outside as well as within the region. For example, measures such as the Strategic Petroleum Reserve, higher oil inventories, and energy-sharing agreements can be implemented to reduce the demand to which the economies of the United States and the rest of the world are vulnerable to politically motivated embargoes or sudden cuts in production such as occurred during the Iranian revolution or the Iraq–Iran War.

Within the region, steps can be taken that would reduce the degree of vulnerability associated with any level of dependence, but such steps may conflict with other interests, as outlined below.

Vulnerability versus Trade and Financial Surpluses.   One of the sources of vulnerability in the region is the risk of domestic turmoil and instability within any one of the producing countries. Given the level of its oil production, Saudi Arabia is of special concern in this regard, but instability in any one of the producers could prove to be disruptive in the region.

Although higher levels of government expenditures will increase imports and reduce financial surpluses, a rapid growth in government expenditures may also contribute to domestic instability. The inflow of foreign workers necessary to sustain more rapid domestic development growth may be socially disruptive. In addition, the dislocations and changes in lifestyle caused by rapid economic development may also put traditional social and political allowances under stress.

Vulnerability versus Military Expenditures and Military Exposure. At least until the Iranian revolution, the United States maintained a limited military capability in the gulf and followed a policy of non-intervention. Until then, the U.S. government relied on the existence of Iranian military forces and the shah to maintain security in the region. As long as Iran's military was seen as being capable and the shah as supportive of U.S. interests, the threat of Soviet intervention and the threat of military conflicts within the region were minimized. Iraq, for example, was not likely to attack Iran or move on other Arab producers in the region as long as Iran was a threat. Iran's military forces, including its naval capability, were also a credible threat against sustained terrorist activities. Iranian forces, for example, were employed in support of the government of Oman when that government was threatened by rebel forces.

Although the Carter administration and now the Reagan administration have taken steps to improve U.S. military capabilities in the region, public consensus does not yet exist in the United States regarding (1) the security threats to oil production in the region, (2) the degree to which U.S. forces in the region could eliminate or reduce those threats, (3) the desirability of committing such forces, and (4) the circumstances under which those forces would be used. As a consequence, access by the oil-consuming nations to oil production in the region remains vulnerable to war among states in the region, acts of terrorism, and intervention by outsiders, in particular the Soviet Union.

Vulnerability versus U.S. Support of Israel. It also is arged by some that there is a fundamental conflict between U.S. support for Israel and U.S. economic interests in the region as they relate not only to oil but also to trade and finance. In this observer's view, it is not likely that Arab oil price and production decisions are influenced by U.S. support for Israel or that oil price and production levels would be modified if there were a settlement. Until a settlement is achieved, however, the United States and other oil-consuming nations will remain vulnerable to another oil embargo should another war break out and perhaps major, long-term production cuts should a future war spread to the gulf.

More importantly, the lack of a Palestinian settlement makes it more difficult for the United States to reduce the other security threats in the region. For example, U.S. involvement in the Arab-Israeli conflict makes it difficult for the United States to obtain support from the Europeans and Japanese for collective security arrangements. As long as the Arab-Israeli conflict continues, Japan and the European nations will continue to fear that a security arrangement with the United States will involve them in a future Arab-Israeli war.

Finally, the lack of a settlement makes it more difficult for the United States to work out cooperative security arrangements with some of the Arab producers. Saudi Arabia is especially reluctant to allow an explicit U.S. military presence on its soil for fear that such a presence would be utilized against Saudi Arabia should another Arab-Israeli war break out.

U.S. Policy Recommendations

For those of us who want to have our cake and eat it too, an ideal outcome over the next decade would be stable if not declining oil prices and a reduction in U.S. direct and indirect dependence on oil produced in the gulf region. In this regard, U.S. domestic energy policies (as well as domestic energy policies both in other industrial countries and in the large number of developing countries) designed to discourage oil consumption and encourage oil production would go a long way toward enabling us to achieve one or both of those objectives. At a minimum, such policy steps should include the elimination of price controls not only on oil production and consumption but also on natural gas production. Taxes that inhibit energy production should be removed, along with excessive environmental controls and restrictions on production. These and other domestic steps designed to ultimately reduce oil imports (or at least hold oil imports stable) would have a favorable impact on the future course of world oil prices. The oil producers would be less willing to risk charging too high a price for fear that they would lose markets in the future. At a minimum, Saudi Arabia's conservative approach to pricing oil would be reinforced.

At any given level of price and dependence on oil produced in the gulf region, steps can be taken within the United States and within other oil-consuming countries to reduce the vulnerability of the oil-consuming nations to developments within the region, whether it be a threat of an embargo, an actual embargo, or a major and sustained loss of production. Strategic reserves would be useful for dealing with threats of embargoes, actual embargoes, or short-run production cuts, but unless they are of enormous magnitude, such reserves would be quckly depleted in a major and sustained production cut. Oil-sharing agreements may turn out to be useful in the face of a major shutdown, but this observer remains skeptical.

Since the focus of this study has been on the Arab oil-producing states of the gulf, the following policy proposals will be limited to policies specifically designed for that region.

1. Intensify diplomatic and security efforts, in order to reduce the likelihood of oil production disruptions or sustained oil production cuts caused by war or acts of terrorism.

   There exist a number of different ways in which military actions of one kind or another can disrupt or halt oil production and shipping in the gulf region. These security threats include, for example, war between two or more producing states, as exemplified by the Iraq–Iran War. Direct Soviet intervention or Soviet intervention in one or more producing states through the use of proxy forces is another security risk for which political and military deterrents need to be developed in order to reduce the likelihood of such Soviet actions. Contingency responses also need to be developed to reduce the risk that a future Arab–Israeli war would expand and engulf oil transportation and/or oil production in the gulf region. Steps also need to be taken to reduce the likelihood of terrorist activities whether perpetrated by individuals, by dissident groups, or by some nation.

It is not possible in this brief chapter to examine these security risks in depth or to develop specific proposals to reduce those risks. Such a policy review, however, should be broad and not limit itself to any single security threat. In addition, avenues of security cooperation should also be explored with other oil-consuming nations and with the Arab oil-producing states in the region.

Whatever security measures are developed, a major effort should be made to explain and generate public support. To the extent that an expanded U.S. military presence in the region is an element of the security strategy, public support for the expenditures will be required, as well as public acceptance of the prospect that U.S. military forces in the region may be utilized someday. Without public support, an expanded U.S. military presence in the region could be destabilizing because it would not be credible.

Finally, the objective of a stronger U.S. military defense capability in the region would be to reduce the risk that war or some other military action would actually occur. There should thus be an explicit, public commitment that a U.S. military presence would be used as a deterrent and not to force producers in the region to produce at a higher production rate.

2. Regarding oil production rates, the U.S. government should cease pressing governments in the region, including Saudi Arabia, to produce more and to behave as price moderates.

The way to encourage producers in the region to behave as oil price moderates is to adopt a domestic energy policy that will persuade them that price moderation is in their long-run self-interest. Unless such policies are in place, the producers will in any case charge what the market can bear.

3. Regarding the domestic development programs of the Arab producers, and in particular of Saudi Arabia, the U.S. should stand prepared to provide technical assistance where desired and should remove any restraints on private sector flows.

The U.S. government, however, should not press for higher domestic expenditure growth rates. Instead, the Arab governments in the region should be left to decide what pace of domestic development is consistent with their domestic needs as well as their social and political stability.

4. Regarding the financial investment policies of the producers, the U.S. government should maintain open financial markets but not make a special effort to persuade the producers to hold dollar-denominated assets or to invest in the United States.

5. Regarding the domestic political situation in each of the Arab oil-producing nations of the gulf, the United States should adopt a hands off policy and neither encourage or discourage political and social reforms or repressive measures.

In sum, the United States and other industrialized countries should not provide special incentives and should stop spending political capital in efforts to persuade the Arab oil producers of the gulf to increase their production targets. Such efforts are not likely to have any influence on their long-run oil price and production levels and yet create the presumption among the producers that a favor is being granted. In addition, even if production levels were increased, they would be of questionable reliability.

Instead, the United States and other industrialized countries should pursue energy policies (domestic and international) that will reduce dependence on the gulf producers and foreign security policies that give first priority to reducing the sources of risk that threaten to bring about sudden, sharp reductions in output in the region.

In its relations with the oil producers of the gulf, the United States should give primary emphasis to reducing the potential sources of instability. Giving first priority to risk reduction instead of oil production in the Middle East is likely to be the most effective means of bringing about price stability during the 1980s.

IV U.S.-CANADIAN ENERGY RELATIONS

Edward F. Wonder

INTRODUCTION

Over the past decade, both the United States and Canada have become increasingly preoccupied with energy self-sufficiency and vulnerability to disruption of oil supplies. Both countries contemplate substantial investments in very expensive and technologically challenging energy projects, and in both countries government policies, especially in the areas of pricing and regulation of industry activity, have been controversial. In Canada, however, the energy policy debate has gone a major step further, becoming a central element in the definition of federal–provincial relations and of overall U.S.–Canadian relations. The Trudeau government's National Energy Program, announced in October, stands at the center of this debate. In the process, a profound and long-lasting transformation of U.S.–Canadian energy relations has occurred.

U.S. perspectives on U.S.–Canadian energy relations have tended to focus on the size of Canada's energy resources and have frequently assumed that a considerable portion of those resources would eventually find their way to U.S. customers. Indeed, the premise that there is a "continental logic" at work, rationalizing energy flows along north–south lines, has been tempting. Upon closer examination, however, several points become clearer. First, an unqualified

137

view of Canada's energy resources, without regard to the technical, economic, and political factors affecting their development, can be very misleading. Second, the politics of energy policy in Canada have left the basic economic and political ground rules of energy development in Canada very unsettled, posing a substantial impediment to major new energy projects. Finally, rather than a major expansion of oil and gas exports or "continentalist" cooperation, let alone integration of energy markets, the most likely prospect for U.S.-Canadian energy relations, unless governments in both countries act to avoid this, is conflict over energy and energy-related issues.

The supply relationship between the two countries has changed considerably over the past decade. U.S.-Canadian oil and gas relations prior to the 1970s were based on a mutual desire to assure access to markets in order to encourage domestic production. For Canada, this meant a policy of exporting to the United States, while in the United States this need justified a quota system to limit imports, which was not applied to Canada until 1970. In 1973, the peak year of Canadian oil exports to the United States, Canada supplied 17 percent of U.S. gross oil imports. By mid-1979, the Canadian share of U.S. oil imports had fallen to 5 percent, and it has continued to fall as oil exports are phased out. It is worth noting that as the Canadian and Venezuelan shares of a burgeoning U.S. oil import market declined in the early 1970s, the position of Middle Eastern and African suppliers increased.

The primary concern of both countries in the 1970s, however, has been access not to markets, but to supply. For Canada, this has meant a strategy of displacing foreign with domestic supply and reducing exports where they interfere with that goal. The reduction in exports has been most dramatic in the oil sector, where only heavy oil that could not find a Canadian market was unaffected. Gas exports have held steady, and while exports of new volumes have recently been authorized, Canadian needs may grow if domestic use of natural gas expands in order to displace imported oil.

Change has not been confined to supply relationships. The linkages between energy and other bilateral issues are becoming more sensitive. This is especially true of trade and investment relations, where Canadian desires for access to U.S. markets for processed raw materials such as petrochemicals and to reduce U.S. ownership of the Canadian oil and gas industries are potential sources of conflict. Environmental relations, where the long-range transport of air pollutants from mid–American coal-fired generating plants is attracting increasing Canadian attention, may also becoming more touchy.

Canada clearly does not have the ability to "solve" the problem of U.S. dependence on insecure oil imports. Nevertheless, it is likely that energy and energy-related issues, especially investment, will occupy a prominent place in the bilateral agenda. Regional dependence in the United States on Canadian gas, the construction of the Alaskan gas pipeline across Canadian territory, the treatment accorded U.S. energy investment in Canada, and the importance of energy to the political structure of Canada necessarily mean that the United States must be vigilant of the energy policies and problems of its northern neighbor.

Several questions guide the discussion of U.S.–Canadian energy relations presented here. These include:

- How significant are Canadian energy resources, and what are the potential constraints on their development?
- How does the Canadian policy process affect domestic energy and export policies?
- To what extent will exports to the United States occupy an important position within the federal–provincial bargaining process and in the national energy policy that that process might produce?
- What are the energy development and marketing options facing Canada, and what are their implications for the United States?
- What are the factors and interests affecting Canadian energy-pricing policies, and what are the potential consequences of these policies for the pace of energy development and demand growth?
- What will be the nature of the Canadian contribution to U.S. energy supply in the future?
- To what extent will other bilateral issues, such as trade, investment, and environment, develop a more explicit energy content?
- Finally, what are the prospects for future energy cooperation?

I. THE CONTENT OF CANADIAN ENERGY POLICY: RESOURCES AND POLITICS

Resources

Two points are particularly important in considering the Canadian energy resource position. The first is the range of uncertainty in resource data, especially for frontier regions, and a tendency toward conservatism on the part of the federal government in appraising these resources. The second is that major exploration and production activity in the future will tend to concentrate on the so-called frontier areas of the Beaufort Sea, High Arctic, and offshore East Coast, as well as the Alberta tar sands, where significant climatic, technical, and transportation problems, to say nothing of the cost and investment requirements, must be overcome. In any event, substantial lead times on a number of fronts will be dominant factors in determining the level and timing of production in frontier areas.

Crude Oil. Candian conventional oil fields can be classified in two categories—(1) the established producing areas south of the sixtieth parallel and (2) the frontier areas north of the sixtieth parallel and offshore east of Newfoundland. The established producing areas are located in Alberta, Saskatchewan, British Columbia, and to a much lesser extent, western Manitoba.

The last official estimate of Canadian oil supply and requirements was issued by the National Energy Board (NEB) in September 1978. (The NEB is currently revising these estimates.) The NEB in 1978 placed recoverable conventional light and heavy oil reserves at 5.7 billion barrels, with another 5.4 billion (2.2 billion light, 3.12 billion heavy) in reserve additions, bringing the total recoverable conventional crude to over 11 billion barrels.[1] These reserves are in the established producing areas. Far more important are the resources located in frontier, offshore, and tar sands areas. Industry and government officials agree that frontier, offshore, and tar sands resources are the key to anything resembling energy self-sufficiency for Canada.

---

1. National Energy Board, *Canadian Oil Supply and Requirements* (September 1978), p. 3.

Briefly, the prospects for these areas are as follows:

- Canadian Beaufort Sea: Geologic estimates of the Beaufort Sea basin reach 30-40 billion barrels. Dome Petroleum has set a production target of 200,000 b/d by 1985 and 750 b/d by 1990, delivered by tanker and later by pipeline. Estimated development costs to reach the 1990 target are in the area of $25 billion.[2]

- East Coast offshore areas: Estimates of the potential range from 7.4 billion barrels (Department of Energy, Mines, and Resources) to 10 billion off Newfoundland and another 10 billion off Labrador (Acquitaine Oil estimate). Costs per barrel in the Hibernia field are twice that of North Sea oil. Gulf Canada estimates that 300,000 b/d could be available from Hibernia by 1990, if priced at the world level.

- Alberta tar sands: Discovered resources are 931 billion barrels, but due to low recovery rate may yield only 80-190 billion barrels of upgraded crude. Production capacity could exceed 750,000 b/d by 1995, surpassing production of conventional light crude in established areas. Significant constraints include price levels, investment required (possibly $40 billion to achieve a 1 million b/d capacity), and labor and equipment availability.[3]

These data present corporate estimates. Speaking before the Natural Resources and Public Works Committee of the Canadian House of Commons on February 10, 1981, D.F. Sherwin, director of resource geology at the Department of Energy, Mines, and Resources, estimated potential recoverable oil in the Beaufort Sea–Mackenzie Delta area to be 9.4 billion barrels, in East Coast offshore areas to be 7.4 billion barrels, and in the Arctic Island area to be 4.3 billion barrels.

Natural Gas. Canadian gas fields are located in the same general region as the oil fields. Moreover, gas appears to be more abundant than oil in the frontier regions. The NEB's gas reserve estimates, as of February 1979, are presented in Table 4-1. The NEB in December 1979 revised its estimate of discovered conventional reserves in

2. *Oil and Gas Journal*, February 25, 1980, p. 64-65; April 13, 1981, pp. 75-78.
3. NEB, p. 58.

Table 4-1. Canada's Discovered Gas Resources and Estimated Additions, 1978 (*tcf*)

	Discovered 12/31/77	Additions 1978-2000	Ultimate Potential
Conventional producing areas			
Western Canada	65.8	38.0	146
Ontario and Other Eastern Canada	0.3		1
Total	66.1	38.0	147
Frontier areas			
Arctic Islands, Mackenzie-Beaufort	14.5	34.0[a]	63[c]
East Coast offshore	–	18.0[b]	27
Other	–	–	6
Total	14.5	52.0	96

a. Industry figures.

b. Newfoundland forecast, 90 percent probability.

c. Geological Survey of Canada, 90 percent probability.

Source: National Energy Board, *Canadian Natural Gas – Supply and Requirements* (February 1979), pp. 8-10, 32-34.

Western Canada, raising that figure to 72 tcf. The other estimates remained unchanged.[4]

As was the case with oil, there are new or potential producing areas that could force revision of NEB forecasts, but that are not now deliverable due to the absence of transportation systems and/or because they are in very early stages of development. Of the conventional producing areas, the potentially most significant area is Deep Basin in Alberta. The National Energy Board so far has been very cautious in treating Deep Basin and in 1979 credited it with only 1 tcf of established reserves.[5] Canadian Hunter, by far the most bullish source of data on this field, claims, on the other hand, that 440 tcf can be recovered at various levels of price and technology, with

4. NEB, *Reasons for Decision* (November 1979), p. 7-8.

5. NEB, *Canadian Natural Gas Supply and Requirements* (February 1979), p. 19.

50 tcf at today's levels.[6] This estimate is regarded as highly speculative by other companies, whose own estimates are significantly
lower. A figure of 7 tcf for proved reserves in Deep Basin is now
accepted by many. The important fact is that the higher Deep Basin
estimates do not yet rest on a solid foundation of drill data.

Production in the frontier areas could compensate for decline in
conventional areas. Dome Petroleum's estimate for the ultimate
potential in the Beaufort Sea — 320 tcf — overshadows those made by
other sources.[7] In the Arctic Islands, Panarctic expects to identify
reserves of 30 tcf by 1981, with 20 tcf needed to justify a pipeline.
Established Arctic Island reserves are currently 16 tcf. Panarctic believes 60 tcf can be proved in the Arctic Islands in the next fifteen
years or nearly the same level currently proven in conventional
areas.[8]

None of this will make much difference if there are no means to
bring the gas to market. Several projects to transport this gas by pipeline or LNG tanker are currently under study. In all cases, the availability of a market is of key importance to the timing and magnitude
of production in these areas. This raises the issue of whether some
exports at the beginning stage of production could accelerate the
pace at which these fields could be developed. In the cases of both
frontier oil and gas, the companies developing those areas foresee the
use of tankers to move these resources to market as early as possible
in order to generate the cash flow necessary to expand production to
the point where pipelines become economical.

The board has refused to include supply estimates from frontier
areas in its forecasts, since this gas is not yet deliverable to market.
Despite the absence of an official NEB estimate of frontier supply
capability, there is a range of corporate estimates for this area. These
estimates run from a high Dome estimate of 3364 MMCf/d from the
Mackenzie Delta–Beaufort Sea area delivered in 1995 and another
2700 MMCf/d from the Arctic Islands to a more representative Imperial estimate of 1972 MMCf/d from the Mackenzie–Beaufort region
in 1995 and 2800 MMCf/d from the Arctic Islands.[9]

6. Ibid., p. 18.

7. *Oil and Gas Journal*, February 25, 1980, p. 64–65; and NEB, *Canadian Natural Gas*, p. 34.

8. *Oil and Gas Journal*, February 25, 1980, p. 66.

9. NEB, *Canadian Natural Gas*, pp. 38–39.

Coal. In contrast to other resources, coal is more widely distributed throughout Canada, although actual production is concentrated in Alberta (over 40 percent), British Columbia (30 percent), and Saskatchewan (16 percent). Canadian coal resources are on the order of 260 billion tons, but only 2 percent of this—5 billion tons—is economically recoverable. Steam coal accounts for about 88 percent of economically recoverable resources.

Canadian coal production more than doubled between 1970 and 1978, when the total reached 37 million tons. Utility demand for steam coal may now be the greatest incentive for increased production. Metallurgical coal, nearly all of which is exported, mainly to Japan, was more important in the early 1970s. In 1978, coal production was nearly evenly divided among the two types, with steam coal accounting for 55 percent. A very ambitious fourfold increase in coal production is projected for 1990, with the steam proportion growing to 70 percent.

Potential constraints on this expansion include rising production and transportation costs, environmental regulation for both mining and air quality, and higher provincial royalty rates. Major factors governing the production rate will be utility demand and the comparative costs of using western Canadian or eastern U.S. coal in the Ontario Hydro system. Prairie province utilities are likely to use local coal.

While Canadian production of steam coal did not meet demand in 1976, the supply–demand imbalance is expected to be restored in the early 1980s and to remain positive in the early 1990s. Nevertheless, U.S. coal will be likely to retain its transportation cost advantages in Ontario markets, with the result that some of surplus Canadian coal may be exported. Present long-term contracts for future deliveries of U.S. coal amount to about 13 million short tons per year. Some blending of Alberta and U.S. coal will occur in Ontario, but this is limited by technical constraints.

Uranium. Canada possesses substantial uranium resources. The largest deposits lie in southern Ontario and in northern Saskatchewan. Canada ranks second to the United States in uranium resources in the non-Communist world. Table 4–2 presents the most recent uranium resource estimates from the Department of Energy, Mines, and Resources. Canada also may possess 1.2 million tonnes of speculative resources in addition to the categories in Table 4–2.

Table 4-2. Canadian Uranium Resources (*in thousands of tonnes of uranium*)

	Measured	Indicated	Inferred	Prognosticated Plus Speculative[a]
Up to 130/kgu	73	157	238	—
$130 to $200/kgu	4	25	90	—
Total	77	182	328	1800

a. Mineable at prices below $200/kgu.

Source: Department of Energy, Mines, and Resources, *Uranium in Canada: 1979 Assessment of Supply and Requirements* (September 1980).

Production capacity may reach 12.3 stu/yr in 1985 and 15 stu/yr in 1990. Canadian demand, however, has fallen sharply due to a downturn in future reactor orders in Canada. Total operating capacity by 1990 at most will be 14,455 MWe.

The Canadian uranium industry developed in response to export demand (the U.S. and U.K. weapons programs) and will remain predominantly export oriented. The industry received a nearly fatal shock when U.S. military purchases were phased out, starting in 1959. In the 1970s, Canada was a leading member of an international uranium cartel arising, in major part, in response to the slack market resulting from the closure of the U.S. domestic market to foreign uranium. This ban, however, will be lifted entirely by 1984, and U.S. utilities have contracted for significant quantities of Canadian uranium. The prospects for this trade, however, may be influenced by several factors discussed later in this chapter.

Electricity. Electricity interties across the border have existed since early in this century. Currently, one hundred transmission lines, capable of handling 8 GWe of power, link the two countries. Over 50 percent of this transfer capacity ties Ontario to New York and Michigan. New lines will raise the total transmission capacity to 11 GWe by 1985. At that time, this level would constitute 1.4 percent of U.S. generating capacity and 10 percent of Canadian capacity.[10] The

10. Department of Energy, *United States–Canada Electricity Exchanges* (DOE/ERA-0053, February 1979), ch. 1.

United States imported nearly 20,000 GWhr of electricity from Canada in 1977 and over 31,000 GWhr in 1979 (29,000 GWhr net). Cross-border sales provide several benefits, among which are reserve sharing, diversity exchanges (due to noncoincident peaking), surplus sales, cost reduction, economies of scale in generating plant, and coordinated planning through several regional electric reliability councils. How much electricity will be available for exports will depend upon electricity growth rates. Low growth would normally discourage new capacity additions, but the possibility of sales to the United States, where power plant construction lead times are very long, could enable the "prebuilding" of plants in Canada in advance of domestic need, with the electricity sold to the United States and then gradually phased out as Canadian demand eventually increases.

The Political Environment

Numbers, of course, do not tell all the story. Canada would appear to be relatively well situated, at least in terms of potential self-sufficiency. What has eluded Canada during the 1970s, and will be likely to continue to in the early 1980s as well, is consensus on a national energy policy. Not only does this have adverse consequences for energy development, but the absence of consensus between the federal government and the producer provinces saps the political strength of Canada.

Contributing to Canada's energy policy problems is a national political system that is ill suited to the task of managing regional conflict within the country. Unlike the United States, the chief arena in Canada for decisionmaking, implementation, and conflict resolution is not the federal government. Decisionmaking in federal–provincial relations focuses narrowly on direct relations between governments with relatively few links to each other except through direct contacts between their political leaders.[11]

This institutional framework gives rise to an energy policy founded upon bargaining relationships unfolding at two levels—between federal and provincial governments and between consumer and pro-

---

11. See Richard Simeon, *Federal–Provincial Diplomacy: The Making of Recent Policy in Canada* (Toronto: University of Toronto Press, 1972), p. 39; and Wallace D. Koehler, "The Impact of Canadian Energy Policy on Changing Federal–Provincial Relations," *The American Review of Canadian Studies* 7 (Spring 1977):1–32.

ducer provinces. Effective policymaking is often joint policymaking because the necessary policy instruments are shared and because each level has the capacity to frustrate the other. With no clear hierarchy, each side is tempted to tilt the balance against the other. Much of the current conflict between Alberta and the other producer provinces, on the one hand, and the federal government in Ottawa, on the other, can be traced to the current Trudeau government's strongly centralist strategy for strengthening the Canadian confederation.

The efforts of the producer provinces and the federal government to protect and extend their power are the dominant feature of energy policymaking in Canada. The British North America Act of 1867 (BNA) vests the ownership of natural resources and exclusive legislative jurisdiction over them in the provinces where they are located. The federal government, by virtue of its jurisdiction over "the regulation of trade and commerce," can regulate interprovincial and international trade. The provinces can charge royalties and levy taxes on energy industries in their jurisdiction, while the federal government can levy taxes and grant subsidies. However, neither royalties nor taxes can be so high as to prevent the other authority from exercising its valid authority by depriving it of necessary revenues. This principle figures prominently in the current dispute between Ottawa and the producer provinces over oil and gas taxes.

A double-licensing regulatory framework within Canada also reflects this federal–provincial division of power. The Alberta government as early as 1948 established a board to set guidelines for gas sales to customers outside the province and to license export applications (sales to other provinces as well as to the United States were both considered "exports"). Licensing of oil exports was added in 1969. Only gas in amounts surplus to that required to ensure a thirty-year supply–demand ratio (now twenty-five years) for Alberta could be licensed for export. Other producer provinces have similar boards.

A federal National Energy Board was established in 1959 to regulate tariffs, tolls, and traffic on the interprovincial oil and gas pipelines and to license all international exports of oil, gas, and electricity. The purpose of the NEB was to strengthen the federal role in the natural gas trade, which previously had largely been preempted by the Alberta board. As was the case in Alberta, regulatory power was extended to oil much later (in 1970). The NEB is not an independent regulatory agency as such, but makes recommendations to the cabinet through the minister of energy, mines, and resources. As a result, political considerations can, and often do, affect the ultimate disposition of NEB advice.

The issues with which the federal political system must contend stem in many respects from an uneven distribution of industry and natural resources that gives rise to sharply divergent regional economic interests. Ontario, and to a lesser extent Quebec, are the industrial centers of Canada, while oil and gas resources are concentrated in the prairie provinces of Manitoba, Saskatchewan, and Alberta (80 percent of proven oil and gas) as well as in British Columbia and the Northwest and Yukon territories. The provinces of Prince Edward Island, New Brunswick, Nova Scotia, and until recently, Newfoundland (which has now laid claim to offshore oil deposits) have lacked both.

A dominant underlying force in Canadian regionalism is dissatisfaction with the concentration of commercial influence in central Canada.[12] Issues in the taxation and exploitation of provincially administered natural resources as well as resentment at the slow spread of secondary industry outward from central Canada are sources of conflict between western Canada and Ottawa. The western grievance, dating from the 1870s, that federal economic policy has enriched Ontario at western expense is evident in Alberta's response to recent federal energy policy initiatives such as the federal export tax on crude oil, oil and gas price controls, and the use of revenues generated by the export tax to subsidize higher priced imported crude in the Atlantic provinces and Quebec. Alberta perceives these initiatives as a continuation of the transfer of real resources from the provincial to the federal treasury and on to consumers in the eastern provinces and as an unwarranted, even unconstitutional, federal intrusion into areas of provincial prerogative. This grievance is all the more ironic because higher oil and gas prices are shifting purchasing power toward the western provinces, with profound implications for the rate and location of future economic growth in Canada.[13]

This economic regionalism that is central to the politics of energy policy reflects a quite different set of preoccupations than does Que-

12. See the essays by Walter Gainer, Eugene Forsey, and A.E. Safarian in H. Edward English, ed., *Canada–United States Relations*, Proceedings of the Academy of Political Science (1976), vol. 32, no. 2.

13. See Judith D. Maxwell, "Energy Bargaining in a Regional Context," in J. Maxwell, ed., *Policy Review and Outlook, 1978: A Time for Realism* (Montreal: C.D. Howe Research Institute, 1978).

becois nationalism. However, regionalism and Quebecois nationalism share a common relevance to national energy politics in that
they have encouraged a strong centralist response on the part of the
Trudeau government to the questions of constitutional reform and
the distribution of political power in Canada. This centralist thrust
clashes directly with the countersentiment of greater regional autonomy implicit in much of Alberta's energy policy and also apparent in
the brief Clark government's approach to a number of energy policy
issues in 1979, such as oil prices and Newfoundland's ownership
claims.

Another element complicating energy policy is Canadian nationalism and specifically wariness of U.S. domination. The degree of pen-
etration of Canada by U.S. interests is considerable. Seventy percent
or more of various sectors of the oil and gas are foreign owned, as
well as 40 percent of coal production and 50 percent of uranium production, although the Canadian share of ownership in the oil and gas
sectors has been creeping steadily upward toward 50 percent. Controlling foreign investment and energy exports have been prominent
factors in encouraging government regulation of the energy trade
and, more recently, direct participation in the energy industries.

At their most fundamental level, the economic issues of energy
policy in Canada have fallen into two basic categories. The first category of issues focuses on the market price for oil and gas and related
tax and royalty rates that determine how much economic rent is collected, how much is given directly to the consumer by foregoing its
collection, and the allocation among the federal government, producing provinces, and industry of the rent that is collected.[14] The second
focuses on exploration, production, and marketing, especially the
pace and location of production activity. The basic political issue is
who—the federal or provincial governments or the industry—makes
these decisions. Canadian export policy historically has in large part
consisted of compromises made over these basic issues in different
time periods.

14. Ted Greenwood, "Canada's Energy Policy and Exports to the United States (Paper
delivered at the Conference on North American Energy Policy, Carleton University, Ottawa,
October 2-4, 1975).

The Energy Trade

Although a detailed examination of the history of U.S.-Canadian energy relations is beyond the scope of this chapter, it is worth recalling that during the 1950s and 1960s, Canadian perspectives on energy relations with the United States were somewhat different from what they are now. Access to U.S. markets provided additional outlets for shut-in oil and gas production capacity in Alberta. The availability of cheaper imported oil, largely from Venezuela, for supplying eastern Canada, the attractive prices Canadian oil and gas could fetch in the United States, and the need for capital to develop the Alberta oil and gas industries made exports to the United States attractive to governments and industry alike. Indeed, the national oil policy announced in 1961 divided Canada into two markets, with those provinces east of Ontario supplied by imported oil and the rest of Canada supplied indigenously. Oil surplus to demand west of the "Ottawa Valley Line" was exported to the United States. Gas supply did not extend eastward beyond Toronto, making sizable quantities of gas also available for export.

Despite the development of oil and gas exports, Canada's attitude toward its energy dealings with the United States had a somewhat schizophrenic character. On the one hand, both the federal government and the producer provinces sought to secure access to the U.S. market to provide a broader base for developing the Canadian oil and gas industries. Although continentalism was never the declared aim of federal policy, Ottawa on several occasions negotiated with Washington to lift restrictions on U.S. imports of Canadian oil. For its part, the United States was never favorably disposed toward continentalism so long as domesitc American producers found it difficult to compete with Canadian crude in the upper Midwest. Despite contrary suggestions from President Nixon's Oil Import Task Force, which expressed interest in a continental arrangement, Canadian oil finally was placed under the U.S. mandatory oil import control program in 1970.[15]

At the same time, there was considerable sensitivity within Canada to American influence in the energy sector. This was especially evi-

15. James W. McKie, "United States and Canadian Energy Policy," in Cambell Watkins and Michael Walker, eds., *Oil in the Seventies: Essays on Energy Policy* (Vancouver: The Fraser Institute, 1977), pp. 251–54.

dent in regard to pipeline construction, in terms of both the nationality of the industrial consortia building them and their direction (i.e., how much of the Canadian market they served). Heavy American investment in general was controversial with groups all along the Canadian political spectrum.

By the 1970s, the context within which the continental concept had once been considered had changed fundamentally. Growing concern over the resource base and the availability of geographically remote and technologically difficult frontier resources as well as rising nationalist sentiments changed Canadian perspectives on exports, while the question of foreign domination of the oil and gas industries became more politicized. The events of October 1973 only served to accelerate a trend already under way in Canadian policy. Major new Canadian initiatives, such as the 1974 decision to phase out oil exports; the rejection of new gas export license applications beginning in 1970; more direct federal efforts to screen and control foreign investment in Canada; the establishment of a crown corporation, Petro Canada, to give the federal government a direct role in oil production in certain areas; and the adoption of two-tier pricing schemes, in which exports were priced at substantially higher levels than domestically produced and consumed oil and gas, dramatically altered the state of the U.S.-Canadian energy relations.

A brief review of the oil and gas trade statistics for the past two decades indicates a progressively increasing share of Canadian production being allocated to exports, from 23 percent in 1960 to over 50 percent in the early 1970s (see Table 4-3). By the same token, Canadian petroleum supplied no higher than 7.66 percent of total U.S. petroleum demand (in 1973). A more meaningful measurement, in terms of the impact of Canadian exports on American supply security, was the Canadian share of U.S. oil imports—17 percent in 1973—and the much heavier dependence of refineries in the northern tier states upon Canadian supply.

Table 4-3 also indicates the increase of Canadian oil imports as, under the impetus provided by the national oil plan, the energy structures of Quebec and the maritime provinces shifted toward much heavier reliance upon imported oil. By 1975, over 75 percent of Quebec's energy base and 83 percent of the maritime provinces' was in the form of imported oil. Canada was a net exporter of oil until 1975, when imports began to outpace exports.

Table 4–3. Canadian Petroleum Supply (*thousands of barrels per day*)

	1960	1965	1970	1971	1972	1973	1974	1975	1976	1977	1978	1979
Canadian production	532.0	867.1	1382.1	1476.0	1698.4	1962.9	1843.3	1623.1	1437.3	1440.2	1230.0	1608.0
Imports												
Crude	343.1	395.0	568.9	671.1	769.6	883.7	797.7	844.5	755.3	649.8	617.5	430.0
Refined	96.2	162.5	193.3	158.6	147.6	123.6	86.4	46.3	36.0	45.0	55.3	35.0
Exports												
Crude	113.0	295.6	669.8	750.8	951.3	1148.0	907.0	707.3	465.1	270.0	463.1	95.0
Refined	9.9	8.6	36.2	52.1	116.4	149.8	134.7	115.6	na	na	na	192.0

Note: These figures exclude plant-liquified petroleum gases.

Sources: Ministry of Energy, Mines, and Resources, *An Energy Strategy for Canada* (April 1976), p. 162; National Energy Board, *Annual Report* (Washington, D.C., 1977), p. 20; Central Intelligence Agency, *International Energy Statistical Review* (Washington, D.C., March 1976, 1977), p. 10, average over first three quarters of 1978; Canadian Embassy, Washington, D.C.

Gas production and marketing share with oil a large export orientation. The percentage of exported gas increased until it reached approximately 40 percent of Canadian production in 1974 (see Table 4-4). As with oil, these exports provided only a very small share of total U.S. consumption (approximately 5 percent). This minor share of the national market, however, obscures more pronounced regional dependencies, particularly in the U.S. Pacific Northwest. Any decline in the availability of Canadian gas and oil could result, then, in substantial regional dislocation.

II. BILATERAL ENERGY RELATIONS IN THE 1980s

Despite Canada's apparent rich endowment in energy resources, the course of energy development in that country during the 1980s will be determined much more by political and economic than by technical and geologic factors. The dominant feature of the energy landscape in Canada is the unsettled state of the economic ground rules governing oil and gas development, over which the industry and federal and producer province governments are locked in a political struggle for control. This struggle is likely to continue for some time, with effects on the pace of energy development, the pricing and marketing of energy resources, the regime governing energy investments, and the level of exports to the United States. The energy arena provides a battleground for political and economic forces of fundamental importance to the future of Canada. Understanding the nature of this struggle is essential to U.S. policy and the protection of U.S. interests.

The National Energy Program

At the center of the current conflict stands the National Energy Program (NEP), announced by the Liberal government of Pierre Trudeau in October 1980.[16] The objectives of the plan came as no surprise, as its basic thrust had been apparent for several months, although the

16. Ministry of Energy, Mines, and Resources, *The National Energy Program* (October 1980).

Table 4-4. Canadian Marketable Gas Supply (*billions of cubic feet*)

	1960	1965	1970	1971	1972	1973	1974	1975	1976	1977	1978	1979	1980
Canadian production[a]	443.0	1051.0	1868.6	2071.8	2362.1	2520.8	2498.9	2520.2	2458.6	2576.8	2600.0	2600.0	2600.0
Exports	109.8	404.7	780.2	912.2	1009.7	1028.0	959.2	946.9	953.6	1003.0	881.0	1600.0	791.0

a. Production figures for 1978–80 are approximate.

Sources: Ministry of Energy, Mines, and Resources, *An Energy Strategy for Canada* (April 1976), p. 163; National Energy Board, *Annual Report* (Washington, D.C., 1977), p. 20; Canadian Embassy, Washington, D.C.

exact means chosen to achieve these objectives went beyond what many expected. The Liberal party had campaigned on a platform attacking the oil-pricing proposals of the previous Conservative government for imposing an unacceptable burden on consumers while conferring a windfall on the industry and the producer provinces. Had they been implemented, these proposals would have raised domestic oil prices to international levels within a few years and would have resolved a long-standing disagreement between the federal government and the producer provinces over pricing policy. The new government had also issued statements about "Canadianization" of the oil and gas industries prior to issuing the NEP. These initial actions had already precipitated a serious breach between Alberta and Ottawa and led to corporate reconsideration of major investments in several tar sands plants even before the NEP was officially presented.

The NEP contains a number of highly controversial and frequently complicated measures. Although some modification of individual elements in the NEP may yet occur, it offers a forceful statement of the Trudeau government's position on energy policy and of how it intends to use energy policy to achieve a number of broader economic and political objectives.

The strictly energy-related objectives of the program include reducing oil's share of total energy demand to 10 percent and achieving oil self-sufficiency by 1990. A considerable part of the debate over the program centers on whether these objectives are actually achievable under its proposed regimes for pricing, incentives for frontier development, and control of foreign investment. By far the greatest controversy, however, surrounds those measures stemming from what the Trudeau government considers to be the two most crucial issues in the energy arena—restructuring the distribution of oil and gas revenues between the federal and producer province governments to give Ottawa a larger share; and increasing Canadian control, not just ownership, of the energy industry. These two issues go beyond simply energy. At its most fundamental level, the NEP is an attempt by the federal government to assert itself regarding the central question of who will make the economic and political decisions that will shape Canada's future.

The most important elements of the program, stated briefly, are:

Pricing.

- Continuation of administered prices through the establishment of a blended price scheme yielding an average price from separate conventional, oil sand, and imported crude prices, such that the average price to Canadian consumers will not exceed 85 percent of world levels or the U.S. average price, whichever is lower; and
- Encouragement of greater use of natural gas, at the expense of oil, by allowing the gap between gas and oil prices (on a btu basis) to widen, together with new gas pipeline construction east of Montreal.

Taxation.

- A new federal tax on all natural gas, wherever it is sold, to provide a new source of federal revenues;
- An 8 percent tax on all net operating revenues from oil and gas production; and
- A tax on oil and gas consumption to finance the federal government's plan to purchase the assets of the Canadian subsidiaries of one or more foreign-owned major oil corporations.

Incentives. Phasing down and eventual replacement of—except for oil sands and heavy-oil-upgrading equipment—standard depletion allowances with a system of graduated grants for exploration that increase in size as the level of Canadian control in a company increases and are higher for exploration and development on federal lands than on provincial acreage.

"Canadianization." Preferential treatment under tax and incentive programs for Canadian firms, plus a minimal 50 percent Canadian owership goal at the production stage on federal lands (so-called "Canada lands"). In addition, a more vigorous role for Petro Canada in such ventures on Canada lands. Petro Can will be entitled to a 25 percent "carried interest" in frontier and offshore developments, in addition to the ownership share that it already holds in several frontier, offshore, and syncrude projects.

The NEP does not assume a "supply solution" to Canada's oil import problem but, rather, views measures to reduce oil demand to levels consistent with anticipated domestic supply as the major part of the answer. The NEP projects oil demand to be 1.615 million barrels per day in 1985 and 1.475 million in 1990, or nearly 400,000 barrels less than the average daily oil demand in 1979. The estimated level of domestic oil production is 1.355 million barrels per day in 1985 and 1.520 million in 1990. Domestic production in 1979 averaged 1.608 million barrels per day. According to these estimates, Canada would have a very slight surplus of domestic production in 1990.

Another key premise of the NEP is that natural gas is plentiful in Canada relative to oil. Some 14.5 tcf of gas is authorized for export to the United States through 1990, and the NEP projects that a 5.8 tcf additional surplus (surplus to both domestic demand and existing licensed export volumes) could accumulate between 1980 and 1990. Thus, unlike the situation with regard to oil, meeting domestic gas demand, which could rise to 2.5 tcf in 1990, is not a problem. The major issue regarding gas, as will be seen later, is the timing of phasing in production from new sources.

A comparison of the NEP with previous energy strategies reveals an important change in emphasis. Both the Liberal and Conservative parties, when previously in power, concentrated on reducing oil import vulnerability and encouraging production of frontier and unconventional oil and gas resources. The national energy strategy announced by a previous Trudeau government in April 1976 emphasized self-reliance, which was defined in terms of reducing Canadian vulnerability to arbitrary import price changes or prolonged supply disruptions.[17] In practical terms, this would have entailed lowering import dependence to one-third of total oil demand by 1985 and preserving natural gas for domestic use until frontier resources could be brought to market. A later study, commissioned by the Ministry of Energy, Mines, and Resources, emphasized substitution of other energy sources for oil (e.g., to reduce oil's share in primary energy supply from 46 to 30 percent in 2000 and expand use of electricity).[18] The Clark government (1979–1980) committed itself to a

17. Ministry of Energy, Mines, and Resources, *An Energy Strategy for Canada* (1976), sec. IV.

18. Ministry of Energy, Mines, and Resources, *Energy Futures for Canadians* (1978).

net oil import limit of 600,000 b/d by 1985 and a 1 percent annual energy growth rate in order to achieve self-sufficiency by 1990.

In view of the potential for federal–producer province conflict over the issue, the price regimes of the two previous governments merit attention. The strategy of the Trudeau government in 1976 called for gradual movement of domestic oil prices to world levels and near, if not full, commodity pricing for gas within two to four years, as well as for demand growth reduction, a doubling of frontier exploration and development activity, and construction of new delivery systems for frontier resources. The brief Conservative government of Joe Clark concentrated primarily upon revising the energy-pricing agreement worked out with the provinces in 1976, since at the agreed upon rate of increase ($1/b every six months), the gap between world and domestic prices was actually increasing. The Clark government proposed to raise oil prices at the rate of first $4/b and then $4.50/b every year until the world price or 85 percent of the U.S. price, whichever was lower, was reached. This was anticipated to occur in 1984.

The NEP departs from these previous strategies in several important regards. The Trudeau government maintains that past policies overemphasized security of supply, while paying insufficient attention to the ramifications of energy policy for the balance of political and economic power within the country and the control of the industry. The NEP rejects the premise of the previous Conservative government that rapid movement of domestic oil prices, regardless of source, to international levels is the most important step in achieving self-sufficiency and retains a regime of administered prices set according to whether the particular oil is imported, produced from frontier areas or tar sands, or comes from current conventional fields. The NEP proceeds on the belief that the pre-NEP net backs were more than sufficient to make high risk projects attractive without the price levels contemplated by the Clark government and that the priority for federal policy is to restructure the distribution of revenues and achieve Canadian control of the industry.

The Trudeau government contends that the existing distribution of revenues, in which the federal government receives 10 percent and industry and the producer provinces split the rest, enriches the producer provinces, especially Alberta, disproportionately to the rest of Canada, while the federal government provides the incentives to production. In more concrete terms, the federal government found itself with insufficient revenues to finance its energy-related obligations, notably the oil equalization scheme.[19] Moreover, the Trudeau government alleges that a foreign-controlled oil and gas industry is exporting capital from Canada and might not invest higher revenues in Canada.

Thus, the energy program revises the distribution of revenues to give the federal government a larger share—24 percent—leaving the provinces with 43 percent and industry with 33 percent. It would rectify a serious federal budget deficit by generating additional federal revenues through new taxes and moving the compensation payments off budget by financing them through a new surcharge imposed on refineries. The NEP addresses the foreign control issue through new Canadian ownership and control requirements, a more extensive role for Petro Canada, and the purchase of the Canadian subsidiaries of one or more major foreign oil companies. It is fair to say that this program was guaranteed to arouse considerable opposition, since it fundamentally revises the rules of the energy game in Canada.

The issues would be complicated enough were they simply economic in character. What makes resolution more difficult is the political struggle between Ottawa and the producer provinces over who makes such decisions and the tendency for both sides to see it in zero sum terms—that is, one side's loss is the other's gain. Such a perspective does not exactly encourage compromise.

Alberta is intent on protecting jurisdiction over its resources, which it sees as threatened by Liberal policies, and is adamant in demanding the prices offered by the previous Conservative government for what it regards as a rapidly depleting resource. Conventional oil produced in Alberta would, under the NEP, be priced as "old" oil and receive only the current price of $17.75 a barrel. Syncrude and frontier and offshore oil produced on federal land would be priced much closer to international levels. The Alberta government objects to this arrangement, for obvious reasons.

Alberta's immediate response to the NEP was to announce production cuts to force the federal government to accept higher oil

---

19. The subsidy paid to refiners using imported oil is an on-budget expense. The proceeds from the oil export tax and a small gasoline tax, theoretically designed to finance this scheme, are added to the federal government's general revenues. Due to declining exports and import costs much higher than anticipated, the subsidy exceeds returns from the tax by over $3 billion.

prices. Both Alberta and British Columbia maintain that the federal government has no right to tax gas, and referral of the issue to the Supreme Court of Canada is likely following consideration in the provincial courts. For its part, the federal government perceives the energy area as an important testing ground for Prime Minister Trudeau's strongly centralist approach to national unity and constitutional reform issues. Although a compromise on prices may eventually be worked out, the underlying source of the tension between Ottawa and the producer provinces will not disappear.

The jurisdiction issue also arises in regard to the offshore oil resources east of Newfoundland.[20] The Conservative Clark government had promised Newfoundland exclusive ownership and control over offshore resources in an attempt to resolve a jurisdictional dispute originating in the circumstances under which Newfoundland, then a separate dominion, joined the confederation in 1949. The Trudeau government, however, has reasserted federal jurisdiction, while offering Newfoundland 100 percent of provincial type revenues until per capita income there reaches the national average. The issue is not simply how to satisfy Newfoundland's revenue needs, however. Newfoundland, with the prospect of economic growth in sight, wants the right to administer and regulate offshore development in order to maximize the economic benefits to its depressed economy—that is, to have the same prerogatives as other producer provinces.

The consequences of this situation with Newfoundland are potentially serious. Mobil Canada, which has major interests in the Hibernia and Ben Nevis permits, has said that while exploration will continue, commercial development will not take place until the jurisdictional dispute is settled. Other oil companies share this attitude. Referral of the issue to the Supreme Court of Canada is likely here as well.

The struggle between federal and provincial governments over political and economic power in Canada is being played out in the energy area because of the economic stakes involved and because the absence of a clear hierarchy of political authority in that sector

20. Newfoundland was a separate dominion whose constitution was suspended in 1934 in favor of direct rule from London. The constitution was revived at the date of union with Canada in 1949, even if only for a split second. Newfoundland maintains it carried ownership of offshort resources with it into the confederation. The Supreme Court of Canada ruled in 1968 that British Columbia (and by inference other provinces) did not own offshore resources. Newfoundland argues that this does not apply in its case because of the special circumstances of its entry.

makes it an ideal battlefield. It is imperative from the perspective of
U.S. interests to understand that the conflict runs deeper than simply energy and is not likely to be settled for some time.

The National Energy Program and Foreign Investment

Potentially the greatest irritant for U.S.-Canadian relations to
emerge from the National Energy Program is its provisions regarding
foreign investment in Canada's oil and gas industries. Of the top
twenty-five petroleum companies in Canada, seventeen are more
than 50 percent foreign owned and controlled, and these seventeen
account for 72 percent of Canadian oil and gas sales. The Trudeau
government finds this level of foreign control objectionable on a
number of grounds. It maintains that non-Canadian interests receive
the lion's share of the financial benefits of higher domestic oil and
gas prices and that financing new projects through internally generated funds simply perpetuates the lack of opportunity for new Canadian participation. Moreover, it sees foreign companies as controlling
future production decisions as well due to their predominant position in frontier and offshore areas and their extensive role in syncrude development. Finally, the Trude government basically distrusts
the multinationals, on the grounds that the necessarily worldwide
interests of these companies do not coincide with Canadian national
interests and that they cannot be relied upon to treat Canada equita-
bly during a world supply crisis or to maintain a commitment to high
risk and high cost projects in Canada.

It is very significant that the NEP defines the issue of foreign
investment not simply in terms of ownership, which an increase in
Canadian-owned equity might rectify, but in terms of control—that
is, who makes the decisions and on the basis of whose interests.[21]
The NEP sets three objectives regarding foreign investment: (1) at
least 50 percent Canadian ownership of oil and gas production by
1990; (2) Canadian control of a significant number of the larger foreign oil and gas firms; and (3) an early increase in the share of the
oil and gas sector owned by the federal government. Changes in the
depletion allowance and the establishment of an incentive payment
system geared to a Canadian ownership and control test, preferences
in granting new export licenses to Canadian-owned firms, the imposi-

---

21. Ministry of Energy, Mines, and Resources, *National Energy Program*, p. 19.

tion of a 50 percent ownership test at the production stage of projects on territory under federal jurisdiction, and more extensive use of the Foreign Investment Review Agency to prevent nonenergy investments by oil and gas companies and to block purchase of already discovered oil and gas reserves by foreign-controlled firms are intended to help achieve the 50 percent ownership goal.

A more extensive role for state-owned and controlled enterprise is a particularly controversial element of the Trudeau government's strategy to reduce foreign ownership. New crown corporations could be formed to purchase the assets of larger foreign-owned companies using funds raised by special charges on all oil and gas consumption in Canada. The role of Petro Canada would increase by virtue of a proposed 25 percent carried interest in every new and existing right on federal lands. Petro Canada already holds significant positions in a number of important syncrude, frontier, and offshore projects. The effect of expanding the direct role of the federal government in those projects that will be crucial to Canada's energy future will be to enhance its influence dramatically regarding the pace of development and, perhaps even more importantly in the Trudeau government's eyes, its leverage vis-à-vis the producer province governments and the private sector.

The Trudeau government's efforts to impose greater control over foreign energy investment could have a substantial effect on bilateral relations. The foreign corporate interests in question are predominantly U.S. based, and industry charges that the new policy amounts to little more than expropriation. The proposed mandatory carried interest for Petro Canada, the intention to buy out one or more major foreign-owned companies, the retention of price controls, and changes in the fiscal regime governing energy development have had a chilling effect on corporate expenditure plans, especially on the part of the major oil companies such as Imperial Oil (Exxon), Shell Canada, Gulf Canada, and Mobil Canada.

The new incentive system favoring Canadian-owned and controlled enterprises also raises the thorny issue of whether Canada is violating the "national treatment" provisions of the OECD's *Declaration on International Investment and Multinational Enterprises*. Adherents to the declaration agree to

> accord to enterprises operating in their territories and owned or controlled directly or indirectly by nationals of another Member country . . . treatment under their laws, regulations, and administrative practices, consistent with

international law and no less favorable than that accorded in like situations to domestic enterprises.

Adherence to the principle of national treatment is an essential prerequisite to a stable international investment regime. Canada claims that the national treatment provision requires only consultation where policies derogate from the rule and that such policies are not precluded by the declaration, a position that the United States does not fully accept.[22] On the face of it, however, Canada's discretionary use of incentives to favor Canadian firms is in conflict with the "national treatment" provision.

The changes in Canada's treatment of foreign energy investment should be kept in perspective, however. The foreign investment issue is not new. The federal government has exercised control over the establishment of almost all new businesses and the acquisition of existing businesses by foreign firms since 1973, when the Foreign Investment Review Act was promulgated, and earlier had blocked the sale of a Canadian oil company to outside interests in 1971. There also has been continuing concern in some Canadian political sectors of the effect of foreign ownership on the performance of Canadian industry in general, although the intensity of this concern has fluctuated. The return of the Pierre Trudeau-led Liberal party to power in 1980 represents a shift toward a more interventionist government strategy in a number of industrial sectors, not just energy.

Moreover, as the Trudeau government is quick to point out, other industrial countries have established state oil companies and imposed in some cases rather rigid restrictions on foreign oil companies operating within their territory. The latest initiatives reflect a conviction that such extensive foreign ownership as found in Canada (over 50 percent in mining, 55 percent in manufacturing, and over 70 percent in oil and gas) results in an unacceptable level of foreign control over Canada's future and that a strong federal government is essential to preserving Canada's political and economic independence. It would be very mistaken to view the investment provisions of the NEP as a manifestation of an incipient socialism.

The long-range consequences of these initiatives are not easy to gauge. Achievement of a federal–producer province pact on energy pricing, which undoubtedly would result in higher domestic prices,

22. The Canadian position on this point was stated by the minister for external affairs, Allen MacEachen, before the OECD Council of Ministers on June 21, 1976.

could have a salutory effect on the situation, since prices may be of greater importan(e to the industry over the long run than investment regulations. It is not clear that Ottawa is going to set about buying out foreign oil companies wholesale, as the possibility thereof could just as easily serve the purpose of putting the companies on notice that their actions will be carefully scrutinized. There is no thought of uncompensated expropriation. Petro Canada's offer of $1.46 billion for the assets of the Canadian subsidiary of Petrofina S.A. in Belgium has in fact been criticized in some Canadian circles as too generous. Corporate reorganization to establish new, more heavily Canadian-owned subsidiaries to acquire interests in frontier areas, and thus qualify under the incentive system, may be feasible in some cases, as a recent move by Dome Petroleum Ltd. demonstrates. Finally, some companies may simply feel that they can live with the new policies without changes in ownership, despite the smaller grants that would then be available. The head of Imperial Oil, the Exxon subsidiary, recently said as much to a Canadian parliamentary committee.[23]

The most serious problem, from a corporate perspective, may not be the substance of federal policy, onerous as the industry may contend it is, so much as the lack of stability and certainty in the basic energy policy regime. Changes that are adverse to corporate interests have occurred in other producer countries, yet the industry has not gone under. What is essential is a stable planning environment to permit the kinds of high risk investments necessary to develop Canada's resources. The greatest threat posed by the National Energy Program is not expropriation or a reduction in revenues per se, but a continuation of the conflict over who makes the rules, perpetuating an unstable investment environment.

The NEP's treatment of foreign investment becomes doubly important in light of the magnitude of the financial resources needed for the Canadian energy sector. A Canadian government study in 1977 estimated that Canada could meet energy investment demands through the 1980s without a substantial increase in reliance upon foreign funding. This conclusion was based upon increased domestic savings and some reallocation of investment capital from other sectors. A recent study by the Royal Bank of Canada, however, has cast a harsher light on the investment issue. With $1.4 trillion, according to the report, required by the year 2000 (over $700 billion will be in

23. *Wall Street Journal*, February 18, 1981.

the electric utility sector), Ottawa will unavoidably be confronted with the foreign investment issue.[24] Even if only 25 percent of the total investment is slated to come from foreign sources, the report warns that energy investors will confront in Canada difficult and possibly unacceptable levels of risk. The viability and economic prudence of the goal of reducing foreign shareholdings to 50 percent in the energy sector may come to appear increasingly questionable if the necessary capital cannot be attracted as massive energy investments in the United States and elsewhere compete for money.

The Pace of Energy Development

In its effort to address the federal-provincial and foreign investment issues, the Trudeau government's energy strategy raises a fundamental question—Can the program achieve its energy objectives, or will the controversy surrounding its major elements result in serious projects delays and possibly aggravation of Canada's energy situation? Although it is too soon to answer this question with an significant degree of confidence, a number of points warrant mentioning.

Theoretically, the potential inherent in tar sands and frontier oil and gas could enable Canada to satisfy its own requirements and then some. The technical and physical obstacles in many of these areas are substantial, but they are not insurmountable. Several companies warned during the last round of NEB oil supply hearings in 1978 that frontier and syncrude projects might compete with each other to some extent for necessary financial, labor, and equipment resources. It may not be prudent to simply add projected frontier supplies without considering the interaction of project requirements across producing areas. Nevertheless, while technical problems may pose temporary obstacles, their impact on the pace of development may not be the determining one.

The more fundamental impediments are not technical, but political and economic in nature. The political struggle between the provincial and the federal governments creates an environment that does not encourage major new investments, certainly of the magnitude contemplated in the energy sector. So long as energy policy is used as a political tool, the stability in the political and economic ground rules necessary for sizable investment will not be present.

24. *World Business Weekly*, June 23, 1980.

The NEP's approach to pricing policy is another potential impediment. The Trudeau government's position is that a replacement cost approach to pricing new sources, based on cost of production plus a "fair" rate of return, rather than an approach based on the price of imported oil, provides sufficient returns to justify new investment. Moreover, the Trudeau government not only believes that world prices would give only foreign-controlled firms a windfall, it believes also that self-financing of major energy projects would be undesirable, since it would limit new investment opportunities for Canadians.

Finally, the prospective changes in the financial regime governing frontier and syncrude projects and the prospect of a more extensive direct state role in the industry through Petro Can and newly purchased subsidiaries of foreign oil companies could have a substantial impact on exploration and development activity. The previous super-depletion allowance for frontier exploration and development had reduced industry's real expenses to less than 10 cents on the exploration dollar. The new incentive-based grant system may partially offset this loss (grants up to 80 cents on the exploration dollar are possible for Canadian companies), but what may be more important to the pace of development is the fact that this system is discretionary. Some foreign-owned companies may reorganize to take advantage of it. Other foreign companies reluctant to reorganize may simply sell off their Canadian subsidiaries. Although a more "Canadian" industry might result, the time and resources necessary to recoup the loss of expertise that might result from this could delay resource development in physically challenging regions.

The oil and gas industry's reaction to the pricing, tax, and investment and ownership provisions of the National Energy Program has been to slash exploration budgets, place major capital investment in tar sands projects on hold, and where possible, shift production rigs and exploration activity to the United States and elsewhere where the financial returns are higher.[25] Among the projects affected are the Cold Lake and Alsands syncrude projects in Alberta and the Hibernia project off Newfoundland. A sizeable number of the smaller and more aggressive Canadian gas exploration firms, the very ones the NEP is intended to benefit, have moved rigs and exploration budgets south of the border where returns on decontrolled over-

25. *Oil and Gas Journal*, February 9–16, 1981.

thrust gas in the Rocky Mountains are four times those of conventional gas in Canada.

The Canadian oil industry, when it appeared that the previous Conservative government would lift price controls in fairly short order, confidently asserted that self-sufficiency could be achieved by 1990 through rapid development of frontier and unconventional sources, albeit at a hefty $300 billion price tag. Several of the major oil companies (notably Mobil, Shell, and Imperial Oil), however, have gloomily forecast, in testimony to the NEB in early 1981, that Canadian oil supply could be 400,000–600,000 b/d short of the target for 1990 as a result of the program.[26]

Exports and Current Canadian Policy

Although oil and gas exports to the United States were a prominent feature of Canadian energy policy until the 1970s, the lead times for production from new sources and the additional uncertainties affecting major new projects discourage any notion that imports from Canada will provide a significant source of future supply for the United States over the next decade. This is true of both the oil and gas sectors, despite the potential size of Canadian resources. The principal exception to this picture is electricity, where the potential for significant new exports to the United States is far more promising than in the other energy sectors.

The prospects for oil exports are particularly slim. Light crude is available only through exchanges, at approximately 100,000 b/d each way, that were instituted after Canada announced in 1974 that it would phase out oil exports. Although their continuation will avert a shortfall for U.S. northern tier refineries, this remains a temporary solution, and it will remain imperative to develop an alternative supply source (presumably a pipeline from the U.S. West Coast) for the northern tier. Exports of heavy crude, which have been exempt from the general export phaseout, may also gradually decrease through the mid-1980s. The National Energy Program calls for investment in heavy crude upgrading equipment to make this oil usable in Canada.

Although the physical potential for oil exports in the 1990s might be present if syncrude, Beaufort Sea, and East Coast offshore oil

26. *Oil and Gas Journal*, January 26, 1981.

projects all reach their full potential by 1990, the prospects for this are not particularly encouraging, as they will be necessary to replace declining production in conventional areas. It is likely that any Canadian federal government, regardless of party composition, will feel politically compelled to strive for self-sufficiency. This will leave little, if any, room for exports.

The picture in the natural gas sector is somewhat different. Gas exports will likely hold at 1.2-1.8 tcf through 1990 and then will decline under existing licenses. Although recent experience with reserve additions in existing areas and the gas prospects in the High Arctic hold the promise of making continuing exports possible, even at the most optimistic levels, Canadian gas would satisfy only 5-6 percent of total U.S. gas needs. The American Gas Association in late 1980 estimated that 1-2 tcf/yr of Canadian gas might be available in the year 2000.[27] Of course, the importance of this gas on a regional basis will be greater.

The level of gas exports beyond 1990 will be a function of several factors. The development of High Arctic resources will clearly have an important effect on deliverability, although the timing and volume of deliveries are not yet definite. The means of delivery—pipelines and/or liquified natural gas tankers—will be important, since the former would require delivery of larger volumes, and hence larger markets, to be profitable. Transport by LNG tanker would allow the gas to seek markets anywhere. Some LNG will be sold to Japanese customers, and several potential European customers have also shown interest.

Although the industry has argued that exports could help provide a market sufficiently large to allow early production, the Trudeau government has taken the position that Arctic gas is Canada's "safety net" and has cautioned that, consistent with the "safety net" concept, development might not begin as soon as the industry would like if that would entail substantial new exports and, from the government's perspective, political controversy.[28] It should be recalled that a previous Trudeau government had been sorely embarrassed in the early 1970s when extravagant estimates of frontier resources subsequently proved to be unfounded. At the very least, new export applications will be carefully scrutinized, and license validity periods may

27. American Gas Association, *Gas Energy Supply Outlook: 1980-2000* (October 1980).

28. Ministry of Energy, Mines, and Resources, *National Energy Program*, p. 44.

be shorter than in the past (possibly less than ten years). This situation would pose planning problems for the importing U.S. gas utilities and customers.

Marketing gas into eastern Canada as a substitute for oil is not likely to have a major effect on potential exports, given the small size of that market. The NEB estimated in November 1979 that 180 tcf/yr could be sold in eastern Canada by 1990. The National Energy Program projects only a modest increase in Canadian gas demand over previously projected levels, since substitution of gas for oil has been emphasized for several years now. What must be kept in mind, however, is the political importance in Canada of maintaining the commitment to expand gas sales in eastern Canada and the need for U.S. interests to acknowledge this goal when considering the prospects for Canadian gas exports.

Another factor affecting gas export prospects is their marketability in the United States. At present, about 75 percent of NEB–authorized gas export volumes are in fact being taken by U.S. consumers. Most of this shortfall is occurring in California and the Pacific Northwest, where the gas market is fully saturated. Some expansion in Canadian gas imports could occur in the Northeast, where gas accounts for only 6 percent of total energy consumption in New England, as compared to an average of 27 percent nationwide. Canadian gas, which is cheaper than residential fuel oil, could compensate for the unavailability of additional domestic supplies. A change in the U.S. gas-pricing regime that might preclude the rolling in of high-priced Canadian gas with lower cost indigenous supplies could also affect the attractiveness of imports.

The position of the Trudeau government toward exports is designed to discourage any U.S. thoughts that Canada could become once again a major U.S. supplier, let alone a participant in a North American "Common Market," a proposition the Trudeau government rejects. The intention not to allow exports to drive Canadian energy policy or dominate corporate decisionmaking is evident in the Trudeau government's willingness to use its tax powers where necessary to eliminate any encouragement of exports stemming from Canada's two-tier pricing policy, in which exports are priced higher than domestic oil and gas, and in the safety net approach to frontier resources.

Whether this perspective will come into conflict with the need to provide the market to start major projects will be of significant importance, as it is very doubtful that private corporations would accept the withholding of production until a strictly Canadian market was available. Were this to be the case, one might expect frontier exploration and production to either slow or fall into the hands of the state oil company to an even greater extent than now contemplated.

In any event, it should be anticipated that Canada will seek full price for its exports to the United States. Oil exports have been priced at appropriate world levels since 1973, while gas is priced on a btu parity basis with crude oil imported into Canada. Where lower prices are offered or scheduled price increases passed up, they will occur strictly in order to assure the competitiveness of the commodity in the markets they serve.

The discussion in this chapter so far has concentrated upon oil and gas, since these sectors dominate the bilateral energy agenda. The prospects for future trade in bulk power, uranium, and coal, however, are far less bounded by constraints of a supply and demand nature and, with the possible exception of uranium, are less prone to be politicized in the way the oil and gas trade has been. As a result, trade in the electricity sector, defined here to encompass both bulk power and coal and uranium, presents a quite different situation.

As pointed out earlier, with the addition of new high voltage lines, the cross-border transmission capacity could reach 11,000 MWe by 1985 or 1.4 percent of U.S. generating capacity and 10 percent of Canadian capacity. Regional trade will be extensive, especially in the Northeast.

The sale of electricity generated by surplus capacity, often on an interruptible or seasonal basis, has been a very important but relatively unpoliticized element in bilateral energy relations. Although there may be scope for some additional expansion of this type of arrangement, a more interesting possibility is the construction of Canadian generating capacity dedicated to the U.S. market. In the absence of strictly dedicated plants, Canada might undertake a commitment to sell a sizeable bloc of power to the United States, while retaining the freedom to change the generating mix backing up this commitment. Several Canadian utilities—in Quebec, Manitoba, and Alberta—are investigating the construction of new hydro-electric or coal-fired plants dedicated primarily to U.S. markets.[29] Manitoba

29. *Energy Daily*, (July 28, 1980); *Nucleonics Week*, (April 16, 1981).

Hydro has identified nearly 6,000 MW of undeveloped hydro sites in that province, while Hydro Quebec has indicated a willingness to build 1,800 MW of hydro capacity. In both cases sales would not begin before 1989. Of the large electricity exporters, only Ontario Hydro has shown little interest in dedicated plants per se, although some experts have suggested that Ontario Hydro build nuclear reactors dedicated to the U.S. market, a highly controversial idea from which the provincial government is likely to shy away.

This new type of arrangement, in which electricity export licenses could run as long as twenty-five years under current Canadian federal legislation, could make an important contribution to U.S. energy needs at a regional level. This would be especially true in the case of New England, where current generating capacity is largely oil-fired and thus very expensive to operate and the prospects of shifting to coal or nuclear power are constrained by environmental, political, and transportation (in the case of coal) problems. New England imports of a large bloc of electricity from Canada could conceivably reach 8,000 to 10,000 MW if Canadian electricity was used to back out current oil-fired capacity and meet a substantial portion of demand for new capacity.

The prospects for expanding electricity sales, certainly on the scale just described, are not unlimited. Considerable uncertainties and obstacles exist on both sides of the border. The provincial utilities, at present, do not have a mandate from their respective provincial governments to generate electricity for the purpose of exporting it, and revision of these mandates or establishment of new provincial or even a federal crown corporation for this purpose would appear necessary. Also, political objections can be expected if Canadians see themselves as bearing the environmental costs for projects benefiting U.S. citizens. On the U.S. side of the border, overcoming regulatory obstacles to building new high voltage transmission lines, developing a customer large enough to take imports of such size (whether the existing New England Power Pool is sufficient for sales at this level is an important issue), and obtaining support from state public utility commissions for the take-or-pay contracts necessary to finance the Canadian capacity are important institutional problems. Above all, a means must be found to ensure the reliability of the supply, since, in essence, New Englanders would be building their generating plants in Canada rather than in New England.

American utilities hypothetically should be able to get as much Canadian uranium as they want. With at most 14,445 MW of domestic nuclear capacity by 1990 in service, the Canadian uranium industry will continue to sell the bulk of its output on the export market. The uranium export supply test announced in September 1974, reserving for domestic use enough uranium to ensure a thirty-year reserve for each reactor to start operation in the following ten-year period, will be irrelevant to determining the exportable surplus; and Canadian production capacity will exceed annual Canadian requirements by a factor of five to seven over the 1980s.

There are a number of irritants and potential impediments to bilateral uranium trade. Despite the current softness and declining real prices in the world uranium market, price may be a major point of contention with Canada. Beginning in December 1976, all future Canadian uranium contracts have contained a clause for annual price renegotiation at the prevailing market price, determined by either spot prices or an escalating floor price, whichever is higher. In practice, Ottawa sets the price each year, leading some customers to believe that the contract is virtually worthless on this point. A second irritant is the extraterritorial application of U.S. antitrust law to Canadian subsidiaries of U.S. firms that participated in the international uranium cartel in the 1970s. Finally, provincial government action may also impede Canadian production, especially in regard to royalty rates and, in the case of British Columbia, to temporary (five years in this situation) uranium-mining bans based on environmental considerations. The possible consequence of these developments is that U.S. utilities may not regard Canadian supply as secure.

U.S. coal exports to Ontario will be likely to retain their cost advantage over western Canadian oil, due in large part to continuation of their edge in lower transportation costs. This disadvantage does not affect users in the prairie provinces and, when combined with the low sulfur content of Alberta coal, will be likely to lead to a situation in which utilities in those provinces build coal-fired capacity using local coal. Ontario Hydro, the largest utility customer of U.S. coal, has begun blending U.S. coal with low sulfur Alberta coal in order to reduce emissions. In 1980, Ontario Hydro planned to import 11 million imperial tons of U.S. coal and to use 2.7 million tons of Alberta coal. Nevertheless, the National Coal Association expected U.S. coal exports to Canada to grow by 2 million tons by 1983.[30]

30. *Coal Week*, October 29, 1979.

III. CONCLUSIONS

The prospects for any significant increase in oil and gas supply from Canada are not promising. Where exports are increased, this will most likely be of limited duration and linked to Canadian interest in efficiently managing the introduction of new high cost energy projects into the domestic supply system. The unsettled state of political relations within the country and the potentially adverse effect of major elements of federal energy policy on the pace of oil and gas development may jeopardize or at least substantially delay the achievement of Canadian domestic energy objectives, let alone create the conditions for substantially increased oil and gas exports to the United States. The electricity sector may offer an exception to this prospect, but even in that sector there exist potential impediments to exports.

In any event, given the lead times involved in developing frontier, offshore, and unconventional oil and gas resources, the impact of new production areas will not be felt before the late 1980s at the earliest. This situation would not change even if the Progressive Conservative party formed the next government and reintroduced a more market-oriented approach to prices and eased the investment measures.

Rather than concentrate on increasing exports, bilateral energy relations in the 1980s will have to cope with a number of challenges that will arise in the context of declining export availability:[31]

- Facilitating both the adjustment to supply problems in the oil and gas sectors and the integration of new supply from unconventional and frontier sources;

- Taking maximum advantage of the complementarity of oil and gas transportation needs of both countries, where present; and

- Promoting the efficient utilization of productive capacity.

Aside from possible increases in electricity exports, the major benefit of successfully coping with these challenges will be to remove one more country from dependence on the world oil market and back the oil currently imported by Canada out into the world market.

---

31. This discussion draws upon Paul Daniel and Richard Shaffner, "Lessons From Bilateral Trade in Energy Resources," in C. Bergie and A. Hero, eds., *Natural Resources in U.S.-Canadian Relations* (Colorado Springs: Westview, 1980), vol. 1.

The quantities as involved are limited—certainly so in relation to U.S. imports—but the act itself of achieving a measure of self-sufficiency in an industrial country is of major economic and political importance.

Declining export volumes, rising prices, and the huge investment requirements may strengthen the relationship of energy to other items on the bilateral agenda. Indeed, there is fear in Canada that energy supply questions could overshadow a very broad agenda of bilateral issues in which many problems remain to be solved. One linkage that may become more evident is that between energy and the overall pattern of U.S.-Canadian trade, in which the United States pays for its oil and gas imports from Canada with manufactured goods, a trade pattern that Canadians resist. Another linkage involves foreign investment and Canadian control over the economy. The NEP's provisions in this area have already drawn U.S. and European protests.

Developing realistic expectations regarding supply from Canada is particularly important for the United States, since one of the consequences of declining oil and gas availability will be the need for replacement sources for those regions affected—namely, the U.S. Pacific Northwest, California, and the northern tier states. The completion of the Alcan pipeline, the construction of a northern tier oil pipeline, and the development of other oil and gas supplies take on added importance in this context. This does not preclude important forms of cooperation, such as tar sands R&D and unilateral efforts to reduce the cross-border transmission of airborne pollutants, but these measures should not be undertaken on the premise that more exports will be available as a result.

Although the issue has not been discussed in this chapter, it is essential that the United States recognize the importance for bilateral cooperation of completing the Alaskan natural gas pipeline. United States failure to complete its portion of this project would deliver a blow to bilateral relations. The prebuilding of the Canadian portion of this line, which has proceeded on the basis of assurances from President Carter that the Alaskan portion would be built or Canadian expenses compensated for, is politically very controversial within Canada, and collapse of the project would be a very serious development. The United States clearly confronts a dilemma here, in view of both the political importance of the project and its somewhat shaky economics as presently constituted. Nonetheless, the onus is on the United States to honor its commitment to Canada.

Planning for alternatives to dwindling Canadian supply, at this writing, appears to be a more prudent course of action than predicating U.S. policy toward Canada in the energy sector on the assumption that new U.S. initiatives can elicit substantially higher exports. Such assumptions are likely to be invalidated so long as the political framework for energy policy in Canada is battled over and export policy remains a major federal weapon in this battle. The United States must avoid intruding upon this struggle, which reaches to the very foundation of the political and economic structure of Canada. Despite its resource endowment, Canada is not in a position to extricate the United States from its energy predicament.

V U.S.-MEXICAN ENERGY RELATIONS

Edward F. Wonder

INTRODUCTION

Seven years after the oil embargo of 1973–1974, the United States remains dependent upon imported oil. Considerable attention, if not with significant effect, has been given to at least diversifying the sources of U.S. oil imports to avoid being held hostage by any single supplier. In this context, word of major new hydrocarbon discoveries in Mexico in the mid–1970s raised, for some U.S. experts, the question of whether Mexico could be the key to unlock the OPEC padlock. Indeed, some U.S. experts foresaw a new Saudi Arabia just south of the Rio Grande, if only the United States took the right steps to bring this about. Upon closer examination, the new Saudi Arabia analogy is misleading, and the assumption of U.S. ability to determine Mexican policy is outright mistaken. Mexican perspectives on the role of oil in economic development and the political, economic, and social factors operating within Mexico not just in regard to oil policy but to general political and economic affairs as well lead to a quite different picture from that posited by the proponents of the new Saudi Arabia thesis. These considerations encourage a more guarded view of Mexican oil policy and its impact on both Mexico and the United States.

Historically, the U.S.–Mexican relationship has not been a happy one for Mexico. U.S. military interventions, the loss of half of Mexican territory to the United States in 1848, and foreign—especially U.S.—economic domination have been Mexico's lot. One exception to this state of affairs stands out—the nationalization of the foreign oil companies in 1938, which was the culmination of forces set in motion by the revolutionary constitution of 1917 and its vesting of ownership of subsoil resources in the nation itself.

At the same time, the memory of Mexico's rise and fall from world petroleum prominence in the 1920s conditions the attitudes of Mexican elites. It is an experience no one in Mexico wants to repeat. Accordingly, the national petroleum company, Petroleos Mexicanos (Pemex), has been charged since 1938 with a "social mission" to ensure that petroleum development addresses Mexico's pressing socioeconomic problems. For Mexico, oil and gas production is not just another industry.

The U.S. desire to relieve dependence on insecure sources of oil and Mexico's imperative of using hydrocarbon revenues to finance economic development and address domestic socioeconomic needs raise a number of issues and questions.

- What is Mexico's oil and gas potential and its world significance?
- What, if any, technological and financial factors constrain production?
- What are the principal political and economic forces within Mexico that will shape oil and gas policy in the coming years?
- What are prospective Mexican production and export levels and marketing strategies?
- How is oil and gas being used within Mexico to achieve broader political and economic objectives, such as trade and investment diversification and industrial growth, and what are the implications of this "strategic" use of oil policy for U.S. interests?
- How do oil and gas relations relate to other issues on the agenda of U.S.–Mexican relations?

In addressing the above points, this chapter will briefly review Mexico's energy resources, identifying not only the range of estimates for various energy sources, but also where these estimates have proven controversial. The bulk of the chapter is devoted to a discussion of the political, social, and economic context of energy development in Mexico and how this context affects production and export policy and relations with the United States, an area that "technical" analyses of Mexico's hydrocarbon resources tend to underemphasize or ignore.

I. MEXICAN ENERGY RESOURCES

Estimates of Mexican resources that have appeared in numerous recent studies and official Mexican pronouncements have generated considerable, and in too many cases unfounded, speculation as to the significance of Mexico's oil and gas deposits. This speculation ranges from statements that Mexico is a new Saudi Arabia, or even another Middle East, to more cautious assessments stressing the limits of current drill-based data, the poor technical characteristics of some major fields, and the long-term potential implications of growing Mexican domestic demand.[1]

A number of factors must be kept in mind when considering estimates of Mexican energy resources.

- In some cases, the exploratory and developmental drill data is insufficient to make estimates of total resources with a high level of confidence;

- Official Mexican estimates have been conditioned by political considerations, if not consciously manipulated for political purposes;

- Changes in assessment methodology have a considerable impact upon assessments of the significance of Mexico's oil and gas resources; and

- Political, economic, and social factors, as well as technical ones, will affect possible production and export levels.

---

1. See, for example, Bruce Netschert, *Mexico: Potential Petroleum Giant* (National Economic Research Associates, September, 1978); William D. Metz, "Mexico: The Premier Oil Discovery in the Western Hemisphere," *Science* 202, (December 28, 1978):1281–65; Richard B. Mancke, *Mexican Oil and Natural Gas* (New York: Praeger, 1979); David Ronfeldt et al., *Mexico's Petroleum and U. S. Policy: Implications for the 1980s* (Rand Corporation, R–2510–DOE, June 1980; hereafter cited as Rand report).

The purpose of the following discussion is not to present a best-guess estimate, but to delineate the range of opinion and to illustrate the impact of the above-mentioned factors.

Several points need to be made regarding the terminology in which official Mexican estimates are made. Pemex's estimates of Mexican hydrocarbon resources include both oil and gas, a point sometimes lost when the unaware presume that the total refers to oil. As a rule of thumb, the approximate ratio of oil to gas in these figures is 65:35, with significant deviation from this on a field-by-field basis. Moreoever, Pemex's conversion ratio of gas to oil is 5000 cubic feet per barrel of oil equivalent, whereas a 6000 cubic feet per barrel ratio is more common elsewhere. This tends to overstate the oil portion of the total by 20 percent.

The most enthusiastic perspectives on Mexico also have tended to fix upon estimates of potential resources, which, as used by Pemex, refer to all ultimately recoverable resources, including cumulative production, proven and probable resources, and undiscovered resources.[2] Pemex also, in 1978, placed some of what should be considered as probable reserves in the proven category, resulting in a one-time increase in the proven reserve category. The implications of Pemex's definitional and presentational approach for the actual numbers and what they really represent are all too frequently overlooked.

Oil

President Jose Lopez Portillo announced, in September 1980, that with total potential hydrocarbon reserves estimated at a combined 250 billion barrels, Mexico had 60.1 billion barrels that were considered proved and another 38 billion barrels in the probable category. The figure for proven reserves was hiked again in March 1981, to 67.8 billion barrels.[3] Approximately two-thirds of this is oil.

The accuracy of Pemex's data is a point of some controversy. Some observers regard the estimates as conservative and believe that with greater exploration in new areas, major increases may be in store. Others believe that the present estimates obscure important technical factors and are not fully supportable on the basis of drill

2. Rand report, p. 4.

3. *Oil and Gas Journal*, March 30, 1981. The 1980 figures come from the *Fourth State of the Nation Report*, delivered by President Lopez Portillo, September 1, 1980.

data and that publicizing major resource holdings serves various political and economic ends, such as maintaining the confidence of the international financial community in Mexico's economy, bolstering Pemex's bureaucratic power, justifying domestically the production and export program in the face of conservationist and nationalist sentiments, and increasing bargaining leverage vis-à-vis the United States on trade and immigration issues.[4] These same observers believe that it was no coincidence that major discoveries were first announced in 1976 and 1977, when the newly installed Lopez Portillo government had to restore the confidence of domestic business leaders and the International Monetary Fund and other creditors in the government's ability to curb inflation, end capital flight, and reduce dependence on external borrowing.

Three areas currently possess the greatest known oil potential— the Reforma area, the offshore Campeche Bay area, and Chicontepec. The northeastern basin is a major source of nonassociated gas. Reforma and Campeche form a major part of the southern zone, currently the most important source of crude for Mexico. Over 82 percent of oil production and 86 percent of gas production in 1978 occurred in the southern zone. New exploration efforts in the early 1970s resulted in discovery of the huge Reforma fields in the southern states of Chiapas and Tabasco. Serious seismic work began in the Bay of Campeche in 1972 and drilling in 1974.

The discovery of major hydrocarbon resources in Reforma and the Bay of Campeche inspired the attention given Mexican oil and gas since 1976. Not only are individual fields very large (at least one supergiant, the first discovered worldwide since 1970), but production costs are relatively low in comparison to other recent discoveries, such as Prudhoe Bay and the North Sea. Productivity per well is high in both regions, although the proportion of heavier crude is higher in Campeche Bay, a fact that has led Pemex to raise the heavy portion of its export barrel to 60 percent. Associated gas is much lower in Campeche fields than in Reforma.

The largest component of Mexico's oil resources is located not in Reforma and the Bay of Campeche, but in the Chicontepec area in central Mexico. Over 106 billion barrels of total potential oil resources are to be found there and over 11 billion barrels of proven

4. See, for example, George Grayson, *The Politics of Mexican Oil* (Pittsburgh: University of Pittsburgh Press, 1980), ch. 3.

oil reserves. The geology of Chicontepec, however, makes its status a curious one. The petroleum in Chicontepec is found in overlapping sandstone beds, minimizing exploration risks but presenting very poor reservoir characteristics. As a result of this latter feature, the area had been left undeveloped for decades, despite the known presence of hydrocarbons. Production per well is low, in sharp contrast to the high productivity in the southern zone, and ranges from 5 to 150 b/d. Formation fracturing is required to improve very low permeability. Due to low depth, costs per well should·be low ($300,000 per well), but Pemex estimates that 16,000 wells will be necessary, bringing the investment, including associated facilities, to develop the area to nearly $9 billion, according to a 1980 estimate.[5] Discounted resource costs may range from $3 to $9 per barrel in marginal areas or much greater than in the southern zone.[6]

Assessing the significance of Chicontepec poses a dilemma. Some experts believe there has been insufficient drilling to determine reservoir characteristics. Difficult geology creates major uncertainty as to how much oil can be recovered. As a result, it would appear prudent to treat Chicontepec as a separate category in assessing Mexico's oil potential, but in doing so, it must be recognized that this undercuts the expectations of a new Saudi Arabia, which in any event appear to have involved a confusion of Mexico's potential resource with Saudi Arabia's proven reserves.

Based upon a more cautious assessment, a recent Rand Corporation study estimates that at the end of 1979, Mexico had proved reserves of 21.5 billion barrels of petroleum liquids (crude plus natural gas liquids), probable reserves of at least 18.9 billion barrels, and a total recoverable resource of 48.1 billion barrels, including that already produced (estimated to be 7.7 billion barrels).[7] Some experts, however, believe that even this estimate, to be validated, requires more drill data and that an even more cautious estimate than Rand's may be appropriate, given what solid data there is at present. In addition, both the Rand team and other more cautious analysts include a much smaller amount of Chicontepec oil in the category of proved reserves than does Pemex.

The same study estimates that there is a 90 percent probability that Mexico will produce more than 68.7 billion barrels, but only a

---

5. As reported in Rand report, p. 21.

6. Ibid. See also "Mexico Report," *Oil and Gas Journal*, August 20, 1979.

7. Rand report, p. 29.

10 percent probability that it will produce more than 121.4 billion barrels.[8] Resolution of methodological issues, such as whether to emphasize the potential of the total Mexican sedimentary basin or to focus on the small number of most productive areas, would have a significant bearing on resource estimates.

Gas

In addition to the gas associated with oil in the southern zone (12.2 tcf proved in Reforma, of which 1.3 tcf has been produced; 0.75 tcf proved in Campeche[9]), major deposits of nonassociated gas are located in several basins in northeastern Mexico. At the end of 1979, approximately 9 tcf were proved in the Burgos Basin, of which 4 tcf had been produced, with potential recoverable resources of at least 10.2, and possibly as much as 14.5, tcf. The Sabinas Basin may be one of the greatest sources of gas in North America if most of its known prospects prove to be productive. The Sabinas Basin is likely to contain at least 18 tcf of ultimately recoverable gas and possibly (with decreasing probability) 53 tcf. According to Rand, excluding most of Chicontepec, Mexico may have proved gas reserves of 34.6 tcf, probable reserves of 24.5 tcf, and a potential total recoverable resource of 72.2 tcf, including that already produced.[10] The Rand study estimates that there is a 90 percent probability that Mexico will ultimately produce more than 131.3 tcf and a 10 percent probability that it will produce more than 214.6 tcf of gas.

Regardless of whether one chooses official Mexican or more conservative independent estimates of Mexican hydrocarbon resources, it is clear that Mexico will become one of the most important sources of conventional petroleum in the world. However, at known levels of proven oil reserves, taking into account geologic and technical uncertainties, Mexico is in the league of Iraq and Venezuela and possibly some day of Kuwait. The comparisons with Saudi Arabia often ignore the fact that the official 250 billion barrel figure for Mexico is an estimate of potential resources, a dominant portion of which are located in the Chicontepec region and a third of which would be gas. Saudi Arabia's proved oil reserves are 167 billion barrels. Mexico's

8. Ibid.

9. Ibid., pp. 17-30.

10. Ibid., p. 29.

known proved gas resources place it at the same level as The Netherlands, and it may become as important as Algeria. A major caveat to
all of the above is that only 20 percent of the area of possible petroleum interest in Mexico has been explored. At present, the most
optimistic estimates, such as Bernardo Grossling's 600-billion-barrel
figure for the total hydrocarbon potential of all Mexico, must be
regarded as highly speculative.

Coal

Although attention in the United States and elsewhere has concentrated on Mexico's oil and gas, for obvious reasons, Mexico also possesses other energy resources that may become increasingly important in the future in meeting the energy needs of Mexican industry
and, toward the end of the century, providing alternatives to oil and
gas. Mexico's coal deposits are of fairly low grade, but are suitable
for electric power production. Proved coal reserves are around 2 billion tons.[11] Following completion of existing coal-fired plants, in
1986 coal will supply around 10 percent of Mexico's electricity.
Most coal production will be dedicated for use in the steel and metallurgical industries.

Geothermal

Mexico has geothermal resources, but their size is very speculative.
Two geothermal plants are already in operation, and three more are
planned by 1983. Expansion of the largest geothermal plant would
raise its capacity to 400 MW by 1985. The prospects for expansion
of geothermal use are tied to the technology and are confined to
remote, semiarid areas near the U.S. border. In any event, geothermal energy may supply only 7-8 percent of Mexico's electricity by
the year 2000.

---

11. Comision Federal de Electricidad figures.

Nuclear

Mexico is currently building two 654 MW plants to go on line in 1982 and 1983. Expansion of nuclear power, which received significant attention in the energy program announced in November 1980, is a politically and economically important issue in terms of both the requisite commitment of technical resources to such a project and the choice of reactor vendor. This matter is discussed later in this chapter. The availability of uranium will be a key factor, and at present, Mexico's uranium potential is estimated to be from 300,000–400,000 tonnes according to Mexican estimates. Although less than 20 percent of hydro potential has been tapped, the remaining hydro potential is concentrated in southeastern and south central Mexico. This leaves nuclear as the major substitute for oil and gas in producing electricity.

The significance of nonoil and nongas resources should not be slighted. The national energy program discussed later indicates that perhaps greater attention is being paid to alternative energy sources, especially in the electricity sector. Development of alternatives would reserve oil and gas for earning foreign exchange, satisfying domestic oil and gas demand, and providing feedstocks for a petrochemical industry, while providing energy sources for the day when oil and gas production begins to decline. Nonetheless, for the next decade or longer, oil and gas will be of primary importance to Mexico's economic and political prospects and to its foreign economic policy and diplomacy. The following analysis, thus, concentrates upon oil and gas policy and the broader economic and political uses to which Mexico is putting oil and gas.

II. ENERGY POLICYMAKING AND MEXICAN OIL AND GAS

Although it was the reports of major discoveries in the southern zone and the resource data provided by the Mexican government itself that grabbed attention in the United States, the economic, social, and political issues accompanying oil development and the ability of Mexico to cope with these are in the long run of the greatest interest to the United States. Oil development poses a major challenge to the political and economic modernization of Mexico. The failure of other societies to meet this challenge, most notably in the case of Iran, provides sufficient testimony to the importance to U.S. interests of Mexico's maintaining political and economic stability while addressing its underlying problems.

Economic and Social Factors and Production Policy

Disequilibrium in the external sector of the Mexican economy, domestic inflation, and the revenue needs of industrialization and overall economic development plans exert a very strong influence on Mexican oil and gas policies, especially regarding exports. Mexican government authorities often speak of a need to avoid economic "indigestion" caused by too large an inflow of oil-generated export earnings. This is a somewhat simple way of describing a very complex problem that oil exports both generate and offer as a remedy.

The influence of the external sector of the economy on oil policy can be seen in the decision by President Lopez Portillo, upon taking office in 1976, to publicize new discoveries and to expand oil and gas production and exports. This step was necessitated by the economic situation Lopez Portillo inherited from his predecessor.

The economic development strategy of the preceding Echeverria government had been financed by substantial external borrowing and an expansionary monetary policy. (Mexico was throughout much of this period, from 1971 to 1974, a net oil importer.) The result was a rising external public debt (32.3 percent of exports in 1976 were required to service this debt), high inflation, and a serious current account deficit. This situation led to the flight of private capital from the country and two devaluations of the peso, whose exchange rate with the dollar is politically as much as economically important in Mexico, and to the subsequent imposition, in 1977, of an austerity program by the International Monetary Fund that limited Mexico's external borrowing and public spending. Lopez Portillo was convinced that oil exports were the solution to these problems and soon replaced those Pemex officials he regarded as too conservation oriented with ones, notably the new director general, Jorge Diaz Serrano, supportive of raising production and exports.[12]

12. Grayson, ch. 3.

A major objective of the Six-Year Plan for oil and gas production announced in 1976 was to earn foreign exchange. The plan called for an increase in oil production from 984,219 b/d in 1976 to 2.25 mbd in 1982, with half this output exported. Gas production was to double to 3.6 bcfd in the same period. Pemex's capital expenditures were heavily development—rather than exploration—oriented in order to meet this target. Expansion of the refinery and petrochemical industries was similarly intended to earn foreign exchange.

The status of the external sector of the economy remains a critical determinant of oil policy. External debt service in 1979 required 64 percent of all export revenues. The 1979 current account deficit was $4.2 billion and approached $6 billion in 1980, while the portion of oil and gas revenues in total exports has risen to over 70 percent. Mexico was one of the largest borrowers in the Euro-dollar market in the 1978–1980 period. Meanwhile, the value of manufactured exports is falling in real terms. To a major extent, the growth in imports, which has kept Mexico in a current account deficit (in fact, in only one year since 1946 has Mexico not run a current account deficit), is due to Pemex's equipment purchases abroad.[13] The strategy of the Lopez Portillo administration has been to emphasize development of new export industries in order to rectify this dependence on oil exports, but as discussed later, oil and gas exports are needed to generate the capital to finance this program.

The weight of oil revenues in the economy will continue to increase. An early estimate of 1981 crude oil export revenues projects them to reach 75 percent of total exports.[14] Pemex's share of total public sector revenues is likely to rise above the 21.4 percent share in 1979. Pemex is by far the largest borrower in the state-affiliated sector of the economy and the source of the greatest expenditures (43.7 percent in 1979), reflecting the swift pace at which production has expanded.[15] The impact of new export industries on the balance of trade will not be felt for several years, leaving oil as the primary earner of foreign exchange.

Mexico's difficulties in regard to oil exports are not confined to the external sector of the economy. Fear of petrodollar-induced

13. See Banco Nacional de Comercio Exterior, S.A., *Comercio Exterior de Mexico*, September 1980 and September 1979.

14. Banco Nacional de Mexico, S.A., *Review of the Economic Situation of Mexico*, January 1981, p. 25.

15. Banco Nacional, *Comercio Exterior de Mexico*, September 1980.

inflation is a major factor in policymaking. One U.S. observer has argued that Mexico's program of expanding oil production while attempting to stabilize the economy has been financed by inflation and government revenues coming increasingly from oil exports.[16] The effect of inflation itself is regressive, and wage rates have not kept pace with inflation. The prices of capital goods of the sort imported by Pemex increased faster than did crude prices in 1976-1978, and Pemex's capital goods imports have a short-term inflationary impact.

High inflation, now over 30 percent, poses a difficult dilemma for Mexican authorities. It creates implicit pressure to devalue the peso in order to maintain trade competitiveness, which is of fundamental importance to Mexican efforts at industrialization and development of a wider range of export goods. Yet devaluation raises import costs, especially of foodstuffs. Political sensitivities have led to a phased devaluation strategy.

Heavy borrowing abroad, which has exceeded official targets, creates pressure to expand oil production and exports to yield sufficient foreign exchange to maintain the value of the peso. However, this would mean a larger ratio of oil revenues to nonservice gross domestic product, which is already 22 percent. A substantially higher ratio could damage the manufacturing sector and render the economy potentially more vulnerable over the long run to the fate experienced by other economies based on a single commodity. Whether Mexico may indeed be following this path is a matter of great importance.

The relationship of oil revenues to industrialization and overall economic development is a third economic factor influencing oil policy. The economy's ability to absorb export revenues without skewing the economic base is cited frequently by Mexican authorities as the most important constraint on oil production and exports. President Lopez Portillo has reiterated on several occasions that the pace of domestic economic development, rather than oil reserve size or export demand, will determine oil and gas production levels.[17] The national energy program links export levels to the need to generate sufficient revenue to maintain an 8 percent GDP growth rate, which is the target rate set by Mexico's numerous economic plans.

16. Laura Randall, "The Political Economy of Mexican Oil 1976-1979" (paper presented at Conference on U.S.-Mexico Energy Relations, Arizona State University, December 14, 1979).

17. See Lopez Portillo, *Fourth State of the Nation Report*, September 1, 1980.

Large-scale economic planning is a prominent component in Mexico's approach to coping with the economic consequences of higher oil and gas production. Central to economic development is the relative balance among different sectors of the economy, particularly the industrial and agricultural sectors, and job formation. With both oil revenues (almost $10 billion in 1980 and a projected $19 billion in 1981, compared with $3.98 billion in 1979) and oil's share of total export revenues expanding rapidly, the chief Mexican task is to decide how best to use these revenues. Since taking office, the Lopez Portillo administration has embarked upon a massive exercise in indicative planning, producing eleven sectoral plans and a global plan to identify ways to utilize oil and gas revenues in promoting economic development. The number and scope of these plans indicate the extensive role to be played by oil and gas revenues in the growth process.

The most prominent of the sectoral plans, the National Industrial Development Plan announced in 1979, emphasized exports of consumer goods and industrial expansion and increased Mexican value added and production of capital goods and incentives to investment in areas away from existing industrial regions. The plan projects an annual rate of industrial growth of 12 percent by 1982 and relies upon increased petroleum export revenues (gas exports significantly were not included, as the gas export deal with the United States was then under negotiation) to finance the plan, together with foreign borrowing. Foreign borrowing would remain integral to economic development, covering what was predicted to be a $2 billion current account deficit (a figure no longer realistic) resulting from the plan during the 1979–1982 period. Without the plan, the government projected an almost $3.2 billion current account surplus in the same period due to oil sales. Despite the emphasis on geographical decentralization of new industrial activity, the nature of many of the goods whose production was stressed (steel, cement, electrical goods, auto parts) is capital intensive. Underpricing of energy inputs subsidizes these industries and, by overstating profits, encourages expansion of capital-intensive industry, despite unemployment.

The so-called master blueprint, the 1980–1982 Global Development Plan released in April 1980, has redirected priorities somewhat, emphasizing the depressed agricultural sector, where a food crisis is growing as the birth rate outstrips falling production. Again, oil revenues are of key importance. The global plan proposes to divert

68 percent of Pemex's total gross earnings over the three-year period of the plan to "priority" sectors. The plan also seeks to eliminate serious transportation bottlenecks that impede industrialization and to increase steel output in order to hold back imports. At a projected 8 percent real economic growth rate, the plan anticipates generating two million new jobs by the end of 1982, but this will meet only new labor demand, currently running at 700,000 new jobs per year. Much more is needed to make a dent in the backlog of under- and unemployment.

The redirection of Pemex's revenues is significant, as Pemex has had to retain a higher share of its earnings in the past to help finance its own expansion program. Moreover, due to much lower domestic oil and gas prices, most of Pemex's earnings come from exports, which may place the Mexican government in a quandary over how to finance economic development while controlling foreign borrowing and holding oil exports steady at the 1.5 million barrels per day level set by the national energy program.

A number of factors constrain the ability of these plans to achieve their economic objectives, beyond the often-cited fact that the programs of one president are not binding on his successor. (The planning horizon, thus, is six years, or a *sexenio*.) The plans are themselves of the indicative sort, in that they set targets and encourage industry cooperation through tax and price incentives. Uncertainty as to whether the targets will be achieved by the private sector places added pressure on the state to increase direct involvement in the economy. Due to its strategy of import substitution, Mexico has inherited an inefficient industrial structure, encouraging the underpricing of domestic energy to subsidize exports. Inflation and overvaluation of the peso further diminish export competitiveness and increase the role of oil as the primary earner of foreign exchange. Finally, the linkages between target industries and the supporting industries that are supposed to develop are not at all clear, calling into question the overall economic effectiveness of the plans.[18]

Economic and social development needs influence Mexican energy policy in potentially conflicting directions. One of the most serious threats to Mexico's stability is the failure of job formation to keep pace with expansion of the manpower pool, generating pressures

---

18. Grayson, ch. 5. See also World Bank, *Mexico — Manufacturing Sector: Situation; Prospects; and Policies* (March 1979); and Redvers Opie, "Mexican Industrialization and Petroleum," *Economic Report on Mexico* (August 1979).

for migration to the United States and to urban and now the oil-producing areas within Mexico, where inflation is worse than the national average. Over 50 percent of the potential workforce is under- or unemployed, and under the best of circumstances only a 5-10 percent reduction in this can be expected.[19] Population growth, while presently lower than the 3.2 percent rate of the 1970s, remains high at 2.9 percent. The persistence of unemployment and underemployment raises the issue of whether capital-intensive industrialization is the best course for Mexico to follow, although the Lopez Portillo government has asserted that development of heavy industry is a prerequisite for employment expansion elsewhere in the economy. There is little support among Mexican elites for a more labor-intensive strategy.

The seriousness of the employment issue is compounded by inequality in Mexican society. A 1980 World Bank study estimates that 40 percent of the households in Mexico receive 9-12 percent of total national income and that there has been no significant change in this distribution (although real incomes have increased) since a similar survey in 1963.[20] Over half of the poor families are located in the agricultural sector. The continued existence of a dual society in Mexico is one of the most stubborn problems confronting that country.

The result of these factors is that conflicting pressures tug at Mexican policy. On the one hand, oil exports generate foreign exchange earnings and government revenues that can be used to finance industrialization. On the other, they contribute to already serious inflation and magnify the importance of various bottlenecks in the Mexican economy, particularly in port and handling facilities and transportation. Whether the new-found wealth even reaches the least of Mexico's population is yet another issue, and potentially the most important for political stability.

The Political System and Oil Policy

The Mexican political system confronts, in utilizing oil and gas revenues to promote economic development, a major challenge to its

19. Wayne A. Cornelius, "Mexican Migration to the United States," in Susan Kaufman Purcell, ed., *Mexico-United States Relations* (Academy of Political Science, 1981), p. 20.

20. Joel Bergsman, *Income Distribution and Poverty in Mexico* (World Bank Staff Working Paper No. 395, June 1980).

capacity to adapt to changing economic and political circumstances. This is especially true regarding the government's ability to plan economic development and reduce the serious economic inequities in Mexican society.

Mexican politics have frequently been analyzed in terms of the so-called "authoritarian" model of the Mexican political system, which emphasizes the political primacy of the president, acting in collaboration with a few key individuals, and the continual cooptation of critics of government policies.[21] The continuing validity of this model, and how the system may function if it is not valid, are two important questions that will be of central importance to Mexico's prospects for modernization of the political system and maintaining its record of political stability.

The dominant political coalition is seen in this model as centering around the president himself and operating through the bureaucracy to set policy directions, regulate the patronage system, and adjudicate conflict. The president's leadership of the Partido Revolucionario Institutionel (PRI), the predominant political party, provides a broad political support base. The dominance of the president rests upon both constitutional and extralegal authority that gives him considerable influence over the composition of the legislature and the judiciary, as well as the governorships, such that there is no effective institutional check on his power. The president's control of patronage ensures him control of the internal decisionmaking process. What limits on the president's power that do exist are due to the growth of diverse economic and political interest groups whose cooptation often requires concessions on the part of the dominant authorities or at least a willingness to take turns in benefiting from policy decisions. Moreover, the Mexical political system creates a potential for abrupt and sometimes radical shifts in policy with the presidential succession every six years, as the shift from the Echeverria to the Lopez Portillo presidency demonstrated.

Reality may be more complex than this model implies. The "pendulum" theory of the presidency, in which each incoming president represents a significantly different shade of opinion from that of his predecessor, may be overstated. More relevant are the differences between an "activist" approach to economic and political development and a "consolidating" approach emphasizing economic growth

21. An application of this model to oil policy can be seen in Edward Williams, *The Rebirth of the Mexican Petroleum Industry* (Lexington, Massachusetts: Lexington Books, 1979).

per se and the absence of a single clear ideological character for any particular administration, certainly so over its entire six-year period.[22] The more horizontal rather than vertical organization of the bureaucracy, which results in a decentralized implementation of policy, frequently frustrates the development of overall national policy.

Moreover, the PRI, as the dominant party, encompasses a very wide spectrum of opinion, making the need to build consensus among diverse groups an important aspect of Mexican politics. Recent changes in the electoral law have legalized additional opposition parties, especially on the left, and although their political influence is curtailed by the unwillingness of the national congress to oppose executive action, the opposition parties have been particularly active on oil- and gas-related issues, frequently criticizing "too rapid" expansion of production and the allocation of oil revenues to heavy industry. Oil policy may become one of the most important tests of the president's power and of the validity of the authoritarian model.

Nominally, the official responsibility for setting energy policy rests with the Minister of Patrimony and Industrial Development. In reality, the situation is more complicated, in that Pemex, by virtue of oil's role in financing economic development, has become a very powerful political actor. Pemex's claim on federal expenditures adds to its influence. The potential for competition for influence between Pemex's director general and the minister of patrimony is of considerable importance for oil policy, as the ministry has in the past harbored more nationalist leanings and has advocated a slower pace for oil development. In addition, the Treasury occupies a potentially important position in view of the impact of oil revenues on the economy and the concern for inflation, deficit spending, and public borrowing.

Energy policy is not confined to oil and gas, of course, and other agencies play important roles in their respective sectors. The Comision Federal de Electricidad (CFE) holds responsibility for electricity generation, transmission, and distribution. The National Institute of Nuclear Energy is responsible for nuclear research and development. A separate state-owned industry is responsible for all aspects of the nuclear fuel cycle. A branch of the Ministry of Patrimony is responsi-

22. See Susan Kaufman Purcell and John F. Purcell, "State and Society in Mexico: Must a Stable Policy Be Institutionalized?" *World Politics* 32 (December 1980): 194–227.

ble for reactor regulation, while the CFE has operating authority for reactors. The National Energy Commission is a cabinet level planning group.

Not only are oil revenues central to the process of economic development, they also offer a vehicle by which to increase even more the role of the state in the economy. The planning process already described is integral to this. Two issues arise in this regard, however. The numerous plans offer several ministries a role in the disbursement of funds, and the plans can be a means by which one ministry can attempt to rein in another. Patrimony drew up the national energy program, which may well have been intended in part to restrain Pemex from expanding production more rapidly. Moreover, the political system may function in such a way as to undermine the effectiveness of planning.[23] The need to maintain political alliances can lead to a profusion of plans intended to provide something for everyone rather than develop a clear, consistent set of priorities, since that could create losers as well as winners. The net effect is to preserve the status quo in a society confronting serious economic and social challenges. Modernization of the political regime may in the end prove to be just as important as economic development.

III. RECENT TRENDS AND ISSUES IN BILATERAL ENERGY RELATIONS

Oil and gas policy in Mexico has borne the stamp of two presidents who were quite different in their orientation toward the United States and in their assessment of how petroleum could best serve Mexico's interests. A brief review of their experience helps illuminate how the various factors at play in Mexico can affect oil and gas policy.

Although there was during the 1970s a general commitment to increasing production, there were fundamental differences between the approaches of Echeverria and Lopez Portillo as to the rate of expansion and the destination of exports. During the Echeverria period (1970–1976), a conservationist approach, which advocated minimizing exports in order to ensure future ability to meet rapidly expanding domestic demand, characterized policy. This gradually

23. Ibid.

gave way as a growing need for export revenues coincided with the discovery of the Reforma fields. Mexico resumed net exporter status in 1974, having lost it in 1971. However, nationalist sensitivities, and particularly fear of the United States using oil as an excuse to reassert domination over Mexico, combined with Echeverria's aspirations to increase Mexico's influence among developing countries to emphasize export markets other than the United States.

The succession of Lopez Portillo to the presidency in 1976 brought a greater emphasis on increasing exports. Official reserve figures grew rapidly, as the previous conservationist approach was abandoned, and the focus of market diversification shifted to Brazil, Japan, and Western Europe rather than to the Third World. As already mentioned, the need to improve Mexico's unfavorable balance of payments, ease reliance on external borrowing, and restore business confidence set the terms of oil development and export policy.

Mexican oil export policy under Lopez Portillo came to center around several points—high export prices; expanded volumes, with an emphasis on developing sales of refined products and petrochemicals; market diversification; and large exports to the United States. The nature of these goals suggests that Mexican policy currently serves a number of objectives, among which the hierarcy is not self-evident.[24]

Mexican price policy adopted OPEC standards as a basis. Mexico, due to lower transportation costs to the United States, has sold its oil slightly above the highest world contract prices. At the same time, domestic prices are a fraction (10–15 percent) of the world levels, maintaining a long-standing policy of subsidizing industrialization in order to accelerate economic growth and improve Mexican industry's international competitiveness.

Relations with OPEC, which showed a series of twists and turns under Echeverria, have not been a significant issue under Lopez Portillo. It is questionable whether Mexico would technically qualify for membership, since its oil export revenues are not the major part of the country's total budget and, moreover, Mexico benefits from certain U.S. trade preferences for less-developed countries, both of which facts would seem to disqualify it for membership. Mexico is well placed, however, to be a "free rider" of the cartel without

24. That there might not be a clear or fixed hierarchy would be consistent with the view that the political basis for planning is unstable. See ibid.

jeopardizing its diplomatic flexibility, especially vis-à-vis the United States; and as Lopez Portillo and other Mexican officials have made clear, Mexico has no economic interest in attempting to break the cartel.

The levels of production and exports increased rapidly in the middle and late 1970s. As pointed out earlier, the initial production target of 2.2 million barrels per day, originally set for 1982, was advanced to 1980, partly in response to surging reserve additions and partly in response to the needs of reviving the economy and reducing the overall trade deficit. Crude production averaged 2.12 million b/d through November 1980. Exports, which were 105,000 b/d in 1975, rose to an average 822,493 b/d in the first eleven months of 1980, having been held below the target of 1.1 mbd by bottlenecks in several ports. By the end of 1980, the portion exported to the United States had fallen to 60 percent from 80 percent in 1979.

Natural gas production in 1980 (through November) averaged 3.52 bcfd, about 74 percent produced in association with oil. Over half is produced in the Reforma area, with very little flaring. All of the gas—400 million cf/d in 1980—produced in the Campeche area will be flared until completion of a pipeline in 1981 to the shore. The national energy program, while projecting a 78 percent increase in oil output by 1990 and a 97 percent increase in gas production (4.1 mbd and 6.9 bcfd, respectively), would hold exports to current target levels—1.5 mbd of oil and 300 mcfd of gas—over the same time period. The gas export figure is the level presently committed to the U.S. market. Moreover, the program announced that no more than 50 percent of exports could go to any one country—namely, the United States—and that Mexico would supply no more than 20 percent of the import needs of a specific customer country. The level of exports would be geared to the revenue needs of an 8 percent GDP growth rate (assuming a 5–7 percent per year real increase in oil prices), while the program anticipates that the share of oil and gas exports in overall exports would gradually be reduced to 50 percent as the product structure of exports becomes more balanced. The program also addressed the issue of conservation, setting a goal for domestic oil demand of 2.6 million b/d in 1990.

Several aspects of this program merit attention. Although the projections can run to 1990, they are not binding beyond 1982, when a new president takes office. The position on an export ceiling is especially interesting, given the importance of export revenues to economic strategy. The failure to project an increase beyond 1982 leaves the decision on this point to the next president. The Banco Nacional de Mexico, a private bank, has estimated that the current account deficit could double if oil exports do not continue to grow after 1982.[25] In light of the poor export performance of the agricultural and manufacturing sectors, either larger oil exports or greater foreign borrowing will be necessary to meet the revenue needs for 8 percent GDP growth.

Considerable emphasis has been given to resource upgrading as a means both of establishing a world class integrated petroleum industry and of capturing more value added—all with an eye on exports. The refining targets (1.6 million barrels per day by 1982) may nevertheless slip into the mid-1980s. The costs of this expansion will be high, while the surplus refining capacity in major markets may pose another constraint. Building a refining industry to handle exports as well as domestic needs may be a dubious proposition, since the product slate has to be geared to the needs of the market. A substantial refining capacity devoted to exports could reduce Mexico's flexibility in choosing its markets.

Progress in establishing a petrochemical industry has been more encouraging, especially for ammonia, but is still insufficient to satisfy surging domestic demand before the early 1980s. Mexico could become a net petrochemical exporter after 1985. Natural gas is the primary feedstock for this industry. Overall petrochemical production will almost double by 1982.

Market diversification is a major point in oil export policy. Echeverria's Third World emphasis, and his notice to the United States with a sale to Cuba, quickly gave way under Lopez Portillo to a more realistic emphasis on industrial and large industrializing country markets. By 1979, petroleum sales were under negotiation with Spain, Japan, Canada, France, and Brazil, with Japan, as the potentially largest customer, having agreed to build necessary port facilities. Current sales volumes are shown in Table 5-1.

In the absence of offsetting benefits such as trade and technology packages, higher netbacks favor sales to the United States due to lower transportation costs. Market diversification, however, serves a number of ends, most notably increasing bargaining leverage vis-à-vis the United States on economic issues and developing invest-

25. Banco Nacional, *Review of the Economic Situation of Mexico*, p. 25.

Table 5-1. Mexican Oil Exports, by Destination
(as of December 31, 1980)

Contract Volumes		Additional Oil Export Commitments	
United States	733,000 b/d	Sweden	70,000 b/d
Spain	220,000	Jamaica	13,000
Japan	100,000	Philippines	10,000
France	100,000	Panama	12,000
Canada	50,000	Guatemala	7,500
Israel	45,000	El Salvador	7,000
Brazil	40,000	Honduras	6,000
India	30,000	Haiti	3,500
Costa Rica	7,500	Total	129,000
Nicaragua	7,500		
Yugoslavia	3,000		
Total	1,336,000		

Total contracted and committed 1,465,000 b/d

Source: Petroleum Intelligence Weekly, February 2, 1981.

ment deals with foreign customers, as discussed later. Mexico's use of diversification as a tool of economic policy is demonstrated by Mexico's dealings with Japan, which has been told that an increase to 300,000 b/d will depend on increased Japanese investment in Mexico.[26]

Exports to the United States have been a major—and potentially the politically most sensitive—element in oil policy under Lopez Portillo. Sales to the United States quickly grew from 89,000 b/d in 1975, or two-thirds of Mexico's oil exports, to 318,000 b/d in 1978, nearly all of which was crude. Under the national energy program, the maximum volume that can be made available to the United States would be 750,000 b/d, or a little over the current level. The issue of how much to sell to the United States obviously bears a major relationship to diversification, the decision not to sell more than 50 percent of exports to any one country, and the 20 percent limit on supply of a single country's total oil imports.

The ceiling on gas exports set by the energy program must be viewed in light of the events leading to the conclusion of an agreement with Mexico for the sale of 300 mcfd to the United States at a

26. Petroleum Intelligence Weekly, February 2, 1981.

January 1980 floor price of $3.625 per million btus, subject to a complex escalation formula. This gas supplies less than 1 percent of current U.S. needs. Initially, Pemex had signed a letter of intent in August 1977 to supply 2 bcfd at $2.60 per thousand cubic feet. The U.S. Export–Import Bank tentatively agreed to provide credits for the pipeline to bring the gas to Texas. Secretary of Energy James Schlesinger, in a now well-chronicled episode, rejected the deal because the gas price was pegged to the price of imported no. 2 fuel oil and was higher than that for either Canadian gas imports or domestic gas under proposed deregulation legislation.[27] The Mexican reaction was to revise the plan for the *gasducto* to limit export capacity and expand domestic gas consumption. The eventual agreement has been widely seen as only a partial salvaging of the lost opportunity.

Despite the sensitivity of sales to the United States, the role played by U.S. firms in Mexican oil and gas development is both extensive and politically curious. The 1938 nationalization outlawed private capital, regardless of origin, in the oil and gas industries. A 1959 law gives Pemex a monopoly over primary petrochemical production. Private companies can serve only in a contractor or consultant mode, with ownership confined to secondary petrochemicals. Pemex itself possesses substantial expertise and experience and is nearly self-sufficient technically, although there are weaknesses in design engineering, overall management, and offshore development expertise. Nonetheless, American firms have been hired on a contractor or consultant basis where it clearly serves Mexican interests. DeGolyer and McNaughton were hired in 1977 to verify Pemex's reserve estimates in order to increase the estimates' credibility to the banking community when Mexico was trying to get out from under IMF borrowing guidelines. Sedco was involved in the ill-fated Ixtoc I well, which suffered a serious blowout in 1979. There was considerable U.S. corporate involvement in the construction of the *gasducto*, especially on the part of Tenneco and Bechtel.

Pemex's foreign equipment purchases are a major import cost. The objective of government procurement regulations is the achievement of complete self-sufficiency, and as a general matter, the Mexican government prohibits imports of high technology goods unless they are not manufactured in Mexico. Approximately half of Pemex's

27. Richard Fagan and Henry Nau, "Mexican Gas: The Northern Connection," in R. Fagan, ed., *State and Capitalism in U.S.-Latin American Relations* (Palo Alto: Stanford, 1979); and Grayson, ch. 8.

equipment purchases overall are imports. This percentage is much higher in the refinery and petrochemical plant sector. As a general matter, the growth rate of oil production has exceeded the ability of Mexican industry to keep pace. Historically, U.S. firms have supplied well over 50 percent of imported equipment, and many American firms are now seeking joint venture agreements or service contracts. The signing of service contracts is complicated by the fact that they require the concurrence of the powerful oil workers union, which owns many of Mexico's drilling rigs and handles about 40 percent of Pemex's major machinery purchases.

The U.S. Department of Commerce projects Pemex import contracts to reach a total of $5.7 billion between 1979 and 1986.[28] The major import market will be for offshore drilling equipment, and the similarity of Mexican requirements to those experienced in the U.S. portion of the Gulf of Mexico, together with the proximity of the United States for spare parts and servicing, may enhance U.S. competitiveness. Nevertheless, it must be borne in mind that the scale of foreign (especially U.S.) corporate participation is a politically sensitive matter. Recent controversies over this involvement incorporate many perspectives, from charges of foreign infiltration of Pemex to claims that, in the aftermath of Ixtoc I, offshore operations would be safer if greater use were made of foreign exports.

In addition to its role in economic development, a similarly close linkage between oil export policy and economic strategy has been established in the area of trade policy. Opposition from Mexican manufacturers and labor unions fearful of losing protectionist economic measures forced the government to forego membership in the General Agreement on Trade and Tariffs in March 1980. The trade strategy embarked upon in the wake of the GATT decision links total oil exports beyond a "platform" (first set at 1.2 mbd in March 1980) to customer countries' willingness to grant Mexico's non-oil exports greater and freer access and to increase their investment in Mexico and technological cooperation as means of avoiding the economic "indigestion" that might occur if they simply paid for oil in cash. A number of discussions, some culminating in agreements along these lines, have been held with France, Sweden, Canada, and Japan,

28. *Oil and Gas Journal*, January 14, 1980; also American Chamber of Commerce of Mexico, *Mexico Energy*, January 1980; and Comptroller General of the United States, General Accounting Office, *Prospects for a Stronger United States–Mexico Energy Relationship* (ID-80-11, May 1, 1980).

all countries that Mexico perceives as eager to conclude such arrangements and possibly easier to bargain with than the United States. Recent statements by Mexican officials have stressed achieving wider and preferential access to U.S. markets rather than oil for investment deals.[29]

A precise oil for investment trade-off does not exist, as the Japanese have discovered. With the imposition of a cap on total exports, Mexican authorities have announced that the increased volumes that Japan seeks must come from cancellation of contracts held by other countries, despite Japanese willingness to satisfy Mexican interests.[30]

The impact of its growing status as an oil exporter can also be seen in Mexican foreign policy. The pretensions at Third World leadership during the Echeverria period have given way to a more focused effort at regional leadership and in developing foreign policy positions that protect Mexico's diplomatic independence and complement its economic interests. One of the more notable developments in this area has been the establishment, in collaboration with Venezuela, of a new facility to help finance the oil import bills of Central American and Caribbean countries. Under this program, initially proposed by the Venezuelans, both Mexico and Venezuela will each supply 50 percent of the oil import needs of eligible countries, with 70 percent of the oil sold at market prices and the remaining 30 percent financed through soft loans at 4 percent over five years. If the deferred payments are used for development of domestic energy sources, the terms are reduced to 2 percent interest and a twenty-year repayment period. President Lopez Portillo also proposed, at the United Nations in September 1979, the creation of a global energy plan, providing for rationalization of production and consumption at the global level and coordinated development of new energy sources.

The independence of Mexican foreign policy has long been demonstrated with regard to Cuba, with whom an oil deal was signed in late 1980, and in Central America, where the Lopez Portillo government has maintained that economic aid and working with progressive political factions are the best guarantees of stability in the area over

29. See the addresses by Foreign Minister Jorge Castaneda and Undersecretary of the Treasury Jesus Silva–Herzog Flores to the Forty-Second Annual Conference of the Council on Foreign Relations, New York, reprinted in Banco Nacional, *Comercio Exterior de Mexico* (June 1980).

30. Ibid.

the long run. These initiatives reflect the role of openings toward Cuba as a means of symbolically asserting independence from the United States as well as a belief that a diplomatically isolated Cuba would be even more difficult to control and a growing fear that instability in Central America is becoming a focus of East–West tension and could, if it spreads to Guatemala, ultimately threaten Mexico's border regions. As discussed in the next section, there is significant potential for serious misunderstandings between the United States and Mexico in the area of foreign policy.

The experience of the past few years demonstrates how oil and gas policy has become integral to Mexico's economic development, trade, and foreign policies. The problems that are apparent now and that will be likely to intensify in the future and their implications for overall relations with the United States merit close examination. The following section discusses both the prospects for bilateral energy relations in the coming decade and the impact of energy on the overall U.S.–Mexican relationship.

IV. BILATERAL ENERGY RELATIONS IN THE NEXT TWENTY YEARS

Regardless of how much Mexican oil and gas actually finds its way to U.S. consumers, U.S.–Mexican relations over the next ten to twenty years will be profoundly affected by energy. This will be true not only in the area of production and exports; the impact of energy on other issues on the bilateral agenda—most notably trade, immigration, and foreign policy—will become increasingly apparent. There is considerable potential for disagreement and misunderstanding on a number of points, thus increasing the importance of having a clear notion of what is the real U.S. interest vis-à-vis Mexico and what will be the best framework within which to conduct relations with Mexico. As a result, the questions of how much petroleum Mexico will produce and where it will be exported must be addressed at two levels—implications for U.S. energy security and implications for overall U.S.–Mexican relations.

The range of speculation as to future production rates is vast. Some observers have claimed that 10 million barrels per day is technically possible by the end of the 1980s or the early 1990s, making Mexico the rival of Saudi Arabia.[31] These estimates have encouraged

31. *Petroleum Intelligence Weekly*, February 2, 1981.

the view that Mexico is the key to reducing U.S. vulnerability to OPEC. Far more cautious estimates foresee Mexican production not exceeding 4 million barrels per day by the middle to late 1980s under the best of circumstances. For reasons discussed later, the projections contained in the national energy program may not provide a very accurate guide to the policy of the next Mexican government.

Central to understanding the range of these estimates is an analysis of their assumptions. The effort here will be to present in capsule form the arguments behind various estimates and then to consider what may be the more likely scenarios and what they mean for the United States.

The high production and export argument, in which upwards of a 10 mbd rate is sustained for at least a decade and exports to the United States alone reach 3 mbd (this rate is for the 1990s; by the middle and late 1980s Mexican production would exceed 5 mbd), is predicated on what is technically feasible and assumes at least 110 billion barrels of oil reserves.[32] The argument presumes that Mexico could easily expand production far above what is required for domestic needs. Moreover, the proponents of this position maintain that it would be in Mexico's interest to do so, given the amount of foreign exchange this would earn and the much loftier international political status, particularly vis-à-vis the United States, that would accrue to Mexico. This argument asserts that the key to achieving this level of production is an astute U.S. policy offering various incentives to Mexico, primarily in nonenergy areas (technology transfer, access to U.S. markets for Mexican goods, concessions on immigration), as a quid pro quo for more oil and gas. The proponents of this argument recognize that this production could create political controversy within Mexico, but believe that the quids pro quo would be persuasively attractive.

In a lower production scenario, oil output will not exceed 4 mbd by 1990 and exports 2 mbd. A number of arguments have been made in support of these estimates. The Congressional Research Service has argued that the market for associated gas will be a key parameter governing oil production and that the Mexican domestic gas market will be insufficient to alleviate this constraint. (CRS estimated that, with gas exports, production would reach 3.8 mbd in 1988 and only 3 mbd without.)[33] Other elements contributing to this production

32. See the Netschert, Metz, and Mancke studies.

33. Congressional Research Service, *Mexico's Oil and Gas Policy: An Analysis* (1979).

scenario are Mexico's desire to control inflation and to prevent an imbalance in the economic structure of the country, as well as the associated political problems, from developing. Thus, in addition to technical constraints, economic and political considerations will work to restrain production.

From the standpoint of what is geologically and technically possible over the next twenty years or so, there are two key uncertainties—resource levels and maximum production capacities. The Rand study has defined three representative scenarios that attempt to take into account these uncertainties as well as underlying Mexican preferences and interests.[34] These scenarios are:

- A low production scenario, constrained by a Mexican decision to give priority to long-term supply self-sufficiency, leaving resources in the ground, especially off shore and in Chicontepec, for future generations, and providing minimal exports, which results in production plateauing at 2.5 to 3.5 mbd in the mid-1980s, depending upon whether the recoverable oil resources are 70 or 120 billion barrels;

- A moderate production scenario of from 3.5 to 5.5 mbd peak in the 1980s and 1990s, with resources at 70 or 120 billion barrels, respectively; exports not exceding domestic consumption; and no acceleration of Campeche and Chicontepec production over current projected rates; and

- A high production scenario resembling the high production argument already discussed, with expansion occurring as rapidly as possible as Mexico decides to become a major world oil exporter and with production peaking at from 5 to 7.5 mbd for about a decade beginning in the early 1990s, depending on resource levels.

It is clear that, with a high level of resources and a decision to become a major exporter, Mexico could become one of the leading forces in the world market. Whether it will choose such a role is, of course, another matter.

The high production scenario, according to Rand, appears to be the least likely. The 10 mbd rate mentioned by some is not likely to be achieved, since the necessary high recovery rates to raise the ultimately recoverable resources to the levels necessary to sustain this

34. Rand report, p. 81.

production rate can be realized only by long productive life in the major fields, with heavy reliance upon water injection and other means of supplemental recovery and not by increasing peak production rates.[35] Moreover, the high production rates require high recovery in Chicontepec, which may be achievable only over very long periods of time (seventy-five to one hundred years). Finally, Mexico can be a major exporter (4–5 mbd) for only a decade or two before production falls precipitously, much the same as happened in the first Mexican oil boom in the 1920s. Low or modest production would enable associated gas to be used without large-scale flaring, while Pemex would retain flexibility regarding how much gas it wants to produce by emphasizing production from fields with heavy oil–low gas or light oil–high gas ratios. At the high rates, Pemex would lose whatever flexibility it actually has. Last, long-term energy self-sufficiency would be unattainable in the high production case, given the relatively short period of high production and the rapid growth of domestic demand.

One factor frequently overlooked by the proponents of the high production–export case is the growth of Mexican demand, which was averaging 7–8 percent per year in the late 1970s and could reach 10 percent under the weight of industrial growth. Upward movement of internal prices, substitution by nonoil energy sources, and increased energy efficiency in the capital stock could moderate this rate in the future, but despite their mention in the 1979 Industrial Development Plan, there is no strong political constituency for higher internal prices. Energy subsidies to industry, moreover, are a major element of that plan. This encourages energy inefficiency, yet this situation will be difficult to change, since low prices have been a major element in Pemex's social mission since 1938. If unabated, Mexican internal demand could exceed 4 mbd by 2000 and, in the medium and low production scenarios, could require reduction of exports beginning in the 1990s. At a production rate of 5 mbd through 2010, self-sufficiency could be lost by 2020 as production declines.[36]

Technical considerations, however, define a range of possibilities. The actual production and export levels achieved within this range will reflect economic and political factors as much as technical ones.

35. Ibid., pp. 39–40, 90–91.

36. Gary Hufbauer et al., "Bilateral Trade Relations," in Susan Kaufman Purcell, ed., *Mexico–United States Relations* (Academy of Political Science, 1981), p. 138.

Economic considerations will in all likelihood continue to exercise dominant influence on overall production and export policy. Without an increase in exports beyond the 1.5 mbd limit set in the national energy program, the current account deficit will worsen, and foreign borrowing would in all likelihood have to increase if the 8 percent GDP growth rate target is to be met. Heavier reliance on borrowing would only aggravate the debt service burden and increase Mexican dependence on the international financial community, especially U.S. banks, which may be politically sensitive within Mexico.

At the same time, increasing the inflow of foreign exchange will threaten increased inflation. Based on data presented earlier, one can argue that Mexico is already experiencing the "Venezuelan" syndrome of an inflated, oil-dependent economy. If oil were to cost $60 per barrel in 1985 (assuming a 4 percent annual real price increase and a 14 percent per year increase in nominal terms), exports of 3 million barrels per day in 1985 would earn $65 billion, which could put Mexico on the path traveled by other oil-dependent economies.[37]

Opinion as to whether production should be expanded further, and at what rate, is divided. The young *tecnicos* in the Secretariat of Programming and Budget see Mexico on the verge of an economic takeoff fueled by petroleum revenues and regard the expansion of these financial resources as essential if industrialization and rural development are to proceed. There is much less enthusiasm for rapid oil development from the old line ministries dealing with agriculture, employment, trade, and economic development, which feel that too rapid an oil boom could trigger massive migration within Mexico and generate employment demands that the rate of economic development cannot satisfy. These ministers reportedly persuaded Lopez Portillo in January 1980 not to follow Pemex's advice to expand 1982 production to 4 mbd. The greatest doubts about rapid oil development come from the left, which rejects sales to the United States, and industrialists and bankers, especially the Bank of Mexico, who foresee greater inflation, bottlenecks in the economy, and an overvalued peso. This question of the production rate will undoubtedly resurface under the new president in 1982.

How powerful the fear of inflation and distortion of the economy will prove to be is unclear. Inflation is serious now, yet the money

37. *Latin American Weekly Report*, January 25, 1980.

supply expanded by approximately 33 percent in 1980. If forced to choose between a contractionary economic policy to curb inflation and maintaining 8 percent GDP growth, the next president could well choose economic growth, since rising expectations and the need for an ever-increasing economic pie to satisfy political claims will generate strong political pressures for maintaining a high economic growth rate. Sooner or later, however, the inflation question must be faced. This could set a ceiling on exports higher than the current one, such that the export levels associated with the moderate production scenario—approximately 2-2.5 mbd—may be realized. The decisions in this area—whatever they are—will be of tremendous significance for Mexico's future.

How much of these exports will make their way to the United States is another question. Although over 80 percent of Mexican oil exports in 1979 went to the United States, Mexico has every intention of decreasing this percentage. The national energy program lowers this percentage to 50 percent. The reasons for this policy are numerous, including the domestic political sensitivity of large sales to the United States; widespread concern that the United States will pressure Mexico to increase exports to it and, if overdependent on Mexican oil, may not hesitate to seize the oil fields during a supply crisis; and the greater bargaining leverage that a successful market diversification strategy will provide Mexico, especially in seeking investment deals with other industrial countries. The often-cited nationalism factor is an important determinant of Mexico's policy regarding exports to the United States, but the calculations behind this policy are more complex and utilitarian than this factor implies.

Although some experts initially regarded the prospects for successful diversification as somewhat marginal, Mexico has not been wanting for customers. Strict destination controls and a refusal to sell in the spot market ensure that Mexican oil reaches its stated destination and is not rerouted to the United States. A port facility expansion and development program should, by the mid-1980s, provide Mexico with facilities to handle 5 million barrels per day. Mexico's ability to realize a higher netback from sales to the United States due to lower transportation costs will, in the end, not discourage diversification, especially if Japanese and European customers invest in new port facilities and help overcome other bottlenecks.

If the United States received 50 percent of Mexican oil exports in the moderate production case, or perhaps 1.25 mbd, this would amount to 19 percent of U.S. oil import needs, if imports remain at the average level recorded in the first quarter of 1981, or 6.47 mbd. In global terms, the exports associated with this case could provide a beneficial cushion in the world oil market, assuming consumer country demand does not grow significantly. Both developments—more oil for the United States and more in the world market—would serve U.S. energy security interests.

The future of gas exports depends upon a number of considerations. Mexico has several options, including shutting in nonassociated gas; limiting production to casinghead gas, most of which would be consumed in Mexico in the low or moderate oil production cases (allowing for greater production from low gas–oil ratio offshore fields); or developing the nonassociated fields for export purposes. In the latter case, upwards of 2–3 bcfd could be available, still a very minor share of U.S. needs.[38] If flexibility in oil production is possible, then production of associated gas may not compel gas exports. Growing consumption of gas in the electricity and petrochemical sectors will limit the size of the overall surplus.

At present, oil production in the high gas ratio Reforma fields has stabilized, with the major expansion in oil output to occur in the Bay of Campeche, where the ratio of gas to oil is much lower. This suggests that major new increments in gas exports would require production from the nonassociated gas fields.

The U.S.–Mexican energy relationship may not be confined to oil and gas. A number of opportunities exist to develop cross-border electricity sales. San Diego Gas and Electric signed a letter of intent in February 1980 for the purchase of 60 MW from a geothermal-power station in Mexico, to be delivered from 1983 into the 1990s. A much smaller service of 20,000 kw has begun to a small town neighboring Tijuana.

The state of California has made extensive efforts to develop greater cross-border cooperative arrangements with adjacent Mexican states, and electricity sales are a part of this. Since the cancellation of the Sundesert nuclear project intended to serve the San Diego area, both utilities serving southern California have sought power wherever they can get it. The population growth in the U.S. Southwest in general would appear to encourage greater resort to cross-border supplies. The Mexicali and Tijuana regions are also growing,

---

38. American Gas Association, *The Gas Energy Supply Outlook: 1980–2000*, A Report of the AGA Gas Supply Committee (October 1980), p. 19.

and cross-border sales would enable the Mexicans to bring on new capacity in advance of when it would have to be firmly committed to the domestic market. The same rationale proved persuasive much earlier in regard to development of Canadian hydroelectric complexes. Historically, the United States has sent more electricity southward than it receives in return (approximately 150 million kwhr to Mexico in 1978, with 50 million kwhr going the other way), but the prospects are that this pattern will be better balanced in the future. A joint Department of Energy–CFE study of electricity exchanges was completed in 1980.

A final area of potential importance to the future of the energy relationship is the role of nuclear power in Mexico. Mexico would not be the first producer country to argue that generating electricity with nuclear power is preferable to using oil and gas for this purpose. In 1977, 8 percent of Mexican gas production was used to generate electricity. This will increase considerably, due to conversion of several generating stations to gas. The oil burned in utility boilers represents at present 10 percent of total production. With greater industrialization, especially in new areas, the electricity sector will grow, raising the issue of substitutes for hydrocarbons in order to reserve oil and gas for more profitable use.

A planning study released in early 1981 set a goal of 20,000 MWe of nuclear capacity to be installed by the year 2000. Gradual acquisition of the technology is a prominent feature of this program. Prior to issuance of this report, separate market and technical studies were completed on behalf of Mexico by reactor vendors from France, Canada, and Sweden. Although U.S. vendors would like to sell to Mexico (the two reactors under construction at Laguna Verde are of U.S. origin), the prospects for U.S. firms winning new contracts are diminished by Mexican unhappiness with the U.S. government over now settled fuel supply problems. Nevertheless, the ambitious program that Mexico contemplates will pose substantial technological and human resource challenges to Mexico.

The impact of energy on bilateral relations is not confined to production and export levels. Trade, migration, and foreign policy issues will be indirectly affected by energy in the ways discussed in the previous section. How much importance the United States should accord the oil and gas export question vis-à-vis these other issues is a matter of major significance to how bilateral relations are approached in the coming years.

Mexico is the United States' third largest trading partner overall, its fourth most important export market, and due to oil imports, its third largest source of imports. Roughly two-thirds of Mexico's trade is with the United States, and the implications for Mexican dependence on cyclical fluctuations in the U.S. economy are not lost upon the Mexican government. However, the U.S. share of Mexico's overall trade deficit is much lower due to oil sales. The United States is the largest source of private investment in Mexico, with a $4.7 billion total in 1979, or 69 percent of the total foreign investment, and will in all likelihood remain so. (Japanese investment, by contrast, is a little more than 5 percent of the total.) The border industry program, in which assembly plants on the Mexican side of the U.S.-Mexican border operate under in-bond arrangements, is an especially thriving element in the Mexican economy and in U.S.-Mexican trade.

There is significant potential for conflict over trade issues. Mexico's decision not to join the GATT, because it might constrain the use of subsidies and other policy tools central to the National Industrial Plan, poses problems for trade relations with the United States. Rising domestic costs and reluctance to devalue the peso will erode the competitiveness of Mexican manufactured exports, creating incentives to continue subsidies and to set export performance and local requirements for foreign investors. The United States views these measures as unfair trade practices.

This potential for conflict in the trade area stems in major part from the enormous gap between the two economies. Moreover, as a former high-ranking U.S. Treasury Department official has argued, an additional source of potential misunderstanding lies in Mexico's tendency to set economic targets and reserve the right to choose policy tools, while the United States emphasizes "rules of the game" rather than specific goals.[39] This difference reflects America's global economic role and adherence to multilateral trade regimes that restrict the choice of policy tools, as well as the asymmetry of the economies. Although oil exports may have alleviated somewhat the balance of payments constraints on Mexican development policy and helped to make the economy more outward looking, selective subsidies and import substitution will remain important policy tools in Mexico. In the absence of a subsidy–countervailing measures agree-

---

39. Hufbauer, p. 139–44. See also the essays by Maria del Rosario Green and Rene Villareal and Rocide Villareal in the same volume for more academic Mexican views on the subject.

ment or its equivalent with the United States, the use of subsidies to compensate for the effects of inflation and a fixed exchange rate may subject Mexican exports to the United States to countervailing duty proceedings, regardless of whether or not they cause material injury to U.S. industry.

Migration is a second and highly emotional issue in bilateral relations. How many illegal Mexican immigrants have entered the United States, let alone how many have remained, is unclear, although the estimates are in the area of five million. Some U.S. economists believe there may actually be a shortage of unskilled labor in the United States in the coming decades that such immigrants could relieve.[40] Nevertheless, illegal immigration is a very sensitive issue in the United States, as the recent recommendation of the (U.S.) President's Select Commission on Immigration and Refugee Policy to limit more tightly the level of new immigrants attests.

From Mexico's standpoint, however, illegal immigration to the United States is seen not as a problem, but as a solution to the lack of opportunity within Mexico for unskilled labor, especially in the agricultural regions. The rate of migration in the future will depend on a number of factors, including the real wage differential between the two countries (estimated by one expert to be 13:1 for agricultural work); inflation in Mexico; the rate of growth in the labor force, which could rise from the current 700,000–800,000 per year to 1.2 million per year by 1990; the rate of new job creation, approximately 700,000–800,000 per year; and the backlog of under- and unemployed already in Mexico.[41] The prospect is for continuing illegal immigration and considerabl friction with Mexico over U.S. attempts to restrict it. It remains to be seen whether the kind of industrialization presently being fueled by oil will eventually make a dent in this problem.

Finally, foreign policy is a potentially fertile area for misunderstanding, especially over Cuba and Central America. This is not simply the result of U.S. reluctance to accept greater Mexican diplomatic status. The two countries act from within different frameworks. As a global power, the United States tends to see regional issues in a

40. Clark W. Reynolds, "Labor Market Projections for the United States and Mexico and Their Relevance to Current Migration Controversies," *Food Research Institute Studies* 17 (Stanford University Food Research Institute, 1980). For a different perspective see Grayson, chs. 5, 10.

41. Cornelius, p. 70.

broader, international perspective, while Mexico acts as a regional power, emphasizing economic and political strategies for regional problems such as the joint oil facility with Venezuela. Although the United States has in the past looked the other way at Mexico's relations with Cuba, Mexico's support for the Sandinistas in Nicaragua and its opposition to the junta in El Salvador have not been as readily accepted in Washington. The potential for misunderstanding over regional issues is great, especially if the United States adopts more militarist strategies for dealing with unrest in Central America or supports military dictatorships.

Although the discussion here is not consciously intended to be overly pessimistic, the important point is that there are several issues of major importance whose handling will determine the course of U.S.-Mexican relations in the coming years. Actual Mexican energy supply to the United States is only one issue and should not be allowed to drive the overall relationship.

V. CONCLUSIONS

Too often public discussion in the United States, more outside the government than within, has been dominated by arguments that Mexican oil and gas are vital to U.S. energy security, that bilateral relations turn on energy, and that the United States should do all it can to get more Mexican oil and gas. The more the United States gets, the more its interests are served. Then we can "stick it to the Saudis." Is this an accurate rendition of U.S. interests? Does the policy implied on the part of Mexico serve Mexican interests?

As Jorge Castaneda, the Mexican foreign minister, reminded the readers of the *Washington Post*, "Mexico is a country, not an oil well!" Pressing for the highest technically feasible production runs many risks. Not only could this exacerbate domestic political sensitivities within Mexico, in the long run the consequences of high production (8-10 mbd) for Mexico could be economic and political destabilization. The prospects of this destabilization occurring over the next twenty to thirty years in a country of what will then be over one hundred million people, with the welfare of the United States increasingly dependent on Mexican energy and with a burgeoning Hispanic population in the United States, are ominous for the United States. This is a nightmare scenario for the Mexicans because of what they fear will be a temptation for the United States to intervene militarily. It must be asked whether the much higher Mexican oil exports associated with the scenario are a particularly wise answer to U.S. energy and diplomatic problems if the production rate required leads to internal instability within Mexico. If events in Iran and elsewhere in the Middle East offer a clear lesson, it is that overdependence on a particular supplier or suppliers is foolhardy.

A more moderate production rate holds numerous attractions for both countries.[42] For Mexico, it would place less strain on the political system, in that this rate may find support from a broad spectrum of elites within Mexico. Export revenues would still be sizable, without seriously overheating the economy. Mexico would attain greater international and regional status and could continue to diversify its economic relations. The specter of Yankee imperialism might appear less threatening if the United States was not overly dependent on Mexican oil. This production rate could still mean more oil and possibly gas for the United States, and the supplier may remain more secure and stable in the process.

The current Mexican emphasis on diversification of oil customers serves U.S. energy security interests by increasing the alternatives for other industrial states more heavily dependent than the United States on Middle Eastern oil and by adding to the margin of excess supply in the world oil market. At the same time, even if only 50 percent of Mexican oil exports come to the United States, the amount received will still increase in volumetric terms. What is clear is that increased imports from Mexico will not alleviate the U.S. need to develop new sources of energy supply and improve the efficiency of energy use. Nor, it must be added, will imports from Mexico allow the United States to turn away from the implications of political and military developments in the Persian Gulf for U.S. foreign policy and national security interests.

What approach the United States should take in dealing with Mexico is of crucial importance. The primary U.S. interest vis-à-vis Mexico is Mexican economic stability and progressive political development. Energy is subordinate to this interest, and it is clear from the evidence that energy is closely intertwined with other bilateral issues. For a number of reasons, then, energy should not—and

42. Rand report, ch. 4; Grayson, ch. 10.

cannot—be singled out as the primary element in the bilateral relationship.

The arguments for package industrial deals, quids pro quo based on immigration and trade concessions and massive technology transfer in return for more oil and gas, appear to rest on the very dubious assumptions that U.S. policy holds the key to Mexican oil development and that 10 mbd is within easy grasp. Several questions must be asked of this approach. Does the history of U.S.-Mexican interaction provide encouraging evidence that this assumption is valid? Are Mexican self-interests sufficient in themselves to lead to higher, albeit moderate, oil production without U.S. pressure to bring about this result?

There is not much evidence to support the presumption that such a linkage approach would work, let alone that it is desirable. The arguments for technology transfer in the oil sector tend to underestimate both Pemex's capabilities and the high probability that considerable transfer will take place through normal commercial mechanisms without much prodding as production expands into offshore and difficult recovery areas. Much of the equipment and rig business will come to the United States in any event. The growth of the Mexican economy will attract technology and capital in other economic sectors as well. The numerous trade and social issues affecting bilateral relations clearly require more focused attention, but do so regardless of the oil issue. It is not evident that horse trading is either appropriate, in light of Mexican sensitivities on the issues and concern at being pressured to increase exports, or effective. How one assigns weights to different parts of the bargain and ensures that each side will deliver on what it promises are additional question marks surrounding this approach.[43]

It is also not clear that these approaches are necessary to receive more oil and gas, especially if Mexican interests are likely to lead to higher production and exports anyway. Certainly as the process of presidential succession begins in Mexico in 1981, new U.S. initiatives to encourage more production would only be misunderstood. The more troubling—and unlikely—case would be if Mexico opted for a low production level. Economically, phasing out exports would be very painful, but a reversion to more Echeverria like policies could

43. Grayson, ch. 7; see also Richard R. Fagan, "Mexican Petroleum and U.S. National Security," *International Security* 4 (Summer 1979): 39-53.

confront the United States with some difficult choices, as this policy could presage greater friction in U.S.-Mexican relations.

Constructive approaches to the major issues on the bilateral agenda, in which satisfactory resolution of one paves the way for resolution of the next, much in the way implied by Lopez Portillo's concept of a "package approach," could help improve the overall political environment of bilateral relations. This could make it easier for Mexican authorities to maintain exports to the United States at relatively significant levels. This approach may be more congruent with political and economic realities on both sides of the border.

Oil is clearly changing the basic parameters of U.S.-Mexican relations. This is evident in the issue areas discussed in this chapter.[44] Whether this process leads to greater conflict and misunderstanding or whether the two countries can work harmoniously to promote their mutual interests will become increasingly important issues of U.S. foreign policy.

The framework within which the United States approaches its relations with Mexico will be of major importance. The United States can approach Mexico from a primarily international perspective, treating Mexico as any other developing country and regional power, subject to the same rules as the rest without any preference.[45] Given the nature of trade and migration issues, this approach would be likely to lead to greater conflict and ignores the inescapable consequences of sharing a common border. The United States can also deal with Mexico on a primarily bilateral basis, with some willingness to give and accommodate on such matters as export subsidies. Or it can cultivate a special relationship, with bargains struck and joint programs developed on the major issues between the two countries. Whether the United States could bureaucratically implement such an approach and overcome the likely protectionist impulses from domestic interest groups is not clear, nor is it evident that this relationship would be acceptable to Mexico, if it entailed major concessions on the part of Mexico. Much now depends on the predilections of the next Mexican president and his administration.

Whether or not a coherent U.S. policy toward Mexico develops, bilateral relations will face a considerable challenge in the years

44. See Robert L. Ayres, "The Future of the Relationship," in Susan Kaufman Purcell, ed., *Mexico-United States Relations* (Academy of Political Science, 1981), for discussion of alternative scenarios for future bilateral relations.

45. Ibid. See also Rand report, pp. 94–97; and Fagan.

ahead. Mexico is slowly changing, as is the United States. Mexico's ability to achieve rapid economic growth and industrialization without debilitating inflation and political instability will be of fundamental importance over the next twenty years. The basic U.S. interest regarding Mexico is nor more oil, but a prosperous, stable, and progressive Mexico.

VI U.S.-VENEZUELAN ENERGY RELATIONS

Edward F. Wonder

INTRODUCTION

Venezuela's role in international affairs, its relations with the United States, and its own political and economic development in this century have been inextricably tied to oil. Venezuela exports more oil than any other nation in the Western Hemisphere—1.9 mbd in 1978, 2 mbd in 1979, and approximately the same in 1980. Almost 34 percent of Venezuela's crude oil exports go directly to the United States—almost 50 percent, if product refined in Aruba and Curacao is counted. While the recent discoveries in Mexico have atracted considerable attention, the continuing importance of Venezuela to hemispheric oil trade remains undiminished. Although total Mexican production will be greater, Mexican exports may lag behind until later in the 1980s.

Historically, Venezuelan oil has been particularly important during periods of supply shortfalls and disruptions such as occurred in 1973–1974 and, more recently, in 1979 and 1980. Venezuela, moreover, was the second largest foreign crude oil supplier for the United States (behind Canada) until 1973, when Saudi Arabia and Nigeria passed it. Nonetheless, the United States has frequently tended to lump Venezuela together with all OPEC countries, in the process appearing insensitive to Venezuela's long-standing importance in oil

217

supply to the U.S. East Coast and to repeated Venezuelan efforts to receive both U.S. recognition as a secure source and the preferential access to the U.S. market that Venezuela feels this reliability should justify.

At the same time, Venezuela confronts a range of challenges of crucial importance to its economic and political future. These stem from the decline of reserves of light crude, the substantial technical and financial problems associated with developing the Orinoco heavy oil belt, and the difficulties of maintaining economic stability in an economy admittedly overdependent on oil revenues. Venezuela's success in overcoming these challenges and in continuing the democratic government that distinguishes it from many other Latin American countries is of overriding interest to the United States.

There are a number of fundamentally important questions that arise in regard to Venezuela's oil policy and the relationship of that policy to the country's economic and political prospects and its relations with the United States and other countries. These are:

- How much oil can Venezuela produce, and what will be the quality of the export barrel;

- What is the relationship of oil policy to Venezuelan economic development and foreign policies and Venezuelan internal political stability;

- What have been the major elements of Venezuela's international oil policy, and how do they relate to Venezuelan political and economic interests;

- How long (and at what expense) will it take to bring on production from currently untapped sources;

- What efforts can be made to facilitate future Venezuelan petroleum development, and what is Venezuelan strategy regarding the Orinoco oil belt and the place of the U.S. in that strategy; and

- What are likely future directions for Venezuelan international oil policy, and what are their implications for U.S.–Venezuelan relations.

The following discussion focuses first on Venezuela's resources and then proceeds to analyze the political, economic, and technical factors affecting oil policy and possible future trends in oil policy and U.S.–Venezuelan relations.

I. VENEZUELAN ENERGY RESOURCES

Oil

Venezuela started to produce oil in 1914 and was from 1929 to 1970 the world's largest exporter. Venezuelan prospects were so promising in the 1920s and 1930s that they encouraged a shift away from production in Mexico. Venezuela now ranks fourth in oil production within OPEC. Crude production averaged 2.35 million b/d in 1979, of which 2 million b/d were exported. This level was repeated in 1980, and both production and exports have hovered at this general level for the past several years. About one-third of the oil produced is heavy crude, and the heavy share is increasing. Production costs average around $2.70/barrel.[1]

The level and composition of oil reserves is an important factor influencing Venezuelan oil policy. About 19.5 billion barrels of conventional crude resources are proved, and with secondary recovery, another 10-12 billion could be recovered. Venezuelan authorities have estimated that there may also be 10-40 billion barrels in potential oil resources.[2] These potential resources—and the level of uncertainty in the estimates is significant—lie predominantly in offshore areas on the Venezuelan outercontinental shelf, where several recent strikes of medium light crude (30° American Petroleum Institute) have occurred. Offshore exploration has intensified to locate more medium and light crude to offset rapidly dwindling light reserves.

Not only do light reserves threaten to reach exhaustion within a decade, total reserves, at recent production rates averaging from 2.2 to 2.4 million barrels per day since 1977, would not last more than twenty years or so. Venezuela has confronted this problem for some time, however, as proven reserves have not strayed much from the 18 billion barrel range since 1961. Currently, reserve additions tend to reflect improvements in the methods of reserve delineation more than they do significant new discoveries.[3] The growing prepon-

1. This data is drawn from a report by the Congressional Research Service, *Outlook on Venezuela's Petroleum Policy*, prepared for the Energy Subcommittee of the Joint Economic Committee of Congress (February 1980), particularly Section III (hereafter cited as CRS); and also from Ministry of Energy and Mines, *Petroleo y Otros Datos Estadisticos* (annual).

2. CRS, p. 62.

3. *Energy Daily*, June 11, 1979; *Oil and Gas Journal*, January 14, 1980.

derance of heavier crudes will continue in the absence of major discoveries of new light crude resources.

How Venezuela came to find itself in this situation is a complicated matter. A major contributing factor is that as nationalization, which occurred on January 1, 1976, began to loom on the horizon, the international oil companies operating in Venezuela stopped investing in exploration from the mid-1960s onward. Petroleos de Venezuela, the parent company in the state-owned oil industry, has thus had to intensify exploration to compensate. By law, 10 percent of the profits of the operating companies go to Petroleos to support exploration activity. (The nationalization itself is discussed later in this chapter.)

Venezuela has had to undertake a number of policies to cope with its reserve situation. A deliberate policy of protecting light reserves entails:

- Limiting production of crude greater than 22°API to no more than 70 percent of production;

- Concentrating exploration on potential light crude resource areas;

- Investigating new methods of producing heavy and superheavy crudes; and

- Changing the refining pattern to increase heavy-crude-handling capability.

Only half of the remaining proven reserves fall within the greater than 25° API category, and this share has not changed since 1969. Without new light crude discoveries, this fifty-fifty split cannot long be maintained.

The Maracaibo Basin is by far the most productive area (78 percent of 1978 output), but is also the most overworked. Half of Venezuela's total output is achieved through secondary recovery. Due to the technical problems in producing heavy crude, which tend to result in slower production, Venezuelan authorities have set a 15:1 reserves to production ratio as a technical limit on the overall production rate. This ratio is applied to production in each API gravity range. Existing production capacity has operated at a very high rate, but new investment would be required to reach the 3.3 mbd theoretical ceiling implied by the 15:1 ratio. The current maximum production capacity is 2.4 mbd, and an increase to 2.8 mbd is planned. The Sixth Development Plan (1981-1985) for Venezuela has retained the

2.2 mbd average production rate, setting aside the extra 0.6 mbd capacity as a "safety net." Rising real prices have enabled Venezuelan authorities to hold production steady while keeping up the flow of revenues. If real prices reached a plateau or began to decline, Venezuela would face some difficult choices regarding raising production, given the reserve situation.

The quality of Venezuela's export barrel poses additional problems. The predominant product is residual fuel oil. Under the present refining pattern in Venezuela, four barrels of residual fuel oil are produced for every barrel of gasoline. The Venezuelan refineries were built years ago to supply the U.S. market for residual fuel oil, which is used by East Coast electric utilities. About 25 percent of Venezuelan oil exports is residual fuel oil.

Over the next twenty years, in view of the composition of remaining reserves in Venezuela and in the world as a whole, future supplies will increasingly consist of heavy, sulfurous crudes that yield a high volume of residual fuel oil. Demand in the United States and the world in general for residual fuel oil is expected to decline, while that for lighter products, such as distillates and gasoline, increases. This trend could have significant and adverse impact on Venezuela in the absence of a refinery modernization program undertaken by both Venezuela and its customers. Venezuela possesses the largest refining capacity in OPEC—1.5 mbd—although its refineries operate at only two-thirds of capacity. The question of refinery modernization is of major importance and is discussed at greater length later in this chapter.

The best prospects for reserve additions are in offshore areas, where little exploration has taken place until recently. Government estimates of probable offshore resources are in the area of 10 billion barrels of light and medium crude, while other geologists, such as Bernardo Grossling, believe the range is from 20–60 billion barrels.[4] It may take ten to fifteen years of drilling to determine the offshore potential, and so far more gas than oil has been found. Venezuela intends to spend $3–5 billion in the coming decade on offshore exploration. Major volumes of production cannot be expected from these areas before 1985.

A factor of growing importance is Venezuela's domestic oil demand, particularly for gasoline. Venezuelan oil demand averaged

4. CRS, p. 62.

283,000 b/d in 1979, but is growing at a rate in excess of 10 percent per year. Artificially low prices encourage domestic demand and
cut into Petroleos' revenues. The need to satisfy domestic gasoline
demand is an important element in the decision to upgrade domestic
refining capacity, which will allow greater gasoline production. In the
longer term, domestic demand, which at present growth rates could
reach 707,000 b/d by 1990, may be an important element in determining how much oil will be left for export.

The irony in light of what appear to be increasingly serious problems with conventional reserves is that Venezuela possesses an untapped and potentially gigantic oil source in the Orinoco belt. This
area previously had been called a tar belt, but in fact, the hydrocarbons in place are mostly fluid and not bituminous. Its size potentially dwarfs that of Canada's tar sands. The Orinoco belt originally
was thought to hold 700 billion barrels of oil at depths to 6000 feet.
Recent drilling indicates that the Guyana shield, which forms the
border of potential resources, lies at about 20,000 feet. A new exploration campaign to delineate the region and define the most promising areas began in late 1979. The spread of present estimates runs
from 1 trillion to 7 trillion barrels, with the consensus estimate
among experts being 2 trillion. The Venezuelan government, however, speaks most frequently of 700 billion plus barrels.[5] It must be
borne in mind that these are all preliminary estimates.

The gravity of the crude is in the 8–14° API range, and sulfur content is 2–5 percent. There are substantial metallic contaminants. All
three characteristics pose serious processing and utilization problems.
Fluidity problems limit conventional recovery to 8 percent. Secondary recovery could yield 15–18 percent of the oil in place. Steam
injection can aid in recovery of some oil; in situ combustion is necessary to recover most. One of the major uncertainties to be overcome
is how widely applicable various production techniques are over the
entire area. Nevertheless, the Venezuelan government believes that
initial development of the belt can be started with well-known production technologies. Even at a 10 percent recovery rate for the area
as a whole, 100–200 billion barrels could be recoverable. State planners anticipate production of 125,000 b/d of upgraded crude by
1988 and 1 million b/d by the turn of the century, when conventional reserves, if no new additions occur, may be gone. The Ministry

5. *World Business Weekly*, July 21, 1980.

of Energy and Mines estimated in March 1980 that production costs could be in the $5–13 per barrel range.[6] Other estimates run in the $12–20 per barrel range. In all likelihood, the costs will in the end prove to be higher.

Potentially the greatest technical obstacle to developing the Orinoco is the need for a technology to upgrade the oil. Without upgrading, the output would be 95 percent residual, and the metallic impurities, if not removed, would burn out the catalyzers in a conventional refinery. Some upgrading is likely to take place on site, possibly using flexicoking techniques developed originally by Exxon. The costs of an integrated production-upgrading facility are steep — $4.7 billion in 1986 dollars for each 125,000 b/d of capacity, or $37,000 per barrel.[7] The costs involved raise the questions of at what point these projects will become more attractive investments than other sources of petroleum or synthetic fuels both in and outside Venezuela; the scale on which Venezuela finds itself can afford to undertake to upgrade Orinoco oil and how much must be upgraded in customer countries; and the opportunity costs, in terms of foregone investment in other sectors of the Venezuelan economy, that development of the Orinoco presents.

Gas

Venezuela also has significant gas reserves, mostly in the form of associated gas. Legally, only associated gas can be produced. These reserves have been estimated at 35–45 tcf and may last forty years at current rates of production. Flaring has been considerably reduced due to the development of a domestic market for gas, which consumes over 60 percent of production, and gas conservation regulations requiring reinjection of much of the rest. Like other producer countries, Venezuela is eyeing petrochemicals and metallurgical industries as new means of utilizing gas. The Venezuelan iron industry is currently a major user. There are no plans for gas exports. No large markets are within the reach of pipelines, while the investments

---

6. Ministry of Energy and Mines, *Venezuela's Heavy Oil Development Prospects and Plans* (March 1980). See also *Quarterly Economic Review of Venezuela, Surinam, Netherlands Antilles* 3 (1979):10–11; 4 (1979):12; and 1 (1980):15.

7. CRS, p. 95.

required for liquifying the gas would compete with the higher priority oil projects.

Coal

Total coal resources are presently figured at 1.5 billion tonnes of high sulfur coal, of which 846 million tonnes are exploitable. Over the long run, coal may assume a more important role in supporting a more regionally diversified industrialization process.

Hydro

Venezuela's hydro potential is considerable and well distributed. Present capacity is near 2500 MW and may expand to meet 50-80 percent of electricity demand in the mid-1980s. Electricity itself will increase from meeting 6 percent of energy needs to 12 percent in the same time frame.[8]

Nuclear

Venezuela has one small research reactor, and there has been some talk of beginning a modest nuclear program. Such a program would encounter numerous constraints, including a lack of engineering manpower, little domestic uranium, and substantial front-end costs. Given the priorities set elsewhere in the energy sector, the prospects for such a program are not good.

II. ECONOMIC AND POLITICAL ENVIRONMENT OF VENEZUELAN OIL POLICY

One of the most important aspects of the structure of the Venezuelan economy is its dual character. The petroleum industry, although it employs only 1 percent of the labor force, is by far the

---

8. U.S. Senate, Committee on Energy and Natural Resources, *The Western Hemisphere Energy System*, a report by Conant and Associates, 96th Cong., 1st sess., November 1979, p. 54.

dominant sector of the economy, a trait shared with many other oil-exporting countries. Other economic sectors, although they employ more people, contribute proportionately less to economic growth. The economy as a whole is subsidized by oil, and a major objective of Venezuelan economic development policy is to lessen that dependence. Underutilization of manpower and urban migration are important social problems. The relationship between oil policy and these broader economic and social problems warrants closer examination.

At the same time, what is remarkable, given the patronage and the political influences on industrial policy found in the Venezuelan economy as a whole, is the degree to which the oil industry has been relatively insulated from this. The prospect for continuation of this absence of politicization in the face of major production and investment decisions in the oil industry is an issue of fundamental importance.

Economic and Social Factors

The pivotal importance of oil revenues to the Venezuelan economy creates a number of factors and considerations that influence and constrain Venezuelan oil policy. Oil export revenues in recent years have represented 30 percent of gross domestic product, nearly 75 percent of government revenues, and over 90 percent of foreign exchange earnings.[9] The agricultural sector, in contrast, generates only 6 percent of GDP. The nonoil industrial sector is both inefficient and lacks diversity, as it is based primarily on other extractive and resource-based industries and suffers from political patronage and poor management. In short, despite its declining conventional reserve position and the high cost of Orinoco oil, Venezuela has no economic alternative to continued oil exports.

Venezuela is a long way from achieving diversified economic growth. Income from oil exports in 1980 was approximately $17 bil-

9. Robert D. Bond, *The Political Economy of Venezuela: 1981-1986*, Latin American Studies Program, Woodrow Wilson International Center for Scholars (March 9, 1981); *Quarterly Economic Review of Venezuela* (various issues). See also Enrique Baloyra, "Oil Policies and Budgets in Venezuela, 1938-1968," *Latin American Research Review* (Summer 1974): 28-74, for a historical analysis of the importance of oil and the government budget.

lion, or almost 96 percent of total export earnings.[10] The manufacturing sector, despite accounting for about 15 percent of GDP and employing 17 percent of the labor force, has suffered low growth rates the past two years (2 percent in 1980), after experiencing an average growth rate of 9 percent per year in the 1970s. Venezuela also continues to be a net importer of foodstuffs. Real GDP declined 1 percent in 1980. Rising world oil prices, rather than expansion of nonoil exports, gave Venezuela in 1980 its first current account surplus in three years.

Venezuela's foreign public debt has risen substantially in recent years as borrowing has increased, not to cover balance of payments needs, but to finance large-scale development projects in steel, aluminum, hydropower, and public works; compensate for government subsidies; and cover large deficits in state-owned enterprises. Venezuela's total public debt rose to $25 billion in 1980, the third largest in Latin America after Brazil and Mexico. Debt service in 1979 amounted to one-seventh of export earnings.[11] In 1974, Venezuela's outstanding public debt had been only $1.9 billion and the amount owed foreign banks less than $1 billion. Pledges to control the growth of external debt and to run state enterprises more efficiently were major elements in the successful electoral campaign waged by the current president, Luis Herrera Campins, in 1978.

Inflation, almost nonexistent prior to 1973–1974, is a serious problem and is running at over 23 percent according to official figures and possibly 30 percent according to private economists. This is far in excess of what Venezuelans were accustomed to even in the late 1970s. Failure to reduce inflation could force reimposition of the price controls on certain basic items that were lifted in August 1979.

Despite having the highest per capita income in Latin America in the late 1970s, the distribution of income leaves the poorest 50 percent of the population with only 14 percent of the national income.[12] The most important social development in recent decades, however, has been the rapid growth of an urban middle class, which has generated demand for improved social services and housing, a factor of no mean political importance, and a growing claim on the revenues allocated to economic development.

10. Bond.

11. "Survey of Venezuela," *International Herald Tribune*, May 1980, p. 95.

12. Bond.

What course the Venezuelan government charts for economic development, thus, is of fundamental importance, given the magnitude of these underlying problems. The government has been virtually the only primary recycler of oil wealth within the economy and plays a key role in planning economic development. The creation of the Venezuelan Investment Fund in May 1974 was a major step by the government, in the wake of the 1973-1974 oil price hike, to accumulate and conserve foreign exchange reserves for future use and to act as a development bank for industrial diversification projects.

The government of Carlos Andres Perez (1974-1978) drew upon Venezuela's oil surplus to finance large-scale industrialization through government investment in heavy industrial projects requiring importation of large quantities of capital goods. Prominent examples of these projects include several steel works, dams, and petrochemical plants. Heavy external borrowing was also crucial to this undertaking. These projects are capital intensive and create little direct employment, and their impact on exports will not be felt in any substantial way for some time.

The Fifth Development Plan (1976-1980) had as a target a total of $23 billion in public investment, about 20 percent of which was to be in the petroleum sector.[13] Actual investment may reach $40 billion. High capital goods imports forced Venezuela's balance of payments into the red in 1978, while the pace of expansion in some areas, such as steel, led to shortages of skilled labor and falling productivity. Significant inflation also appeared for the first time during this period, and the money supply tripled in size. Discontent with these undesirable economic side effects of Perez's strategy contributed to Herrera's victory in the 1978 presidential election.

The Herrera government unveiled the Sixth Development Plan in July 1980. This plan, which is basically a list of public expenditure targets and investment projects rather than an economic development strategy per se, emphasizes expansion of education, housing, and public services, in contrast to Perez' emphasis on heavy industry. President Herrera had pledged during the electoral campaign to expand public services, but with the exception of housing, these sectors will not contribute greatly to overall economic growth. The plan projects expenditure of an additional $24 billion in the petroleum

13. See Petro-Pablo Kuczynski, "The Economic Development of Venezuela: A Summary View as of 1975-1976," in R. Bond, ed., *Contemporary Venezuela and Its Role in International Affairs* (New York: New York University Press for the Council on Foreign Relations, 1977).

industry for offshore exploration and development of the Orinoco. A 6 percent GDP rate over the period of the plan is the goal.

Venezuela's range of development strategies is narrow. High wage rates make combining industrialization with high factory employment, as found in some Asian countries, not really feasible. Continued dependence on oil is undesirable, too, yet the continued flow of oil revenues is vital to financing economic development. The current strategy appears to combine growth in resource-based industries with an urban services economy. A major factor in determining the success of this approach is Venezuela's ability to manage its oil industry and the meshing of the public and private sectors of the economy. So long as it is dependent on oil, Venezuela's economy is highly vulnerable.

Politics and Policymaking

Since the nationalization of foreign-owned oil companies in 1976, considerable effort has been made in Venezuela to avoid politicizing oil policy, in the sense of making it a political campaign issue or a matter of impassioned debate. Both major parties recognized from the start that oil is too important to the economy to play politics with. Petroleos consequently has been free of the patronage and corruption that undermine the management of other state-owned industries. Nonetheless, oil policy is not left to the hands of technocrats; indeed, it would be highly surprising if this were otherwise in light of the political significance of oil both before and after nationalization and its role in the economy.

As a general rule, the "externally" oriented aspects of oil policy and the more political elements of that policy are the responsibility of the Ministry of Energy and Mines, currently headed by Dr. Humberto Calderon Berti. The ministry sets broad policy guidelines every year for such matters as production, the mixture of heavy and light oil, the amount of associated gas to be used, and reference values for tax purposes. Petroleos, as the parent company, determines general operating policy in light of these guidelines and monitors and supervises the operating companies' activities. The ministry leaves technical matters in the hands of Petroleos.

Petroleos and its operating units, of which Maraven and Lagoven, having respectively taken over the Shell and Exxon concessions, are the most prominent, are treated almost like private companies, especially in the tax area. The flow of revenue to the government, which comes from taxes paid to Petroleos and not directly from oil sales, follows essentially the same path as it did before nationalization. The subsidiaries technically compete with each other, and Petroleos is an independently run, unsubsidized operation that finances internally a considerable portion of its expenditures.

Although an independent Petroleos was sought from the start, its activities have not been entirely free from political controversy. Petroleos' use of technical assistance and service contracts with the foreign companies it replaced has been politically sensitive. These contracts are based on Article 5 of the Organic Law on which nationalization was based. This article allows such arrangements where they are necessary for the effective performance of Petroleos' functions. Following nationalization, the government negotiated four-year technical assistance and service contracts with the former foreign operating companies to assure continuity in operations. These contracts were attacked within Venezuela, however, as being little more than a thinly disguised form of continuing compensation for nationalization, and in 1980 flat service fees replaced per barrel payments to the foreign companies.

The same Article 5 also allows the state to form partnerships with private (i.e., foreign) entities for a fixed period of time, so long as the state retains control. Approval of both chambers of the Venezuelan Congress is required to establish a joint venture. None have been proposed, and no one seriously believes that any would be, as a joint venture with a foreign oil company could be politically explosive.

Venezuela has taken a number of steps to decrease dependence on the international oil companies, including negotiation of contracts directly with the end user utilities and refineries, thus avoiding reliance on the middle man role of the oil companies and with other state oil companies in importer countries.[14] Venezuela has also not sold oil in the spot market, basing sales only on long-term contracts.

Another area where Petroleos is not unchecked is control of the Orinoco development. Authority for planning the development of the Orinoco was transferred from the Ministry of Energy and Mines

14. An address by Dr. Humberto Calderon Berti, minister of energy and mines, to the National Academy of Science, Washington, D.C. March 6, 1980.

to Petroleos in 1977, but construction authorization remains with the ministry, which has reasserted its influence under the present regime. All four operating companies—Lagoven, Meneven, Maraven, and Corpoven—are involved in different operations in the Orinoco. The present leaderships of both the ministry and Petroleos have sought to avoid engaging in a bureaucratic struggle for determining the pace of this development. Under different leadership in the future, this might not be the case.

The development of the Orinoco, in addition to the service contracts with foreign companies, is one of the few major oil-related issues to emerge in the political arena since nationalization. The Perez government opposed even exploration in the Orinoco on the grounds that this oil should be reserved for future generations, and the Accion Democratica candidate, representing Perez' party, ran in the 1978 presidential election with this plank in his platform. The COPEI party candidate, Luis Herrera Campins, advocated initiation of exploration and limited development and authorized this upon assuming the presidency in 1979. Given the investments underway now, it is unlikely that election of the Accion Democratica candidate in 1983 will lead to a reversal of the Orinoco development plans. Nevertheless, how fast to proceed, and with what foreign involvement, will remain potentially important political issues.

In addition to helping to finance economic development, oil has proven to be of fundamental importance to the maintenance of a democratic political system in Venezuela. Several factors account for Venezuela's ability to sustain democratic government in the face of a legacy of military rule. One is a political style based on adherence to certain "rules of the game." Venezuela's first taste of popular rule came in 1945–1948. However, efforts by the Accion Democratica government of Romulo Betancourt to institute large-scale structural reforms in the economy and society were carried out in such a way as to alienate the major political actors in the society. A military coup and exile for democratic leaders followed, and democratic rule did not return until 1958.

This experience of lost opportunity during the *trienio*, as it is called, led the exiled leaders of the main political parties to agree to limit destructive political competition. Over the 1960s, a characteristic leadership style emerged, emphasizing consultation and avoidance of ideological disputes.[15] This style has contributed significantly to

15. Bond. *Political Economy.*

the success of Venezuelan democracy and its progression to a competitive and predominantly two-party system.

Two other factors, in addition to leadership style, have been crucial.[16] The first is strong party organization, in which both the COPEI and Accion Democratica parties, the major ones, encompass a broad spectrum of groups. This, plus a tradition of leadership autonomy, facilitates political concession making and compromise.

The second is the constant flow of oil revenues to the government. This enables the government to meet the claims of competing groups, especially for public services, without resorting to redistribution. The oil revenues also have enabled the state to leave some economic sectors to private industry (commerce, manufacturing), while reserving others to itself (steel, petrochemicals, electricity). This latter benefit has been more political than economic, in so far as it has contributed to political peace, since both privately and publicly owned industries are inefficient and poorly managed.

As Robert Bond points out, the political challenges facing Venezuela in the 1980s reflect long-standing economic and social problems.[17] These include restructuring the economy away from dependence on oil, integrating new segments of the population into the economy, and addressing serious problems in industrial management and the underutilization of Venezuela's human resources. The continued flow of oil revenue is crucial to the success of the political system in meeting these challenges, as it provides the state with the resources necessary to address these problems and satisfy political demands, particularly from the urban middle class. Nevertheless, over the longer run, some Venezuelans wonder what the political consequences will be if oil production begins to drop in the 1990s and Venezuela still has not achieved balanced economic development.

III.   RECENT EXPERIENCE IN BILATERAL ENERGY RELATIONS

Several trends and developments in Venezuelan oil policy over the past twenty years have had important implications for Venezuelan-U.S. relations. The first is an emphasis on institutionalizing cooperation. This theme has taken several concrete forms—in the search

16. Ibid.
17. Ibid.

for a special oil relationship with the United States, in producer concertation through OPEC, and in proposals for a producer–consumer dialogue. The second is the nationalization of the foreign oil companies, which took place on January 1, 1976. The third is Venezuela's refusal to participate in politically inspired oil export embargoes and its cooperation with consumers during unexpected supply shortfalls. In addition, Venezuela has proposed various forms of regional and hemispheric energy cooperation, particularly from a financial standpoint, and has begun to focus more of its diplomatic energies on the Caribbean and Central America.

Venezuela's emphasis on institutionalizing cooperation in the energy sector is a manifestation of a distinctive foreign policy style, which some experts relate to the way in which the institutionalization of democracy has been approached within Venezuela, and the importance of acceptance of "rules of the game" to that process. Tugwell describes this style as a willingness not just to work together to solve problems, but to build institutional frameworks to handle problems on a more organized, long-term basis and to disaggregate conflicts in order to prevent one issue from overlapping with others and to avoid letting adversarial aspects of political relations obscure opportunities for cooperation in other areas.[18] Active Venezuelan participation in OPEC, the Andean Pact, the Latin American Economic System, and the Latin American Energy Organization is, in this view, a reflection of this style.

Venezuela, for a number of years, sought a special energy relationship with the United States. Venezuela proposed such an arrangement in 1959, when imposition of an import quote program in the United States appeared imminent. Minister of Mines and Hydrocarbons Perez Alfonso proposed that a government-to-government agreement among the hemisphere's major suppliers (i.e., the United States, Canada, and Venezuela) be established to rationalize shipments and overall production. Under the terms of this proposal, the United States would grant a preference to regional suppliers, guaranteeing them a specified proportion of the U.S. market.[19] The quotas would be allocated directly to governments rather than to the oil companies, as Perez Alfonso wanted to reduce Venezuelan depend-

---

18. Franklin Tugwell, "Venezuelan Foreign Policy" (Unpublished manuscript, n.d.)

19. See Franklin Tugwell, *The Politics of Oil in Venezuela* (Stanford: Stanford University Press, 1975), ch. 3.

ence on the international oil companies. The model for this proposal, as it was in Venezuela's subsequent advocacy of OPEC, was the U. S. system for prorationing domestic production in order to avoid oversupply. This is important, since Venezuela has consistently sought to establish a proprationing system, first on a regional and then on a global basis, from this time on through the 1970s and still regards establishment of such a system as an eventual objective.

While clearly serving Venezuelan interests, this proposal reflected certain preferences that are still present in Venezuelan policy:

- Continuous and institutionalized discussions;

- A secure share of the U.S. market;

- Government-to-government transactions, reducing the independence of multinational oil companies; and

- Provision of a stable basis for long-term planning and production control.

Perez Alfonso's proposal and subsequent Venezuelan efforts to persuade the United States to change its mind after only Mexico and Canada were granted exemptions from import quotas were unproductive, although later in 1972 and 1973 the United States suggested the possibility of guaranteed market access for Orinoco crude in return for long-term security for U.S. oil companies operating in Venezuela, an impossible proposition for Venezuela at the time.[20]

The idea of producer concertation, which would achieve at another level of action Venezuelan objectives regarding prorationing, decreased dependence on the oil companies, and so forth, led to the creation of OPEC. The price cuts imposed by the major oil companies in 1959 and 1960 convinced Venezuela that national approaches to regulating multinational oil companies would be ineffective if they were not coordinated with other producers. Perez Alfonso, with Saudi Arabian help, became the major architect in establishing OPEC. Venezuela was a leading force in OPEC in the 1960s and in the 1970s emerged as a moderating force within that organization, opposing steps that could lead to chaos in world markets as OPEC lost whatever utility it had in coordinating pricing policies.

20. Ibid., pp. 139–40. Public opposition that developed when word of the discussions leaked forced the Caldera government to adopt a defensive, nationalistic position in discussions with U.S. government representatives.

Producer-consumer dialogue and cooperation, at both regional and global levels, has been a third major institutional element in Venezuelan policy. Perez Alfonso had initially hoped that OPEC could evolve into a producer-consumer relationship, carrying out on a world scale what Venezuela in 1959 had proposed should be done on a regional level. Venezuelan officials have continued to advocate a long-term understanding in which guaranteed OPEC supply would be exchanged for market access, financial assets, and technology in a regime in which price increases would be based upon a semiautomatic adjustment mechanism providing much greater predictability than is the case at present.[21]

More recently, Venezuela has come to concentrate on the financial problems of resource-poor developing countries. Venezuela has collaborated with international financial institutions and has increasingly channeled funds directly to Central America and the Caribbean countries. Venezuela established its own oil-financing facility in 1975 to subsidize Central American oil imports through an extensive loan program. In 1975 financial assistance disbursements were 25 percent of the Venezuelan current account surplus, and in 1975–1979 $5.7 billion were allocated for this purpose. A joint Venezuelan–Mexican program established in 1980 to help Central American countries with their oil bills is intended to replace the unilateral program begun in 1975, which had simply become too expensive. This joint facility, established at Venezuelan initiative, will entail the extension of low interest loans to finance 30 percent of each country's bill, with a reduction in the interest rate and extension of the payback period if the loaned money is invested in indigenous energy development.

In addition to unilateral and now bilateral efforts to help poor oil-importing countries with rising oil bills, Venezuela has also promoted multinational undertakings. Venezuela has on several occasions proposed replenishment of OPEC's special fund for economic aid. The Venezuelan minister of energy and mines in March 1980 proposed the establishment of an inter-American energy development fund to coordinate and help finance where other sources of money might not be forthcoming the development of energy resources in the West-

---

21. Address by President Luis Herrera Campins to the OPEC Secretariat, Vienna, February 14, 1980.

ern Hemisphere.[22] This fund would provide seed money rather than assume a major project-financing role and would be administered through an existing international financial institution, such as the World Bank or the Inter-American Development Bank. The fund would concentrate on developing the energy resources of currently non-energy-producing countries. Venezuela has maintained that participation should be open to all countries in the Americas, including Canada and the United States, despite opposition to this from elsewhere in Latin America.

Nationalization was the second major development in recent years. Although Venezuela had pioneered many of the strategies designed to increase the oil producer governments' share of oil revenues, such as the fifty-fifty formula for splitting profits with foreign companies, the payment of royalties in crude, and the establishment of regulatory agencies. Venezuela remained concerned at the independence of the companies. In the 1960s the companies' falling expenditures for facility maintenance and exploration and the serious depletion of light crude reserves became the dominant issues.

The Hydrocarbon Law of 1943 had given the government a larger share of profits in exchange for a forty-year extension on concessions. As a result of this law, all concessions were to expire in 1983. The Hydrocarbons Reversion Law of 1971 called for the state to assume ownership of all oil company property and the concessions when they expired. Rising taxes and loss to the state of the power to set prices had discouraged the companies from making further investments in Venezuela. Production began to fall. The oil price hikes in 1973–1974 finally gave Venezuela the fiscal resources to nationalize the oil companies, which was finalized on January 1, 1976.

Venezuela offered compensation, but on the basis of net book value, not the estimated value of profits that the companies might have realized had they held their concessions until 1983. The Venezuelans regarded this settlement as generous, maintaining that had the concessions continued to their expiration date, no compensation would have been required. A little less than half of the total compensation, which was just over $1 billion, was held up over tax claims. This issue still has not been completely resolved.

Finally, Venezuela has been a reliable supplier despite the turmoil through which the international oil system has gone in recent years.

---

22. Address of Minister of Energy and Mines Calderon Berti before the Venezuelan–American Association of the United States, New York, March 4, 1980.

This extends not only to not participating in oil embargoes, but also to maintaining production at high levels throughout periods of supply shortfall, as during the Iran crisis in 1979 and the Iran-Iraq War in 1980. This contributes to the flexibility of the supply system in coping with these shortfalls.

From the Venezuelan perspective, however, the question arises as to whether the United States has taken Venezuela for granted. Venequelan sensitivity on this point can be traced back to the failure on several occasions of Venezuelan authorities to persuade U.S. officials that Venezuela should be granted preferential treatment as a "regional" supplier under the oil import quota program. Soon after the import quotas were lifted for all suppliers in 1973, Venezuela found itself subject to restrictions in the Trade Reform Act of 1974 enacted by Congress to penalize OPEC for the oil embargo. Of course, this had not been an OPEC embargo, and Venezuela had not taken part. Although financially insignificant, inclusion in the group of countries subject to the trade measures was in Venezuelan eyes a symbol of the U.S. failure to recognize Venezuela's record of reliability. More recently, legislation to back out oil imports from the East Coast, largely through conversion of utility boilers to coal, was proposed by the Carter administration without any real consideration of how it might affect specific suppliers. While this would take a considerable length of time to accomplish, this proposal was seen simply as another U.S. failure to distinguish between reliable and politically friendly suppliers and the rest.

These trends—institutionalized cooperation, state control of the oil industry, supply reliability—will in all likelihood persist in the coming decades and characterize the direction of Venezuelan oil policy. There also have been, however, other developments, in addition to those that are specifically oil related, that are of importance. This is especially true in the area of foreign policy.

The overall climate of Venezuelan-U.S. relations improved toward the end of the 1970s as the new Herrera government adopted more regional and subregional diplomatic ambitions, in contrast to the broader reach of Venezuelan foreign policy under President Perez. During the Perez period, Venezuela had taken an activist and more adversarial role in the North-South dialogue, supporting cartelization of nonenergy raw materials and commodities, and was a prime mover in the establishment of the Latin American economic system, which was intended to facilitate communication among Latin American states in dealing with the United States.[23] Venezuela also resumed diplomatic and trade relations with Cuba under the Perez government, lent strong support to Panama during the negotiation of the Panama Canal Treaty, and backed the Sandinista Liberation Front in Nicaragua and opposed U.S. proposals in the Organization of American States to impose an inter-American peace-keeping force between the two sides in the Nicaraguan civil war. Venezuela also sought the leadership of the Andean Pact, an institution for regional economic integration that has imposed greater control over multinational corporations.

Under President Herrera, Venezuelan diplomatic attention has focused more on Central America and the Caribbean.[24] The Venezuelan–Mexican program for financial assistance to oil-importing countries in the region is one manifestation of this. Venezuela has also channeled financial aid to Nicaragua to help the process of economic restoration and to encourage the revolutionary junta there to follow a course of democratic pluralism and moderation. Both initiatives are based on the premise that economic assistance is the most effective approach to promoting political stability in the region.

Where the current government has departed from past policy is in its more adversarial approach toward Cuba, where specific disputes with that country as well as concern over Cuban military activities in Central America have led Venezuela to withdraw its diplomats from Havana. The most significant departure, however, has been Venezuela's support of the ruling junta in El Salvador, where the ruling COPEI Social Christians have identified with the Christian Democratic civilians, led by Napolean Duarte, in the Salvadorean junta. This support for Duarte reflects a belief that the civilians in the junta represent the political center in El Salvador, as well as personal and ideological links between COPEI's leaders and Duarte, who spent seven years in political exile in Venezuela.

One of the most interesting diplomatic developments related to this general foreign policy focus has been the emergence of greater

23. See John D. Martz, "Venezuelan Foreign Policy Toward Latin America," and Robert Bond, "Venezuela's Role in International Affairs," in R. Bond, ed., *Contemporary Venezuela* (New York: NYU Press for the Council on Foreign Relations, 1977), for a discussion of the Perez government's foreign policy.

24. R. Bond, *Venezuela, the Caribbean Basin, and the Crisis in Central America*, prepared for the workshop on "The International Aspects of the Crisis in Latin America," Woodrow Wilson International Center for Scholars, Washington, D.C., April 2-3, 1981.

coordination with Mexico. This is reflected in the joint oil facility, where the two countries agreed to supply half of each recipient's oil import needs, thus consciously avoiding any impression of carving out spheres of economic influence in the region, despite the logistical advantages of dividing the area so each fully supplied those countries closest to it. Moreover, despite their difference of views over Cuba and El Salvador, where Mexico backs the more progressive and democratic elements among the opponents of the junta, both governments have expressed a desire to harmonize their policies to prevent the region from becoming a locus of East-West conflict and outside intervention.[25] This is especially true regarding El Salvador, where they have offered their joint good offices to help find a peaceful settlement.

Although Venezuela's positions on subregional issues would appear to coincide with those of the Reagan administration, there are important differences. Venezuela clearly desires an end to oligarchical governments and is very concerned about the potential for intervention by outside forces, including the United States as well as the Soviet Union and Cuba. Nevertheless, despite Venezuelan sensitivity at appearing to be a "stalking horse" for the United States in Latin America, this complementarity of positions is an important development.

IV. ENERGY RELATIONS IN THE 1980s AND 1990s

The direction taken by Venezuelan oil policy and Venezuelan–U.S. energy relations in the coming decades will reflect a number of factors. The level of exports supportable by conventional reserves, the pace and magnitude of Orinoco development and related marketing and refining policy decisions, and the relationships between oil development and economic development and regional cooperation will be of major importance in setting this direction.

Even with a planned increase in production capacity, the limited size of conventional reserves, especially of the lighter crudes, will not be likely to lead to an expansion of production and exports beyond the current levels. Venezuela will in all likelihood continue to rely

25. *New York Times*, April 9, 1981.

upon rising oil prices rather than higher production to keep up the flow of oil revenues to its treasury. After 1985, the production level will depend largely upon the outcome of the search for new sources if a decline is to be avoided. This search has proven less successful than originally hoped.

The growing share of heavy oil in proved reserves creates the potential for an even heavier export barrel. Venezuela is currently shifting its refining policy to meet changing U.S. demand patterns and rising domestic gasoline consumption. Venezuela has dedicated $2–3 billion over the next six years to convert its refineries to maximum distillate production and to refine very heavy crudes. Venezuela is also considering construction of a new joint refinery with Mexico to centralize refinery operations for small Central American markets. Much of the burden of refinery modernization necessarily falls upon customer states, however. Venezuelan officials have discussed the possibility of extending long-term supply arrangements for upgraded refineries.[26]

Rapidly growing domestic oil consumption may come to have a considerable impact on how much oil Venezuela can export. As in many other producer countries, domestic oil is substantially underpriced. The growth rate of domestic consumption has risen from 4.8 percent in 1974 to the current rate in excess of 10 percent. Gasoline represents 60 percent of demand, which places additional value on light crude protection. The Herrera government so far has been unwilling to raise prices substantially, and for any Venezuelan government, this would be a very sensitive step in political terms. An OPEC study is reported to show Venezuelan oil consumption reaching 506,000 b/d in 1985, 794,000 b/d in 1990, and 1,245,000 b/d by 1995.[27] With no expansion of production beyond 2.2 mbd, exports could fall to 1.4–1.5 mbd in 1990. Whether this would result in less foreign exchange earnings for Venezuela would depend on the real rate of increase of world oil prices. Venezuela could thus find itself having to consider increasing production of conventional crude, possibly advancing the pace of Orinoco development, or raising domestic prices to slow demand growth. Moreover, since domestically consumed oil is badly underpriced, Petroleos could realize lower overall profits than had exports held steady. This would mean

26. *Oil and Gas Journal*, March 31, 1980; *World Business Weekly*, April 20, 1981.

27. *Petroleum Intelligence Weekly*, September 8, 1980.

lower tax revenues for the government and possibly less money available to finance exploration and development, which has been supported in the past by internally generated capital.

Over the long run, the development plans for the Orinoco are crucial. The development strategy for the Orinoco is still in the formulation stage. Venezuelan officials believe the problems encountered there will be primarily political and economic rather than technical. The most important aspect of this strategy, however, is that the Venezuelan government believes that Orinoco crude should be viewed essentially as a competitor, in cost and timing terms, to unconventional and alternative energy sources coming on stream toward the end of the century and not something whose exploitation should be rushed.[28] For Venezuela and the world as a whole, the major task is to manage the transition to such sources as smoothly as possible.

The Ministry of Energy and Mines provided a preliminary look at Venezuela's plans for the Orinoco in March 1980.[29] The long-term production goal is 1 million b/d by the year 2000. This plan assumes continuation of the conservation policy limiting production capacity for conventional crude to 2.8 million b/d and limited success in finding new light and medium crude. Any change in those assumptions could result in a shift in this target. In the absence of compelling economic and political considerations, the conservative nature of these assumptions, in that they already associate this target with a bad case scenario for more accessible oil, does not encourage much belief that this target would be moved forward. Improvements in the offshore oil situation, for example, would tend to work for delay in reaching this target.

In the short term, several targets have been set:

- 125,000 b/d of upgraded crude by 1988, yielding a synthetic crude of 28° API, free of sulfur and metals, and with a 45 percent light products yield in conventional refineries; and

- 50,000 b/d by 1983, and 75,000 b/d by 1988, of nonupgraded crude (12-15° API).

---

28. See Alberto Quiros Corradi (President of Maraven), "Energy and the Exercize of Power," *Foreign Affairs*, Summer 1979, esp. pp. 1161–64.

29. Ministry of Energy and Mines, *Heavy Oil Development*.

Possibly 250,000-300,000 b/d of Orinoco crude could be available by 1990, depending on how many additional projects are defined.

Marketing strategy is especially important to the development of Orinoco oil, given its heaviness, 4 percent sulfur content, and metallic impurities. Petroleos is now considering three marketing options, making available:

- A synthetic crude, which would draw a premium over natural crude due to its freedom from impurities and which would enable Petroven to retain marketing flexibility.

- A blend of Orinoco and medium crudes from either producing areas, which would draw a higher price than either of its two components if sold alone. The long-term viability of this option would be limited by a closing of the light–heavy crude price gap and declining availability of lighter crudes in the 1990s.

- Untreated Orinoco crude, which must be diluted to make it transportable, thus boosting costs.[30]

The cost of Orinoco crude-upgrading plants (the 125,000 b/d plant to be built by Lagoven by 1988 will cost over $4.7 billion alone, with $7 billion required for the entire Lagoven project) will limit Venezuela's ability by itself to upgrade Orinoco crude. Consequently, the Venezuelan government has argued that consumer countries must provide most of this upgrading capacity and maintains that the global trend toward a heavier barrel will necessitate the requisite investments anyway. Brazil and France have expressed interest in building their own facilities to handle this oil. As an incentive, Venezuela would guarantee a 10- to 15-year supply of Orinoco oil to such facilities, but would not offer preferential pricing, as France has sought.[31]

Venezuelan authorities believe that Orinoco crude will cost less to develop than Canadian tar sands or U.S. oil shale and have offered specific investment figures in the $300-10,000 per barrel per day range, depending on location. Venezuelan estimates of the production costs for the development of synthetic crude run from $5-13 per barrel.[32] These figures are regarded by many outside experts as optimistic, and it is highly likely that prices could escalate substan-

30. *Financial Times*, June 27, 1980.
31. Ibid.
32. Corradi, p. 1163.

tially as the turn of the century target, which would necessitate production from technically more demanding areas, is approached.

However, the central question may not be simply the commercial competitiveness of Orinoco crude in the 1990s, but the attractiveness of this investment as well in relation to other energy projects elsewhere in the world. This question will turn on a number of factors, including the size of the world oil market, price levels, the availability of conventional oil, and the progress made in major consuming countries in adopting alternative energy sources. Although a 1 million barrel per day target has been set for the end of the century, the identification of individual projects has not proceeded beyond establishing the first major increment of Orinoco production capacity.

The higher costs associated with Orinoco oil could mean lower per barrel revenues, depending upon where world prices stand at the time. This would confront Venezuela with potential economic worries, especially if diversification of the country's industrial base proceeds slowly. Venezuela has broached the idea of a guaranteed U.S. market for Venezuelan manufactured goods, something the United States sees as incompatible with multilateral approaches to trade negotiations and existing international trade agreements. The lifting of the restrictions under the 1974 Trade Reform Act and the reextension of the generalized system of preferences to Venezuela have been important steps, at least symbolically, although Venezuelan exports to the United States continue to consist of oil and a few primary commodities.

The issue of foreign participation in the Orinoco is an important one. Venezuela has signed a number of agreements with foreign countries for technical cooperation in developing the Orinoco. Agreements with France and West Germany provide for studies of techniques for processing the crudes found in the belt. Potentially far more important is a technical assistance agreement with Canada. Consultations between Canada and Venezuela on heavy oil and tar sands development have been going on since 1973. Since April 1977, the Syncrude and Great Canadian Oil Sands consortia have been involved. An agreement for joint projects and technical cooperation related to heavy oil production was signed in January 1979 with the Alberta Oil Sands Technical and Research Authority.

The United States and Venezuela signed an agreement on March 6, 1980, for periodic R&D and technical exchanges, personnel exchanges, equipment testing, and joint technical and R&D projects in oil and other energy areas. This is an umbrella type agreement, under which specific cooperative arrangements were subsequently designated. The agreement itself is not as specific as the Alberta-Venezuela pact. Among the potentially most promising projects was to be the testing of the U.S. Department of Energy's "downhill" steam generator in Venezuela, which could be very important to the production of viscous heavy oil. However, cutbacks in the U.S. FY 1982 budget have threatened the implementation of this and other projects under this agreement.

The initial U.S. conception of this agreement involved exchanging technology for oil, but this was subsequently supplanted by a politically less sensitive R&D cooperation approach intended to establish a base for such an arrangement, if one appeared feasible at a later date. There had been considerable pressure from some sectors in the Congress to adopt the more ambitious approach. Whether such an exchange approach in fact is necessary, if the Orinoco proves to be an attractive commercial proposition, or achievable, since the technology is in corporate hands, is quite another matter. This leads, however, to the issue of potential corporate involvement in the Orinoco.

Foreign corporations, such as Bechtel, Foster-Wheeler, and others, are already playing an important project-planning and coordination role. The Lummus Corporation was selected in April 1981 to coordinate Lagoven's 125,000 b/d project. This involvement is all based on service contracts. A joint venture is politically out of the question, however, and the Venezuelan government does not regard foreign corporate capital as necessary. Nevertheless, extensive foreign involvement, even through service contracts, could prove to be controversial if it appeared that the government was condoning a repenetration of the Venezuelan oil industry by foreign interests. Concern has already been expressed that all the bidders on the contract won by Lummus were foreign. Lummus' willingness to hire more Venezuelan subcontractors apparently was a major factor in the decision to award it the contract. In general, the hiring of Venezuelan firms as subcontractors and the transfer of know-how, not just technology, will have an important bearing on whether technical service contracts for foreign firms will prove to be controversial or not. The Venezuelan goal is technical self-sufficiency as much as it is bringing on a new source of oil.

The most difficult challenge facing Venezuela over the next twenty years will not necessarily be developing the Orinoco per se, but promoting more diversified economic growth. "Sowing the petroleum"—that is, using it to finance economic growth—has long been a popular phrase in the Venezuelan political lexicon. Dependence on oil income will continue throughout the century, making it imperative to find foreign markets for Venezuelan oil. The magnitude of world needs suggest that this will not be a problem. What could pose problems are a significant delay in bringing on substantial Orinoco production, a leveling off or decline of world oil prices in real terms or declining production of conventional crude, and the failure of reserve additions to keep pace with production. Any of these developments would have an adverse impact on the oil revenues that have proven to be of fundamental importance to both political and economic development in Venezuela.

Achievement of a significant degree of diversification in the industrial structure of the country, and particularly in the composition of exports, will take many years. Success in accomplishing this so far has not been marked. Failure to achieve the objective of a diversified economy could, over the long run, especially if oil revenues begin to slide, have serious political repercussions within the country.

At the least, Venezuela will encounter a number of important and difficult choices in confronting the need for economic diversification and more balanced economic growth. It is not clear at all that maintaining economic growth at 5–6 percent per year, curbing inflation, controlling the level of foreign debt, developing the Orinoco, and investing in nonoil industrial and public service sectors without diverting funds from elsewhere can be achieved without some trade-offs. The trade-offs that are struck will be of lasting significance for Venezuela.

While progress toward a balanced economy and a more equitable distribution of income is crucial, Venezuela enjoys several advantages in confronting its future. It has the resources to industrialize. Political parties on the far left have not taken root, while so far, the urban poor have not proven to be a major source of discontent.[33] Nonetheless, demands for social services, housing, and jobs will in all likelihood grow, and the Venezuelan government must have a steady source of income to respond if political disaffection is to be avoided.

The principal elements of Venezuelan oil policy for the next two decades are being set in place, and the United States figures prominently in all of them. This is true not only of the Orinoco develop-

33. Bond, *Political Economy*.

ment, which too easily could distract U.S. decisionmakers from other important Venezuelan interests and initiatives. Nonenergy trade with the United States, if it develops, could have a profound impact on the prospects for Venezuelan economic development. The success of Venezuela's proposals for regional energy cooperation rests to a major degree on how skillfully the United States reacts to other countries assuming greater regional influence and leadership.

V. CONCLUSIONS

The successful ability of Venezuela to weather politically important changes in its economic structure is of direct and overriding interest to the United States. Energy relations should be viewed as a means to promoting this interest, and U.S. perspectives on the prospects for the Orinoco should be formulated in this light. These prospects are clearly intriguing, although the scale and timing of likely production and the impact on world supply, and on U.S. supply security in particular, should not be overestimated. Nevertheless, the fact that Venezuela has been a traditional and reliable U.S. supplier is encouraging.

It is clear that the time frame for this development is very long term — the 1990s at the earliest. The tentative development and production schedule for the Orinoco will not yield even 1 million barrels per day until the year 2000, if then. In the near term, the Venezuelan export barrel is growing increasingly unattractive and in the long run is vulnerable to fuel-switching strategies. Both the United States and Venezuela must make investments in refinery modernization to accommodate this change. It does not appear that Venezuela can help alleviate U.S. supply security problems in the near term, but the United States can do much to support Venezuelan interests. A policy more attentive to those interests could have a major payoff in the long run, even if Venezuela does not supply a major share of the U.S. market.

U.S. technology may figure prominently in development of the Orinoco. Whether its availability could speed development of the Orinoco is another matter, and the evidence suggests that this alone will not be the governing factor. Access to the U.S. market will be of substantial, if not greater, significance.

Venezuela by itself simply may not be able to support the investments required in upgrading plants. Rather, it has offered long-term assured supply to countries building their own upgrading plants. The Venezuelans view Orinoco crude as deriving its maximum value after world conventional production has peaked and presumably the price of syncrude has been bid up. Moreover, speeding up production could become a political issue within the country. The firming up of offshore prospects for medium and light crude, if this transpires, will be of major importance to determining how long conventional crude will be produced in major quantities and could encourage a more relaxed attitude toward Orinoco development. The direction of trends in conventional oil production and reserves, then, may be a key factor in determining the pace of Orinoco development.

The Venezuelans run a potentially serious risk in a more relaxed strategy. The longer Orinoco development is delayed, the higher may be the value of the crude, but a continuation of new conventional sources entering into production elsewhere or initiation of large-scale self-sufficiency projects in the major importing states could make investment in the Orinoco less attractive. Nevertheless, the current Venezuelan definition of national interest appears to recommend a cautious approach, and U.S. policymakers must ask what the benefits of pushing for more rapid development would be for long-term mutual interests.

Venezuela has launched a number of initiatives to alleviate the economic problems of developing countries and to fund hemispheric energy development. This general concept deserves support. The United States can work quietly to help ensure the reconciliation of these and other similar undertakings, such as that of a World Bank energy-financing agency, and to contribute money and expertise. What does appear necessary is a more concerted U.S. effort to focus on Venezuelan interests and affairs as a totality and not to let energy needs drive its Venezuelan policy.

VII U.S.-JAPANESE ENERGY RELATIONS

FOREWORD—*John E. Gray and*
Yoshizane Iwasa

The Foreword and Preface to this book describe the background, purpose, and overall activities of the Atlantic Council's Energy Policy Committee, whose members are identified on pages ix-xii. Early in 1980, that committee's examination of U.S.-Japanese energy relationships, undertaken in cooperation with Japanese associates, elicited a proposal from the Committee for Energy Policy Promotion[1] and the Institute of Energy Economics,[2] both based in Tokyo,

1. The Committee for Energy Policy Promotion (Japan) was established in November 1973 under the initiative of the four leading economic organizations in Japan—the Federation of Economic Organizations, the Japan Chamber of Commerce and Industry, the Japan Committee for Economic Development, and the Kansai Economic Federation—for the purpose of making recommendations to the government of Japan on a comprehensive energy policy and promoting large-scale international and national energy projects, thereby contributing to the stabilization of supply and demand of energy in Japan and in the world. The members of the committee consist of representatives of seventy-seven companies from various industrial sectors, men of learning and experience, and experts in international problems.

2. The Institute of Energy Economics (Japan) was incorporated in 1966 on a private nonprofit basis under the auspices of leading companies in Japan. The activities of the institute are to collect and process information related to energy matters in Japan and other countries; review and analyze energy issues affecting the domestic and international economy; provide information capable of serving as a basis for planning and policy formation by both government and private business; study and evaluate problems of the environment and

247

to upgrade the committee's case study to a joint project. It was felt that a joint project was needed because of the significance of establishing better understanding about each other's energy conditions for expanding and improving U.S.-Japanese bilateral energy relations and because of the substantial effects individual and bilateral actions of Japan and the United States can have on the future of these two countries, the Asia–Pacific region, and the world.

Yoshizane Iwasa, counselor of the Fuji Bank, became chairman of a committee of Japanese experts organized as a counterpart to the Atlantic Council's Energy Policy Committee. He was assisted by Mamoru Sueda, secretary general of the Committee for Energy Policy Promotion, and Dr. Toyoaki Ikuta, president of the Institute of Energy Economics. The members of this committee are listed at the end of this section. Dr. Ikuta and the commitee produced a working paper to parallel the case study written for the Atlantic Council by Milton Klein. Representatives of both committees then met on several occasions to review the two working papers and to formulate a series of joint U.S.-Japanese policy recommendations. The U.S. and Japanese working papers and the joint policy recommendations are published in this Atlantic Council Policy Paper and are being published simultaneously in Japanese by the Committee for Energy Policy Promotion and the Institute of Energy Economics in Japan. We are pleased to report that all of the analyses produced in the course of the project, together with this policy paper, will be published as books simultaneously in the United States and in Japan later this year. We are deeply appreciative for the extent and value of these exchanges and the prospect that we may contribute to enhanced relations between the United States and Japan.

Special thanks go to the Tinker Foundation, the Battelle Memorial Institute, and the many corporations and individuals without whose support this project would not have been possible. We should add that the views expressed in the Policy Paper which constitutes this chapter are those of our joint committees. It should be clear also that while the report sets forth our overall views, no particular member of the committees should necessarily be assumed to subscribe to all the specific views presented.

---

conservation in energy-related industries; and maintain close relationships, through exchange of information and opinion, with the government, private and public organizations, and educational institutions.

Our joint committees worked hard and well to produce from diverse experience these collegial policy recommendations and the two related case studies. Given the breadth of the issues and the range of the options, it is with gratitude that we have concluded the work with substantial consensus. We recognize that we have done so, in some instances, by sticking to general principles, rather than presenting detailed solutions. We are most grateful for the opportunity to have participated in the work of a group of highly knowledgeable people willing to contribute their time and expertise in such a constructive and harmonious manner.

John E. Gray	Yoshizane Iwasa
Chairman	Chairman
Energy Policy Committee	Japan–U.S. Energy Relationships
The Atlantic Council	Committee
of the United States	The Committee for Energy
	Policy Promotion, Japan

Members of
Japan–U.S. Energy Relationships Committee[3]

Chairman
Yoshizane Iwasa, counselor, The Fuji Bank, Ltd.

Members
Kiyoshi Hama, managing director—petroleum, Mitsubishi
    Corporation
Yuji Idemitsu, director and general manager, Overseas Operations,
    Idemitsu Kosan Co., Ltd.
Akira Imao, managing director, The Kansai Electric
    Power Co., Inc.
Hidezo Inaba, chairman of the board of directors, Japan Industrial
    Policy Research Institute
Joutaro Inoue, managing director, The Chubu Electric
    Power Co., Inc.
Kimimichi Ishikawa, managing director, Nippon Oil Co., Ltd.

---

3. Members of the Atlantic Council's Energy Policy Committee are listed on pages ix–xii.

Kenji Kasai, executive managing director, Mitsui and Co., Ltd.
Watari Mizuno, managing director, The Tokyo Electric
  Power Co., Inc.
Yoshihiro Nakayama, advisor, Niigata Engineering Co., Ltd.
Kazuo Sugiura, director, Toa Nenryo Kogyo Co., Ltd.
Toshihiro Tajima, deputy president, The Industrial Bank of Japan
Nobuhiko Ushiba, advisor to the Ministry of Foreign Affairs
Shigeharu Yamamoto, executive vice-president, Toyota
  Motor Co., Ltd.
Yokichi Yoshida, managing director, Tokyo Shibaura
  Electric Co., Ltd.

Coordinator
Toyoaki Ikuta, president, The Institute of Energy Economics

Secretary General
Mamoru Sueda, secretary general, The Committee for Energy
  Policy Promotion

Secretariat
Takao Sato, manager, Research Division, Committee for Energy
  Policy Promotion.
Hideo Ohba, chief economist, Institute of Energy Economics.
Eiji Takano, staff economist, Institute of Energy Economics.

I. U.S.-JAPAN ENERGY RELATIONS:
AN AMERICAN VIEW
Milton Klein

1. Introduction

The post-World War II period saw the development of an extraordinarily close relationship between the United States and Japan. Japan adopted at a rapid pace many of the characteristics of Western societies, particularly those of the United States. In the aftermath of the war, new Japanese institutions were developed with substantial guidance by the United States. Strong economic and cultural ties developed, though the traditional Japanese culture and approach to societal relationships remained strong and in a number of respects different than American and European methods. In the field of military security, the United States provided the strategic defense capability for the Pacific region, while Japanese military activities were confined to the development of domestic defense forces. The resulting relationship was one in which Japan for the most part followed the lead of the United States in world affairs, although not always unquestioningly.

As time has passed, the economic and industrial strength of Japan has grown markedly, so that today Japan stands as one of the world's strongest industrial powers, second only to the United States among the non-Communist nations. With that growth, Japan has begun to develop strong economic and cultural relationships with other countries of the western Pacific and Southeast Asia, particularly taking a substantial role in the development of the less-developed countries of the area. In recent years, the establishment of new relationships with China has assumed importance. At the same time, the U.S. global role has in a relative sense diminished.

With these changes, the relationship between the United States and Japan has been undergoing change. Japan no longer has the economic and political dependence on the United States that it once had. But its strategic dependence remains. The peace-keeping role of the United States is of great importance to Japan; it sees no alternative. Yet the credibility of the United States as the foundation of Japanese security has come into question in Japan: Can the United States be depended upon to act if the situation demands?

The effects of these changes have been growing commercial competition and a greater independence by Japan in setting its course. The energy problems facing the industrial world have been a major element in that changing relationship.

The energy situations of the two countries differ in a number of respects (see Figures 7-1 through 7-3 and Table 7-1):

1. Japan has virtually no domestic oil resources and only limited coal and other potential energy sources. Except for oil, the United States is rich in domestic energy resources—coal, uranium, natural gas, solar insulation.

2. Japan imports nearly 90 percent of its energy and 99.8 percent of its oil; the United States imports 20 percent of its energy,

Table 7-1. Primary Energy Supply Patterns, 1977 (*percent*)

	Japan	Germany	U.K.	France	Italy	Canada	U.S.A.
Oil	73.3	53.0	43.9	59.4	66.4	43.5	48.1
Solid fuels	15.7	27.1	33.9	18.0	7.4	8.5	19.6
Gas	3.5	14.9	17.1	10.1	16.1	17.8	25.5
Nuclear	2.1	3.3	4.7	2.3	0.6	3.3	3.5
Hydro/ geothermal	5.4	1.5	0.4	10.2	9.5	26.9	3.3
Total	100	100	100	100	100	100	100
Dependence on imported energy	87.5	55.4	26.3	74.0	80.0	Δ 6.1	20.4
Dependence on imported oil	99.8	96.1	57.8	99.0	98.8	12.8	45.8

Source: OECD.

45 percent of its oil. Three fourths of Japan's oil imports have been from the Middle East, while only about one-fourth of U.S. oil imports are from that region.

3. Oil constitutes nearly three-fourths of Japan's energy supply, as compared to slightly less than half in the case of the United States.

4. Industry accounts for a much greater share of energy consumption in Japan than in the United States (50 percent in Japan versus 33 percent in the United States in 1977). Japan's per capita energy consumption in the transportation and residential–commercial sectors is less than one-fourth that of the United States.

5. Japan consumes one-third as much energy per capita and about one-half per unit of GNP than does the United States.

Thus, Japan is substantially more dependent on imports to meet its energy requirements than is the United States and uses energy more efficiently, with industry accounting for the major fraction of its consumption.

Though these differences are significant in terms of the possible choices for action, both countries are highly vulnerable to oil supply disruptions and escalating oil prices. With varying degrees of urgency

Figure 7-1. Energy Consumption Patterns, 1979.

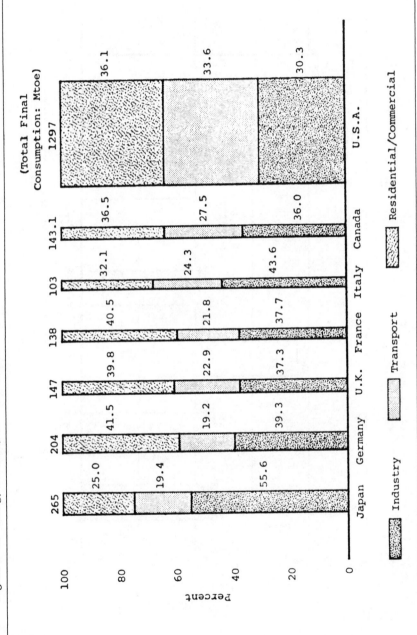

Source: OECD.

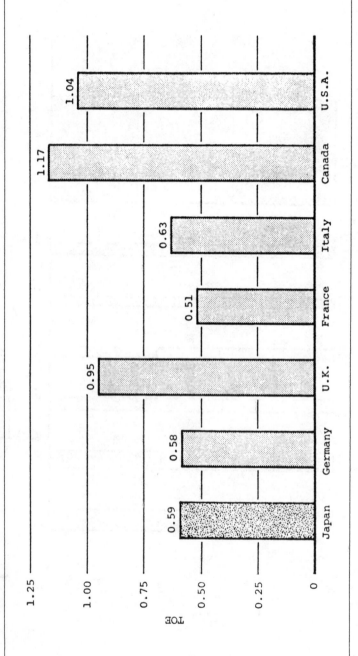

Figure 7-2. Total Primary Energy Requirements per GDP, 1979.

Source: OECD.

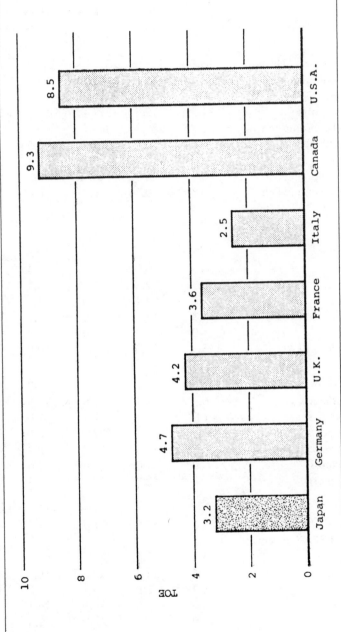

Figure 7-3. Total Primary Energy Requirements per Capita, 1979.

Source: OECD.

Table 7-2. Key Energy Indicators and Data, Japan (*mtoe*)

	1960	1973	1979	1985	1990
General					
Energy demand (TPE)	93.8	342.0	370.0	501.9	622.2
Energy production	58.1	39.2	49.6	86.6	136.8
Production (TPE)	0.62	0.11	0.13	0.17	0.22
Net oil imports	31.2	279.5	277.4	326.9	326.8
Total oil consumption	29.2	259.7	262.5	309.0	309.2
TPE-GDP ratio	0.69	0.69	0.59	0.56	0.55
Per capita TPE	1.0	3.1	3.2	4.1	4.9
Oil consumption (GDP)	0.21	0.52	0.42	0.35	0.27
Oil consumption (TPE)	0.31	0.76	0.71	0.62	0.50
Supply					
Production					
Solid fuels	42.6	15.9	11.2	12.8	12.8
Oil	0.5	0.7	0.5	1.4	1.7
Gas	0.7	2.6	2.3	5.4	6.4
Nuclear	0	2.4	15.0	36.5	71.3
Hydro/geothermal	14.3	17.6	20.6	27.2	36.0
Other	0	0	0	3.3	8.6
Electricity (TWH)	115.5	470.3	573.4	740.0	937.0
Trade					
Coal exports	0	- 0.4	- 1.3	0	0
Coal imports	6.4	42.4	42.6	70.8	97.4
Oil exports	- 1.0	- 2.0	- 1.3	0	0
Oil imports	32.1	251.5	278.7	326.9	326.8
Oil bunkers	- 1.6	-13.5	- 9.9	-19.3	-19.3
Gas exports	0	0	0	0	0
Gas imports	0	2.8	16.7	35.2	53.9
Demand					
TFC	58.6	245.9	271.9	351.5	434.9
Shares of TFC (percent)					
Oil	33.4	67.1	68.5	62.1	54.8
Solid fuels	49.4	15.4	12.2	16.0	15.6
Gas	3.2	2.9	3.1	4.3	5.0
Electricity	14.0	14.6	16.1	16.1	16.5
Other	0	0	0	1.4	8.1

Table 7-2. continued

	1960	1973	1979	1985	1990
Reference Items					
GDP (1975 US$ billion)	136.8	496.8	632.0	888.5	1131.7
Population (million)	93.3	108.7	115.9	122.0	126.0
Growth Rates					
Percent per year	1960-1973	1973-1979	1979-1985	1985-1990	
TPE	10.5	1.3	5.2	4.4	
GDP	10.4	4.1	5.8	5.0	
TFC	11.7	1.7	4.4	4.4	
TPE-GDP ratio	0	-2.7	-0.6	-0.5	
Energy production	-3.0	4.0	9.7	9.6	
Net oil imports	18.4	-0.1	2.8	0	
Oil consumption	15.3	0.2	2.8	0	

Source: International Energy Agency.

and success, both have initiated programs aimed at reducing their vulnerability—programs that include improving the efficiency of energy use (conservation), substituting other fuels for oil, encouraging the use of domestic resources, and diversifying foreign sources of supply. But their different situations have led to differences in emphasis. With its virtually complete lack of domestic energy resources, Japan has been turning more aggressively than the United States to the use of nuclear power. Though it has only limited resources of coal, Japan has also begun to move in the direction of greater coal utilization, its principal potential coal suppliers being Australia, Canada, China, the United States, and South Africa. Nevertheless, the fundamental differences in the energy framework of the two countries will remain. Projections of the effects of these policies on energy balances are shown in Tables 7-2 and 7-3.

Over the years, Japan's oil has been largely supplied by the international oil companies, U.S.-based companies accounting for as much as 70 percent of Japan's crude oil imports. To promote domestic exploration and development of oil and diversification of foreign supply, Japan established the Japan National Oil Corporation (JNOC; previously Japan Petroleum Development Corporation) and restricted foreign ownership of their oil industry. JNOC provides risk money,

Table 7-3. Key Energy Indicators and Data, United States (*mtoe*)

	1960	1973	1979	1985	1990
General					
Energy demand (TPE)	1035.3	1792.5	1877.4	1980.0	2117.0
Energy production	980.3	1510.4	1533.3	1566.0	1765.0
Production (TPE)	0.95	0.04	0.82	0.79	0.83
Net oil imports	83.1	304.6	415.0	438.0	362.0
Total oil consumption	456.9	813.0	868.0	840.0	746.0
TPE–GDP ratio	1.11	1.15	1.04	0.93	0.87
Per capita TPE	5.7	3.5	8.5	8.5	8.7
Oil consumption (GDP)	0.49	0.52	0.48	0.39	0.31
Oil consumption (TPE)	0.44	0.45	0.46	0.42	0.35
Supply					
Production					
Solid fuels	258.2	380.5	438.3	510.0	637.0
Oil	381.1	523.9	489.0	427.0	411.0
Gas	305.5	514.5	460.0	407.0	414.0
Nuclear	0.1	22.1	69.3	126.0	186.0
Hydro/geothermal	35.4	69.4	74.5	86.0	91.0
Other	0	0	2.2	10.0	26.0
Electricity (TWH)	391.6	2086.9	2248.0	2774.0	3274.0
Trade					
Coal exports	-22.3	-32.3	-39.2	-43.0	-50.0
Coal imports	0.2	0.7	3.5	0	0
Oil exports	-10.1	-10.8	-14.0	0	0
Oil imports	93.3	315.5	429.0	438.0	362.0
Oil bunkers	-11.7	- 9.5	-25.0	-25.0	-25.0
Gas exports	- 0.3	- 1.8	- 1.0	0	0
Gas imports	3.7	24.5	29.0	44.0	65.0
Demand					
TFC	823.3	1309.9	1348.8	1377.0	1422.0
Shares of TFC (percent)					
Oil	52.4	53.1	56.3	52.4	47.3
Solid fuels	13.3	7.5	6.3	7.9	9.4
Gas	26.2	27.6	24.2	23.2	23.6
Electricity	8.1	11.8	13.1	15.8	18.1
Other	0	0	0	0.7	1.6

Table 7-3. continued

	1960	1973	1979	1985	1990
Reference Items					
GDP (1975 US$ billion)	932.4	1561.4	1805.3	2127.0	2447.0
Population (million)	130.7	210.4	220.1	233.0	244.0
Growth Rates					
Percent per year		1960-1973	1973-1979	1979-1985	1985-1990
TPE		4.3	0.8	0.9	1.3
GDP		4.0	2.4	2.8	2.8
TFC		3.6	0.5	0.3	0.6
TPE-GDP ratio		0.3	-1.6	-1.8	-1.5
Energy production		3.4	0.3	0.4	2.4
Net oil imports		10.5	5.3	0.9	-3.7
Oil consumption		4.5	1.1	-0.5	-2.3

Source: International Energy Agency.

guidance and technical assistance to private companies. Such companies have obtained concessions in Indonesia, the Middle East, and Africa, and others are in negotiation. JNOC is now involved with companies active in twenty to twenty-five producing countries. In contrast, the oil consumed in the United States is, of course, largely supplied by domestically based companies.

As petroleum-exporting countries have increasingly taken over control of their production and exports and allocated less to the major international oil companies, these companies have cut back their so-called 'third-party' sales in all countries, including Japan. They have continued to supply their affiliated companies in Japan, but overall, supplies by U.S. companies to Japan have been reduced to about 25 percent of Japan's oil demand. In addition to the effect of these acts on total Japanese suppliers, Japanese refiners lost a major fraction of the crude they need for their operations. To take up the slack, Japan has made substantial use of trading companies. For example, JNOC has led negotiations and organized consortia in direct deals with Mexico and Indonesia, providing investment capital and loans in return for crude. These and other circumstances have had the special effect of encouraging Japan to establish closer energy ties with countries in its region, particularly China, Indonesia, and

Australia—ties that can be expected to affect the totality of economic and political relationships.

There are important factors outside of the energy field that also bear on the energy relationships between the United States and Japan. Particularly relevant is strategic defense. The United States has carried, virtually alone, the defense of the Western world's interests in the Mideast; Japan has not been called upon to share this burden. Now there are questions as to U.S. ability and will to carry out that function—questions that call for a reexamination of the role Japan should have in the effort to assure world security. (A recent report[4] of a joint working group of the Atlantic Council and the Japanese Institute for Peace and Security has made recommendations on these matters.)

Trade is another related factor. As a densely populated nation, Japan is highly dependent on imports of many essential products and must export other products to pay for them. Thus, Japan must successfully compete in international markets to meet its economic and social needs. Its principal exports are manufactured products, which have a relatively high energy content. Its imports, apart from fuels, are principally raw materials, food, and livestock. In the postwar era, Japan has given priority to industrialization; its sectoral energy consumption is, at least in part, a reflection of this emphasis. Now it is giving increasing priority to social programs and consumer desires, a number of years later than this occurred in the United States. As a result, Japanese society feels particularly vulnerable in the present difficult world economic climate.

The U.S. economy has, of course, been much more self-contained. However, in recent years, the role of international trade has also assumed increased importance in the United States, exports rising from 4.4 percent of GNP in 1970 to 7.7 percent in 1979 compared to 10.2 percent of GNP for Japan in 1979. Finally, the trade between the two countries is large, each being a major trading partner of the other.

Thus, the energy relationships between the United States and Japan must be viewed against a backdrop of changing and volatile global relationships and fundamentally different energy economies. Yet their common interests make it imperative that, at a minimum, their individual energy difficulties not be divisive and, if possible,

---

4. *The Common Security Interests of Japan, the United States, and NATO* (Washington, D.C. and Tokyo: December, 1980).

that actions on the energy front help to strengthen the ties between them.

2. The Policy Objectives of U.S.-Japan Energy Relationships

As the two largest industrial powers outside the centrally planned economies, the United States and Japan have a strong mutuality of economic and political interests. Both countries have a vital need — and responsibility — to assure the stability of Southeast Asia and the Pacific. Energy is a key element in the achievement of that objective. Today many of the less-developed countries of the region are embarked on a course of rapid economic development. At the same time, there are forces at work, abetted by the Soviet Union, that have the objective of overturning existing regimes for political ends. It is in the interest of both Japan and the United States to encourage the strong development trends of these countries to help maintain peace in the region.

Increasingly, Japan has targeted programs of financial and technical aid for its regional neighbors. In a recent year, it spent $433 million on such programs, while the U.S. AID program spent $308 million in the area in the same year. Countries of the region are dependent on U.S. and Japanese markets for their growth. For the United States and Japan to play a constructive role in the economic and social development of these countries, the economies of Japan and the United States must be sound — so that their markets are available to the LDCs and so that aid flows can continue. The slowdown in growth and the balance of payments problems of the industrialized countries, in large part brought on by the energy problems of the 1970s, can seriously erode this capability.

Furthermore, while the worldwide energy problems have had major effects on the economies of the industrial countries, the effects are even greater for countries in earlier phases of development. Such countries require substantially increasing amounts of energy for their development and can ill afford the sharply higher energy prices. Anything that major energy consumers such as the United States and Japan can do to reduce their own consumption of energy resources, particularly oil, is of value to the LDCs.

Though the United States and Japan have together a particular responsibility in the western Pacific and Southeast Asia, their mutual interests extend to other regions as well. Both are dependent on a healthy worldwide economy, and they have a common interest in maintaining stability throughout the world. Their size and influence place upon them a special responsibility to promote constructive relations not only among their allies but also with the oil-producing states. Furthermore, they must take a leadership role in relations with the developing world and facilitate energy-producing investments in developing countries.

The concerting of policies by the two countries in potential and actual trouble spots can reduce the likelihood or consequences of unfavorable developments. On the other hand, to the extent that their individual interests differ, such problems can be exacerbated. The potential for such difficulties was evident during 1979 and 1980, first with the Iranian oil production shutdown and cutback and the subsequent volatile oil market and then with the taking of U.S. hostages in Tehran. In the wake of the Iranian oil problems, Japan considered its vital interests to be such that it obtained oil from whatever source possible, even though this added pressure on oil prices. (Japan was, of course, not alone in such actions. Some Western European countries also placed demands on the oil market, which enabled prices to be bid up.) After the American hostages were taken in Iran, Japan exercised restraint in oil purchases, but did not follow the U.S. lead in embargoing oil from Iran.

These events help bring into focus the question of the potential solidarity of the two countries in the event of even more serious oil supply disruptions. How they cope individually and together with their energy vulnerability can be of decisive importance in the relationships between them and the peaceful development of the global economy.

3. Issues in the Energy Relationships of Japan and the United States

How can they best cope? An answer requires the exploration of several other questions. What can either country do to enhance the security of energy supply for the other? What can each do for itself? Are there actions in other fields that could strengthen their energy relationships?

What Can the United States Do to Improve the Japanese Energy Position? Japan's needs, like those of others, are for sufficient and reliable sources of energy supply at costs that enable Japan to meet its societal objectives. Until a sufficient transition to other forms of energy can be achieved, oil will continue to be a vital energy source and a source of difficulty. As an oil importer itself in the supply-limited world oil market, under most circumstances there is little the United States can do by itself to provide oil supply security for Japan in an emergency. The principal mechanism for dealing with supply emergencies, supply disruptions, and pressures on oil prices must be through the development and enforcement of strong multilateral arrangements among the principal consuming countries. This mechanism today is the International Energy Agency. The ability to deal with these issues is dependent on the strength of support both the United States and Japan give to that agency.

Even so, there is the potential for misunderstanding. As pointed out earlier, U.S.-based international oil companies have been the major supplier of Japanese oil, and their cutbacks of third-party customers have been particularly difficult for Japan. It appears that the companies have attempted to follow practices that treat all countries they serve in an equitable fashion, to "share the pain" evenly. Yet this feature of oil company operation and the fact that these companies are not subject to U.S. government control have sometimes not been recognized by the Japanese public.

While there is little that the United States can do for Japan with respect to oil on a bilateral basis, there are other energy supply areas in which U.S. action can either be very helpful or damaging. One such area is nuclear power. Increased use of nuclear power has been an essential oil substitution path for Japan. Because the United States is a supplier of enriched uranium and the country long leading the way in the development and use of nuclear power, U.S. policies affect this course, at least in the short run. In recent years, changes in U.S. policies, particularly deriving from antiproliferation objectives, have made the United States a less reliable supplier and raised concerns in Japan as to its ability to meet its nuclear power goals. Furthermore, the seeming ambivalence of the U.S. government toward domestic use of nuclear power has been used to fuel controversy in Japan about nuclear power.

The focus of U.S. policy has been to discourage reprocessing of nuclear fuel and the development and use of the nuclear breeder reactor. These technologies can extend the energy usefulness of uranium manyfold. The United States has argued, in its nonproliferation policy, that uranium resources are sufficiently large so that those steps are not necessary for some time to come. The Japanese view, however, has been that regardless of how much uranium there may be worldwide, the breeder is one of the few sources of energy that can be considered indigenous and therefore would significantly enhance its energy security.

To the extent that U.S. policies slow the Japanese nuclear program, Japan's energy future is made more vulnerable. The legitimate nonproliferation concerns that triggered the U.S. actions are intended to promote international stability. When the factors described in the preceding section are considered, it is at least arguable that the real risks to stability are probably higher from the precarious energy situation facing the countries of the world than from proliferation of nuclear weapons via the nuclear power route.

As Japan diversifies its energy supplies, increased use of coal is also essential, so it is attempting to make a number of arrangements to enhance security of its coal supply. The vast coal reserves of the United States make it an important source, and negotiations have taken place between Japanese and U.S. groups for supply contracts. However, Japan has expressed a concern as to whether U.S. coal-leasing and environmental policies will permit the use of these reserves in quantities sufficient to meet both U.S. demand for coal and export needs, which include those of other countries as well as Japan. It has questioned whether the United States has the ability—or the will—to put in place the infrastructure necessary to ship the large amounts of coal involved within the country and from seaports, particularly through the West Coast, to make the cost of U.S. coal competitive in the Japanese market. It has also expressed concern about U.S. reliability as a supplier in view of past abrupt changes in U.S. policies—for example, the soy bean and nuclear power cases.

It is clear that the United States is in a position to assist Japan along its oil substitution path, and it is in the U.S. self-interest to do so. But doing so will require that the United States adopt policies that facilitate the export of uranium and related services and of coal. To be credible, the policies must be accompanied by consistent action, at least on the part of all agencies of the federal government. A reexamination of the risk to world stability from vulnerable energy supplies compared to that from nuclear weapons proliferation via nuclear power is in order, followed by a new statement of policy and practices that can serve to remove impediments, direct and implied, from the path of Japan's greater use of nuclear power. Clarity and consistency of coal-leasing and environmental control policies are similarly necessary. Federal and state governments must adopt policies that facilitate the necessary investment in infrastructure. As will be noted later, such policies are needed to meet domestic energy needs as well as the needs of others. A favorable climate for the Japanese purchase of U.S. coal has the added merit of improving the trade balance between the two countries.

In an overall sense, this review shows the damaging effect of the twists and turns of U.S. policies in recent times on U.S. allies and U.S. credibility and the vital importance for the United States to define a consistent, understandable set of energy policies and programs, so that Japan, and other countries as well, can know what to expect from the United States over the long run. A review of energy relationships between the two countries reveals that there is no regular mechanism for exploring the full range of bilateral energy issues confronting them. Such a mechanism, involving both government and the private sector, could be useful.

What Can Japan Do To Enhance the U.S. Energy Situation?   As an energy-poor country, it is obvious that there is little Japan can do directly to help the United States meet its energy requirements. The principal, and not unimportant, course that could be beneficial in the near term is price restraint as Japan buys on the world oil market, particularly during periods of shortage. The events of 1979 have shown how "panic" buying actions of the larger consumers can bid up world oil prices. Care in such periods is in the longer term interests of all. The building up and draw-down of oil stocks and the building of strategic oil reserves are important factors in the current oil market and need to be coordinated multilaterally.

How Can the Domestic Energy Policies and Programs of the Two Countries Enhance Their Relationship?   It is vitally important that the policies of both countries reflect the fact that the energy problems they face are deeper than planning for temporary supply disruptions. They are long-run problems brought about by the great dependence the world economy has on a depleting supply of low cost oil. Furthermore, because of the international character of the oil market, the actions of any one consuming country affect the prospects of the others. Success in conservation efforts and in substitution of other fuels for oil is not only beneficial for the individual country, but easing demand on the oil market reduces pressure on the economic and political prices that all pay. Thus, strong domestic energy programs by each of these two major oil consumers are of great value to the other. Both countries have initiated programs to this end.

A recent discussion paper on the vision of policies in the 1980s by the Japanese Ministry of International Trade and Industry (MITI) stated: The 1980s will mark a historic turning point in the energy situation, and the political and economic environment. The manner in which we handle worldwide problems in the coming decade will be key in determining whether we can engineer a promising future.

The MITI study noted that, assuming Japan's economy grows at an average annual rate of 5 percent in the 1980s, a modest rate compared to Japan's past growth, the amount of energy consumed will need to double unless patterns were to change. Thus, it cited energy conservation as the most important need in the coming decade.

One of Japan's accommodations to a lower energy future has been a gradual change in the energy intensiveness of its products. Since 1974-1975, most of Japan's industrial growth has been in high value-added but relatively low energy content products, such as automobiles and consumer electronics. Production of steel and petrochemicals, which are low value-added, high energy content products, has had little growth.

Japan largely uses market forces to achieve its conservation goals. During 1979 the gasoline tax, already the equivalent of $0.75 per gallon, was increased by 25 percent. The aviation fuel tax was doubled, and kerosene prices were deregulated. The recently enacted Energy Conservation Act provides some tax incentives for conservation investments in industry and loans at current interest rates for insulation in homes. Building insulation standards are mandated. But for the most part, Japan continues to rely on market forces and voluntarism. Whether this approach will be adequate is questionable.

Japan, which consumed approximately 5.2 million barrels of oil per day in 1978, has set as targets a limitation of approximately 6.1 mbd in 1985 and 1990. It has also set a goal to reduce dependence on oil from 75 to 50 percent of its energy consumption. To do so will require the vigorous development and introduction of alternative sources to provide more than three times their current usage.

In diversifying its sources of oil, Japan's objective is to increase its imports from Asia to 30 percent of the total by 1990, compared to 22 percent in 1978. It is also investing heavily in domestic onshore and offshore oil production, in an attempt to maintain at least the current relatively low level of domestic production. But such production is unlikely to contribute substantially to Japan's energy needs.

Japan's supply plans also call for a significant increase in liquified natural gas imports, intended to enable increased use of gas in electricity generation and its more widespread use in industry and the domestic sector. Success in achieving these plans requires successful negotiation of long-term contracts with foreign suppliers and timely construction of liquefaction plants abroad and receiving terminals in Japan, where there is difficulty in finding adequate sites.

As noted earlier, Japan's plans to reduce its oil dependence rely heavily on increased use of coal and nuclear power. With respect to coal, Japan has established incentives for use of its domestic resource, but achievement of its alternative supply objectives requires a major increase in steam coal imports—from 1 million tons in 1978 to 54 million tons in 1990. Its high population density places particular stress on emission controls and makes more difficult the finding of suitable sites for coal-using plants as well as port facilities.

The nuclear portion of its supply plan calls for 30 GW of capacity in 1985, 53 GW in 1990, and 78 GW in 1995. (It was approximately 14 GW in 1979.) These plans, though scaled down from earlier ones, remain ambitious and can be achieved, if at all, only by sustained effort. Japan is attempting to obtain adequate supplies of uranium through long-term foreign purchase contracts and overseas investment in uranium properties. To enhance its security of supply, Japan aims to develop an independent nuclear fuel cycle capability, which has been at the center of the bilateral difficulties arising out of the recent U.S. policy on reprocessing and the nuclear breeder.

Hydro and geothermal energy provide small quantities of electricity in Japan, though the Japanese government plans to exploit them as fully as the available resources permit. Japan is supporting research and development on other renewable energy forms, but no major contribution is expected in the near and medium term. A noteworthy feature of Japan's energy program is the close working relationship between the government and Japanese industry. Japan's government places great emphasis on helping its industry secure foreign energy resources and in facilitating the exports that pay for them. Its use of trading firms and consortia, which negotiate multifaceted arrangements, is the most conspicuous example. If a project is in the "national interest," and energy-related activities tend to be, government financing is made available.

While Japan has encountered its share of difficulties in developing, implementing, and financing its energy program, there has been a wide consensus on the course to be followed. This is in marked contrast to the situation in the United States, where there has been great difficulty in achieving a consensus even on fundamentals. The maintenance of oil prices to the consumer at levels below world market prices until very recently had the effect of draining a disproportionate share of world supplies to the United States, reflecting, in the view of the Japanese and others, a lack of will in the United States to take politically difficult but vitally important actions.

Also in contrast to Japan, the relationship between the U.S. government and U.S. industry has been characterized by distrust. This despite the fact that industry is the mechanism that must be counted on to implement new energy directions and to provide the exports that will help the U.S. economy pay for its oil imports. Furthermore, the division of powers in the United States between federal and state governments, coupled with a lack of consensus on the directions to be taken, has added to the difficulties in the taking of necessary actions to improve the U.S. energy position.

Like Japan's, U.S. policy calls for greatly improved energy conservation and large increases in the use of coal and nuclear power. Significant improvements in energy use efficiency have taken place in industry—a reduction of about 12 percent overall in the amount of energy used per unit of production between 1974 and 1978. In the past year, improvements have been noted in the other sectors as well, responding to the much higher oil prices, though in part it is also the result of weakened economic activity. The United States has put in place tax credits for energy-conserving investments and requirements for automobile efficiency. Until recently, in the absence of decontrolled oil and gas prices, the United States had largely depended on regulation and incentives rather than market forces to bring about conservation.

The emphasis on greater use of coal has had some effect, though limited and less than plans call for. The difficulties encountered in reconciling environmental rules with the development of coal production and coal-using facilities have continued. Measures are yet to be firmly established that will enable the necessary investments to be made in domestic transport and port facilities and in mining community development.

With respect to nuclear power, the U.S. government's attitude has in recent years been one of ambivalence. While its stated policy called for much greater use, it has avoided any firm supportive acts. Regulatory actions have tended to stretch schedules. The accident at Three Mile Island has reduced public confidence and exacerbated the regulatory problems. Lack of positive action on the permanent disposal of nuclear waste threatens to impede expanded use of nuclear power, a problem that also threatens Japan's nuclear power program.

The problems the United States has encountered in its moves to alternative supplies have been a matter of concern to the Japanese as well as to other countries. As the world's major oil consumer, success in substitution in the United States is considered essential to a satisfactory world energy future.

The policy of the Carter administration placed great emphasis on the development of new renewable energy sources such as solar, wind, and biomass, setting a target of 20 percent of energy needs from such sources, plus hydropower, by 2000. There is considerable skepticism as to the realism of that target at costs that can be afforded while meeting other national needs.

Both the United States and Japan have embarked on extensive programs of research, development, and demonstration relating to new and improved energy technologies. In 1979, the U.S. government spent $3.8 billion in these efforts, and the Japanese government spent $920 billion. In both countries, significant private sector funds are also devoted to such work; incomplete data indicate that U.S. industry spent more than $1.3 billion and Japanese industry over $510 million in 1979. The programs in both countries cover a broad spectrum of technologies, including conservation, coal combustion and conversion, nuclear power, geothermal energy, solar energy, biomass, ocean energy, and wind energy. While historically Japan has tended to adopt technologies that were pioneered elsewhere, there are signs that it now recognizes a responsibility to be among the leaders in new developments. An MITI discussion paper recommended that R&D spending (including that for energy) should be increased from the 1.7 percent of GNP currently spent to 2.5 percent of GNP by the mid-1980s and to 3 percent by 1990. That paper recommended, further, that Japan pursue the development of creative technologies.

There are major benefits possible through closer energy RD&D cooperation between these two countries and with others. The pursuit of energy technology goals is an expensive undertaking; collaboration can make more effective use of the funds made available. A start in this direction has been made through the IEA RD&D program: the agreement on a synthetic fuels project, SRC-II, is a beginning of collaboration in large demonstration projects, though the future of this particular project is in doubt at this writing. While Japanese policy statements have been supportive of such cooperation, in practice Japan has in the past exhibited reluctance to engage in specific project collaboration. This reluctance apparently stems from a concern about losing a competitive edge, as well as language and cultural difficulties. No doubt the changeable nature of the U.S. government commitment to individual projects is also a deterrent. However, there are signs that this reluctance is giving way to take advantage of greater collaborative efforts.

Table 7-4 is a listing of current U.S.-Japan cooperative agreements in energy technology, bilateral and multilateral. Given the technological capacity and strength of Japan, greater initiative and participation by Japan in RD&D collaboration, particularly of a major hardware nature, would be beneficial. Experience indicates that such collaboration, properly structured, offers important economies and does not alter substantially the relative competitive positions of those participating.

Commercial Competition and U.S.-Japan Energy Relationships. As pointed out earlier, export trade has long been a vital element in Japan's economic life and is of increasing importance to the U.S. economy. Each is a major trading partner of the other, and they compete for third-country markets. Energy and its costs are important factors in their export products.

Japan's aggressive and effective export practices have had political repercussions in the United States and in the European community, as they have made large inroads into markets (e.g., automobiles and

Table 7-4. Agreements in Energy RD&D Between Japan and the United States

---

Bilateral

1. High energy physics—information exchange

2. Fusion—information exchange
   —testing in Doublet III Tokamak, with about $60 million Japanese investment in this USDOE facility

3. Geothermal applications—information exchange

4. Nuclear reactor critical experiments—information exchange
   —cooperative planning for testing

5. Liquid metal fast breeder reactor—information exchange plus some joint experiments:
   general
   safety
   fuel development
   materials dosimetry
   mixed oxide fuel performance codes

Multilateral (all IEA or IEA related)

6. Coal liquification—solvent refined coal
   —joint funding of $1.5 billion project (with Germany)

7. Advanced heat pumps—task sharing (with ten other countries)

8. Coal technical information service—joint funding (with ten other countries)

9. Enhanced oil recovery—task sharing (with five other countries)

10. Nuclear reactor safety—task sharing and some joint funding (with seven other countries)

11. Geothermal—hot, dry rocks
    —joint funding (with four other countries)

12. Solar heating and cooling (3)—task sharing (with thirteen other countries)

13. Wave power—joint funding (with three other countries)

14. Wind energy technology—task sharing plus some joint funding (with nine other countries)

15. Fusion (2)—joint funding of superconducting magnet test facility and materials test facility (with five other countries)

16. Hydrogen production from water—task sharing (with eight other countries)

17. RD&D strategy development—task sharing (with fourteen other countries)

electronics) where unemployment has risen, particularly in this recessionary period. While both countries have subscribed to the international trade treaties, there are practices both alleged and real that affect the competitive picture. This has led to calls in the United States for restricting imports from Japan and the further elimination of the trade barriers erected in Japan. Such problems can color the entire range of bilateral relationships and has particular relevance in any attempt in the United States to make special efforts to assist in Japan's difficult energy situation.

4. Conclusions and Recommendations

The actions on energy matters that Japan and the United States take individually and together will constitute a major element in their future relationships and future world order. To provide for a mutually beneficial future, the following conclusions and recommendations are offered:

1. A secure energy supply for Japan is vital to U.S. interests. The U.S. dependence on oil imports and the international character of the oil market limit the measures that the United States could take in most oil emergencies to mitigate the precarious Japanese oil situation. Emphasis needs to be placed on multilateral actions, particularly among the consuming countries, that can serve to assist Japan as well as the United States and other consuming countries in the event of oil supply disruption. These include:
    a. Strong support and strengthening of the IEA emergency oil-sharing program;
    b. Coordination of oil stocks build-up and draw-down in periods of tight supply as well as market softness; and
    c. Continuing cooperation in demand restraint measures and oil market actions during this era of precarious supply–demand balance.

2. If circumstances arise in which Japanese oil supplies are particularly disrupted, it is in the U.S. interest to do what it can to alleviate such a problem, consistent with commitments to the IEA system.

3. The United States can assist Japan in reducing its dependence on oil by becoming a source of steam coal. The United States should adopt policies that facilitate the export of coal in a reliable fashion, including more certain processes for environmental approvals and policies conducive to infrastructure development, particularly through the West Coast. Japanese investment in U.S. coal properties should be encouraged as a means of enhancing assurance of supply.

4. It is similarly of interest to both the United States and Japan that Japan make full use of nuclear power to reduce its use of oil. The United States should resolve the uncertainties created by its nuclear policy in a manner that will facilitate the use of increasing amounts of nuclear power by Japan as well as by the United States. Cooperation between the United States and Japan to demonstrate solutions to disposal of nuclear waste should be undertaken.

5. Both countries should adopt policies that reduce pressures on the oil market in the longer term as well as the near term.

   a. Strong conservation efforts continue to be of high priority.

   b. Pricing of all forms of energy in both countries should encourage conservation and the development of alternatives to oil.

   c. Both should strengthen other policies and programs that facilitate supply alternatives. In the United States this requires the elimination of inconsistent federal practices and the promotion of policies that recognize the essentiality of greater use of coal and nuclear fuels to replace oil.

   d. Aggressive programs of research, development, and demonstration as well as commercial application of new energy technologies are necessary. Active collaboration in such efforts between Japan and the United States and multilaterally, either privately or government to government, can facilitate the achievement of that objective. Worthy of particular emphasis are projects in:

      Conservation technologies
      Shale oil development
      Coal combustion, including environmental
         control technologies

Coal liquefaction and gasification
Nuclear reactor safety
Breeder development
Solar energy
Fusion.

6. Japan and the United States should take the lead in facilitating energy-producing investments in developing countries and in promoting constructive relationships with oil-producing countries.

7. To provide a suitable political climate for U.S. actions, Japan needs to assure trade policies that will make it less subject to allegations of unfair export practices and import barriers.

8. A regular means of exploring the entire range of bilateral energy issues should be instituted, involving both government and private sector representatives. Among the first items such a group should examine is the means of encouraging coal and uranium exports from the United States to Japan.

Underpinning all such actions for the foreseeable future is the need for both countries to contribute to a credible strategic position that will serve to protect vital sources of oil.

II. JAPAN–U.S. ENERGY RELATIONS:
A JAPANESE VIEW

Toyoaki Ikuta

1. Energy Demand and Supply Structure of Japan

The most notable characteristic of Japan's energy demand and supply structure is the extremely high rate of dependence on oil.

In 1979, for instance, oil accounted for 70 percent of Japan's total primary energy consumption. In comparison, rates of dependence on oil in the Western world were 45 percent in the United States, 43 percent in the United Kingdom, 51 percent in West Germany, and 61 percent in France. Only Italy, with 68 percent, recorded a rate comparable to Japan's. The rate of dependence on oil in Western Europe was 55 percent on the average (Table 7–5).

Table 7-5. Primary Energy Consumption of Major Countries, 1979

	Oil	Natural Gas	Coal	Hydro	Nuclear	Total
Japan						
mtoe	265.4	22.1	58.6	19.9	14.7	380.7
(percent)	(69.7)	(5.8)	(15.4)	(5.2)	(3.9)	(100)
United States						
mtoe	862.9	498.8	384.1	80.1	72.2	1898.1
(percent)	(45.5)	(26.3)	(20.2)	(4.2)	(3.8)	(100)
West Germany						
mtoe	146.9	45.9	78.6	4.0	9.6	285.0
(percent)	(51.5)	(16.1)	(27.6)	(1.4)	(3.4)	(100)
France						
mtoe	118.1	23.3	29.9	14.5	9.6	195.4
(percent)	(60.4)	(11.9)	(15.3)	(7.4)	(4.9)	(100)
United Kingdom						
mtoe	94.1	41.2	76.1	1.3	8.1	220.8
(percent)	(42.6)	(18.7)	(34.5)	(0.6)	(3.7)	(100)
Italy						
mtoe	101.2	22.9	10.0	12.4	1.3	147.8
(percent)	(68.5)	(15.5)	(6.8)	(8.4)	(0.9)	(100)
Western Europe						
mtoe	726.5	185.5	264.0	108.3	41.3	1325.6
(percent)	(54.8)	(14.0)	(12.4)	(8.2)	(3.1)	(100)

Source: BP Statistical Review of the World Oil Industry, 1979.

In addition, Japan has been importing almost all the amounts (99.8 percent) of oil she requires. This rate of dependence on imported oil is also way above the 46 percent of the United States and the 85 percent of Western Europe as a whole.

Moreover, while ratios of Middle Eastern oil (oil from the Persian Gulf countries) to total imported oil in the United States and Western Europe are 25 and 66 percent, respectively, that in Japan is as high as 75 percent (Table 7-6). As a result, Japan's rate of dependence on Middle Eastern oil in its total primary energy supply, which can be obtained by multiplying the foregoing three types of rates,

Table 7-6. Oil Imports of Japan, the United States, and Western Europe by Source, 1979

	Japan	United States	Western Europe
Middle East			
mtoe	205.2	104.6	430.6
(percent)	(74.5)	(24.9)	(66.5)
Asia-Pacific[a]			
mtoe	59.4	25.9	1.2
(percent)	(21.6)	(6.2)	(0.2)
Africa			
mtoe	0.7	123.7	139.1
(percent)	(0.2)	(29.5)	(21.5)
Others			
mtoe	10.3	165.6	76.2
(percent)	(3.7)	(39.4)	(11.8)
Total			
mtoe	275.6	419.8	647.1
(percent)	(100)	(100)	(100)

a. Excludes Communist countries.
Source: BP Statistical Review of World Oil Industry, 1979.

reaches about 51 percent, which is much higher than the U.S.'s 5 percent and Western Europe's 31 percent. This means that a blockade of the Hormuz Strait could cause serious effects on Japan's primary energy supply, while adverse effects caused to the United States would be negligible and those to Western Europe would remain moderate.

This high rate of dependence on oil—and in particular on Middle Eastern oil—makes Japan's energy supply structure extremely vulnerable. Needless to say, Japan has not been idle or reluctant to take measures to improve the vulnerable situation of its energy supply. Since the first oil crisis, Japan has set up measures to deal with emergencies through promulgation of a variety of legislation and establishment of new organizations and has made efforts to facilitate research and development of alternative energies and to promote energy conservation. In particular, energy conservation efforts, primarily in the private sector, have produced the most satisfactory results among major oil-consuming countries. Even so, there is no change in the fact that Japan is still faced with a serious problem of high vulnerability in its energy supply.

2. Objectives and Significance of Japan's Energy Strategies

Because Japan's energy supply structure is so vulnerable, there is no alternative for Japan but to give priority to securing a stable energy supply. This is because the security of Japan's economy fully depends on stability of her energy supply. To secure economic stability means to stabilize politics and the society. Now that Japan has become the second biggest economic power in the free world today, her political, economic, and social climate could have a substantial influence on the Asian and Pacific area and the free world as a whole.

Accordingly, not only for her own national security but also for stability and development of the free world as a whole, it is important for Japan to take measures, such as diversification of energy supply sources and improvements in consumption efficiency and conservation of energy, to alleviate the potential vulnerability of her energy supply structure. At the same time, in view of her international position, it is essential for Japan to cooperate with major countries in planning and enforcing energy strategies. And it is especially important that Japan and the United States, facing each other across the Pacific Ocean and having deep political and economic interrelations, step up cooperation in the energy field.

3. U.S. Domestic Energy Policies as Seen from Japan

Oil. U.S. oil imports had recorded sharp increases in the 1970s, and the nation is now the biggest oil-importing country in the world. At the same time, however, the nation is the largest oil-producing country in the free world, rivaled only by Saudi Arabia. Accordingly, direct and indirect effects of U.S. domestic oil policies on world oil market are formidable.

The price control of U.S. domestic crude oil and the entitlement system worked together as a kind of import subsidy, by keeping U.S. refiners' crude oil acquisition cost artificially lower than the international level. Thus, the phased decontrol of domestic oil initiated by the Carter administration was welcomed by Japan and other oil-importing countries as a very desirable step. This U.S. policy, aimed at reflecting the market mechanism in domestic crude oil price, was furthered by President Reagan's decision on January 28, 1981, to immediately decontrol domestic oil prices and at the same time to abolish the entitlement system.

These two major decisions will, it is hoped, result in increased oil exploration and development activities, as well as in further reduction of oil consumption in the United States. These moves by the United States, the largest oil importer in the free world, toward reducing its pressure on the international petroleum market are viewed favorably by Japan and Western Europe.

Gas. The same can be said concerning U.S. natural gas prices. As a result of price control policies enforced for years, domestic natural gas prices in the United States have been controlled at an extraordinarily low level, whereby consumption has been encouraged and exploration for new gas fields discouraged. For instance, at the beginning of 1980, the average price of natural gas delivered to thermal power plants was $2.04 per million btu, less than half of the $4.30 per million btu for heavy oil.

In view of such situations, the Natural Gas Policy Act effected in 1978 provided for measures that raise natural gas prices in real terms and fully decontrol newly discovered gas prices after 1985. Like crude oil policies, these natural gas policies aim at reduction in consumption and promotion of exploration and development activities, which are also beneficial to countries other than the United States. It is hoped that the new administration under President Reagan will soon come to a decision to accelerate deregulation of new natural gas as it has done with crude oil price.

Coal. As to coal, the United States is believed to have a big surplus power to increase output in light of its vast deposits. In fact, the U.S. government is now planning to greatly expand use of coal by promoting fuel conversion of large-sized boilers for power generation and other purposes from oil and natural gas to coal.

However, because coal mines subject to the new development program are mainly surface-mined Western deposits, several problems remain to be solved, such as environmental regulations in coal-producing areas and arrangement of a transport network to deliver coal to major consuming areas and exporting ports on the East and West Coasts.

As will be discussed later, Japan is planning to increase coal imports sharply after 1985 and therefore expects that the United States will expand its coal-exporting capacity by making constant progress in increasing coal output. It is a solid fact that countries other than Japan also hope that the United States will diminish its rate of dependence on imported oil by increasing coal output and utilization.

Nuclear. As will be discussed in detail later, nuclear-power-related developments in the United States have profound impacts on the nuclear power programs of Japan and the European countries. Therefore it is desirable that the United States should recognize its position, not as a country blessed with natural resources, but as the leading political power in the free world, and resume positive nuclear policies to encourage the use of nuclear power within the country, not only for reducing its dependence on imported oil but also for facilitating the Japanese and European nuclear programs.

R & D. Furthermore, a great deal is also expected of the United States in the field of research and development of new energies other than conventional oil substitutes. In particular, it should be noted that neither Japan nor the Western European countries at present are capable of conducting technological development for new energies on such a large scale as the United States has demonstrated in carrying out the Manhattan Project and the Apollo Project by mobilizing huge financial and human resources.

4. Measures to Expand and Improve Japan-U.S. Energy Relations

a. Measures to Deal with Oil Supply Emergencies. Since the United States and Japan are the two biggest oil-importing countries in the free world, it is important for the two nations to play a positive role under united efforts in making the emergency oil-sharing system of the International Energy Agency effective. Also, to identify and solve difficulties in carrying out the system, Japan and the United States, whose oil industries have already established a close relationship, are required to work together. Furthermore, concerning oil reserves, which individual countries have been building up independently under the instruction of the IEA, it may be beneficial for Japan and the United States to exchange information constantly and to conclude some kind of agreement that permits sharing reserves with each other in case of emergency.

Such an arrangement by the two biggest oil importers will play a significant role in preventing extreme price rises at times of tight market, especially when it is not so tight as to trigger the IEA emergency oil-sharing plan. It goes without saying, however, that this kind of arrangement should be compatible with and in no way disrupt or compete with the existing IEA emergency oil-sharing program.

b. Japan–U.S. Cooperation for Diversification of Oil Supply Sources. As U.S. oil imports are much larger than those of Japan, the range of cooperation that the United States can offer to help Japan diversify her oil supply sources is very limited. This does not mean, however, that there is no room for such cooperation.

For instance, cooperation would be possible between the two countries in oil exploration and development efforts outside the traditional oil-exporting countries that, if successful, will not only facilitate the Japanese diversification of supply sources but will also help ease the world oil supply situation. Similarly, successful U.S.–Japanese cooperation in enhanced oil recovery technologies and investments in known oil fields will also have significant effects. If such cooperative efforts are successfully carried out within the United States, U.S. dependence on foreign oil will be reduced, giving corresponding relief to the international oil market. In addition to these bilateral efforts, the United States could help Japan to diversify its oil supply sources by permitting export of its domestic oil to Japan.

If the United States shows its readiness to allow exports to Japan of its domestic oil, including Alaskan crude oil, about which swap deals had been suggested, and synthetic oils from coal, shale, and the like, in the long run, this will improve the U.S.–Japan energy relationships. Even if there was no definite plan of actual export for the time being, clearly stated U.S. readiness to allow such exports when the case demands would go a long way to enhancing her credibility among the Japanese people. In particular, the issue of whether to approve oil exports to Japan in return for investments made by Japanese firms in the United States should be reviewed constructively not only from the energy supply aspect, but also from the viewpoint of U.S.-Japanese trade relations. The United States can also help Japan's oil source diversification by making available to Japan a portion of the oil destined for the United States from such producer countries as Indonesia and Mexico. As a matter of course, this also requires cooperation of the producer governments themselves. It is conceivable that such an arrangement will be more effective and have more likelihood of being realized in case of emergency than under normal conditions.

c. Expansion of Japan-U.S. Coal Trade. Expanding utilization of coal (steam coal) is one of the measures most expected to reduce Japan's rate of dependence on oil and improve her vulnerable energy supply structure. This will lead to diversification of supply in terms of both region and resource.

Japan is planning to import 22 million tons of steam coal in 1985 and 53.5 million tons in 1990 (sixteen- and forty-fold increases, respectively, over actual imports in 1979). While the majority of imported coal now comes from Australia (70 percent in 1979), it will not be possible nor will it be practical for Japan to depend on Australia alone to import such huge amounts of coal. In this light, Japan now expects much of the United States, the largest coal-producing country in the free world in terms of both deposits and output. An increase in Japan's coal imports from the United States will also be beneficial for the two countries in fields other than energy. For instance, it will contribute not only to the alleviation of trade imbalances between the two countries, which ran nearly $6 billion in favor of Japan in 1977 (Table 7-7), but also to the improvement of the U.S. employment situation.

In view of the above aspects, it is desirable that the United States set up coal utilization expansion programs at the earliest opportunity, including plans for coal exports to Japan. In particular, construction of infrastructures such as railways and port facilities, taking due care to avoid any unnecessary cost rises, is an essential element for realizing shipments of a huge amount of coal from the Pacific coast.

In this context, it is imperative that some kind of U.S.-Japanese joint program take place so that technical, economic, and other uncertainties surrounding U.S. coal exports to Japan can be clarified and necessary measures taken as soon as possible. For example, sub-

Table 7-7. Japan's Trade with the United States

	1977	1978	1979
Total export	19,717 (24.5)[a]	24,915 (25.5)	26,403 (25.6)
Foodstuffs	200 (23.0)	218 (20.8)	189 (15.7)
Light industry products	2095 (20.7)	2343 (21.0)	2201 (18.4)
Heavy chemical industry products	17,146 (25.2)	22,054 (26.4)	23,601 (26.9)
Others	276 (19.9)	300 (17.5)	412 (18.9)
Total imports	12,396 (17.5)	14,790 (18.6)	20,431 (18.5)
Foodstuffs	2734 (27.1)	3564 (31.3)	4423 (30.7)
Crude materials and fuels	4950 (10.9)	5101 (10.9)	7369 (10.9)
Manufactured goods	4639 (31.7)	6020 (30.1)	8505 (31.3)
Others	73 (13.0)	105 (8.5)	133 (8.1)
Export—Import balance	7321	10,125	5972

a. ( )—share percent of United States.
Source: 1980 White Paper on International Trade, MITI.

stantial contribution will be made in the efforts to solve these problems if Japan cooperates, in close collaboration with the U.S.-Japan Coal Conference, whose first session was held in August 1980, in joint works with the Western Coal Export Task Force, which has been organized with the Western Governors' Policy Office (WESTPO) members, as well as representatives of coal, railroad, and other related industries, as the main constituents.

d. Strengthening of Japan-U.S. Nuclear Cooperation. To reduce Japan's dependence on Middle Eastern oil, expansion of nuclear power utilization is as important as that of coal and LNG. According to a provisional forecast on long-term energy demand and supply, Japan plans to install 30 million kilowatts of nuclear power capacity in 1985, 53 million kw in 1990, and 78 million kw in 1995. However, the Three Mile Island accident and nonproliferation policies of the Carter administration have kindled again among the Japanese people so deep a distrust in nuclear power as to make it doubtful whether or not nuclear capacities planned in the provisional forecast can be achieved.

The negative attitude of the U.S. government toward nuclear power development may be reasonable for a country that is one of the largest oil and gas producers in the world and is also blessed with vast coal resources. However, this U.S. attitude has had a very negative effect on Japan and the Western European countries that have no choice but to depend on nuclear power as one of the most important alternative energy sources.

To promote the use of nuclear power, we cannot neglect the issue of nonproliferation. Because of her past experience, Japan is particularly sensitive to the issue and has been playing an active role in the nonproliferation movement. Unfortunately, however, Japan and the United States have different opinions concerning the ways to achieve nonproliferation.

It seems that Japan is not the only country in the world that hopes the United States will, taking different energy situations of individual countries into consideration, take the initiative in carrying out joint programs among the United States, Japan, and the Western European countries, whereby basic technologies of nuclear power generation and techniques of plant operation and management accumulated in individual countries will be fully utilized to establish and improve safety and reliability of nuclear power generation. There should be no argument against the significance of exchanging information of technological and technical developments made by each country, if peaceful utilization of nuclear power is to be expanded.

Also, policies of the United States have had considerable influence on the issue of nuclear fuel cycle, the early establishment of which has been a primary concern of Japan. It is desirable that the United States deepen its understanding of the positions of Japan and the Western European countries and review its policies related to the issue. A joint work of possible part(s) of the nuclear fuel cycle on a bilateral, multilateral, or a regional basis, based on the results of discussion at the conferences of the International Nuclear Fuel Cycle Evaluation, provided it is not counterproductive to the individual efforts of the countries concerned, will be one of major subjects of review for the United States.

Similarly, it is desirable that the United States, in its move to amend the siting regulations of nuclear power plants, should take into consideration that these regulations can have substantial influence on the nuclear power programs of Japan and Western Europe and should, in view of the present level of and possible future progress in nuclear reactor safety technologies, avoid unnecessarily limiting the areas suitable for nuclear power plant sitings. In the longer run, it will also be significant for the United States and Japan to step up mutual cooperation in research and development of advanced types of reactors such as the fast breeder and nuclear fusion technology.

e. *Strengthening and Expansion of Cooperation in R&D for Alternative Energies.* In addition to cooperation related to oil and existing oil substitutes, Japan and the United States should step up and expand collaboration for conducting research and development of unconventional alternative energies. Specifically, strengthening and expanding cooperation for the coal liquefaction programs already in progress would be a desirable precedent. The two countries should also cooperate to promote development and utilization of renewable energies—for example, geothermal and solar.

In this regard, there appears to be plenty of opportunities for the two countries to cooperate with each other in assisting the Asian-Pacific countries in their R&D efforts to develop and utilize such indigenous alternative energy sources as biomass. Japan–U.S. cooperation in this field is practically their responsibility as the two leading countries in the Asia–Pacific region.

f. *Political and Technical Cooperation for Energy Conservation.* As a measure to reduce the rate of dependence on imported oil for the time being, conservation is considered as important as or, in the short run, even more effective than expanded utilization of coal, nuclear power, and other alternative energies; and it is positively carried out by individual countries.

According to statistics prepared by the United Nations, energy consumption per capita in 1978 in major advanced countries were 7737 kilograms oil equivalent (kgoe) in the United States, 4092 kgoe in West Germany, 3546 kgoe in the United Kingdom, 2971 kgoe in France, and 2602 kgoe in Japan (Table 7-8). Also, OECD statistics showed that total energy requirements (TER) per $1000 of gross domestic product in 1978 in these countries were 0.879 tons oil equivalent (toe) in the United States, 0.427 toe in West Germany,

Table 7-8. Total Energy Requirements (TER) of Major Countries per Capita, 1978 (*kgoe*)

	1978	1977
Japan	2602	2589
United States	7737	7874
West Germany	4092	3934
France	2971	2961
United Kingdom	3546	3472
Italy	2197	2128

Source: World Energy Supplies, 1973–1978, United Nations.

Table 7-9. Total Energy Requirements (TER) of Major Countries per Unit of GDP, 1978

	TER (mtoe)	GDP (bill $)	TER/GDP (toe/1000$)
Japan	357.2	973.91	0.367
United States	1857.3	2112.37	0.879
West Germany	272.7	638.88	0.427
France	190.2	471.59	0.403
United Kingdom	211.5	309.21	0.684
Italy	137.4	260.11	0.528

Source: Energy Balances of OECD Countries, 1974/1978.
National Accounts of OECD Countries, 1950–1978, Vol. 1.

0.684 toe in the United Kingdom, 0.403 toe in France, and 0.367 toe in Japan (Tables 7-9 and 7-10).

As indicated by these data, there seems to be plenty of room for energy conservation in the United States, where former President Carter had made conservation one of the most important measures of his energy policy package. In this field, Japan can contribute much to the United States by providing techniques, technologies, and experiences that Japan, being short of natural resources, has accumulated for years.

Accordingly, it is important to promote systematic exchanges of techniques, information, and human resources between the two countries and to elaborate cooperation programs for each one of

Table 7-10. Japan's International Trade (*million dollars, percent*)

	1977	1978	1979
Total export	80,495 (100)	97,543 (100)	103,032 (100)
Foodstuffs	870 (1.1)	1047 (1.1)	1207 (1.2)
Light industry products	10,106 (12.6)	11,133 (11.4)	11,986 (11.6)
Heavy chemical industry products	68,129 (84.6)	83,654 (85.8)	87,662 (85.1)
Others	1390 (1.7)	1710 (1.8)	2177 (2.1)
Total import	70,809 (100)	79,343 (100)	110,672 (100)
Foodstuffs	10,105 (14.2)	11,403 (14.4)	14,415 (13.0)
Crude materials and fuels	45,491 (64.2)	46,716 (58.9)	67,482 (61.0)
(Mineral fuels)	(31,149) ((44.0))	(31,336) ((39.5))	(45,286) ((40.9))
Manufactured goods	14,651 (20.7)	19,992 (25.2)	27,133 (24.5)
Others	562 (0.8)	1231 (1.6)	1642 (1.5)
Export–Import balance	9686	18,200	-7640

Source: 1980 White Paper on International Trade, MITI.

the energy-consuming sectors—namely, transport, industrial, and residential–commercial.

g. Promotion of Information and Human Resources Exchanges. To realize a variety of the measures mentioned thus far, it is important to promote and step up continuous exchanges of information, opinions, and human resources at every level of the public and private sectors between the United States and Japan. Although innumerable opportunities for information and human resource exchanges have already been established between the two countries, it is surprising to learn that few opportunities exist for discussing overall energy problems.

In particular, it is quite rare for the two countries to have significant discussions based on international positions of each country and bilateral relations between them.

Such being the case, much attention is being given to the developments and results of the current project of the Atlantic Council of the United States and the move demonstrated at the Japan–U.S. Businessmen's Conference toward establishing an energy forum.

III. JOINT POLICY RECOMMENDATIONS

- The Energy Policy Committee of the Atlantic Council of the United States
- The Japan–U.S. Energy Relationships Committee of the Committee for Energy Policy Promotion, Japan

The Energy Policy Committee of the Atlantic Council of the United States, chaired by John E. Gray, and the Japan–U.S. Energy Relationships Comittee of the Committee for Energy Policy Promotion, Japan, chaired by Yoshizane Iwasa, have completed a joint study of the energy relationships between Japan and the United States. This joint assessment was undertaken in parallel with and as part of the Atlantic Council's project on international energy relationships in the 1980s, which the council began at the end of 1979.

During the course of this joint work, both parties have come to recognize more fully the significance of U.S.-Japanese energy relationships, the difficulties that both countries face today, and the mutually advantageous actions that they can and should take individually, together, and in concert with other allies in the 1980s. These proposed actions will constitute a major element in their future relations and in future world order.

The disparity in their domestic energy situations and their common interests as the world's two largest importers of oil create special problems and opportunities in the overall bilateral relationship of Japan and the United States. Therefore it is important that the United States and Japan act promptly to improve their respective energy situations. At least as important as unilateral efforts, however, is a cooperative and integrative approach by the two countries on all energy alternatives, including conservation.

Based on the above considerations, the combined committees offer the following conclusions and recommendations for action in order to provide for a mutually beneficial future.

1. The security of oil supplies is vital to the interests of the United States and Japan.[5] In view of this fact, the two countries should cooperate as much as possible, with the United States recognizing Japan's near-total dependence on imports and Japan recognizing the importance of stable pricing of oil in world markets.

For example, the United States specifically should agree to give positive consideration to the sale of U.S. crude oil to Japan under emergency conditions of large-scale Japanese supply interruptions. As well, the United States should modify its export policy to permit the swapping or sale of Alaskan oil to Japan under nonemergency conditions, in order to make more efficient and less expensive use of Alaskan oil by cutting transportation costs. Both steps would have an important symbolic effect on American–Japanese relations and enhance the credibility of existing international plans for petroleum sharing in an emergency.

At the same time, Japan should continue to refrain from unnecessary purchases in the spot market and give prompt and positive consideration to significantly increased investment in U.S. energy development.

2. The United States and Japan should cooperate further to enhance the security of energy supplies and diversification of supply sources.

For example, the two countries should promote increased cooperative oil and gas exploration and development in untapped areas as well as enhanced recovery in existing fields. Both countries should build and maintain sizeable petroleum stocks. The possible sharing of government-controlled stocks under certain emergency conditions — such as emergency conditions short of the IEA "trigger" or beyond the scope of the IEA emergency oil-sharing plan — may be advantageous to both countries and should, therefore, be studied promptly.

3. In carrying out these and other measures, Japan and the United States should both recognize that such actions can be more effective

5. Security issues as they relate to energy are treated in the recently published Joint Policy Paper of the Atlantic Council of the United States and the Japanese Research Institute for Peace and Security, under the title *The Common Security Interests of Japan, the United States, and NATO*, op. cit.

in a multilateral context and should therefore coordinate these steps with appropriate IEA programs.

Specifically, the two countries should take the necessary steps to assure that the IEA emergency oil-sharing plan is credible, realistic, and workable under emergency conditions. To this end, they should cooperate so that IEA plans and procedures are continually coordinated on a regular basis in order to assure that the disparate needs and capabilities of all IEA members under potentially differing emergency conditions are fully taken into account. Continued close consultation with the private energy sector in this regard is indispensable.

4. In order to reduce pressures on the oil markets, the United States and Japan should continue to support policies that will lead to stronger conservation and more efficient use of energy.

Energy pricing in both countries should encourage conservation and the development of alternatives to oil. The United States has taken steps to decontrol all oil and should accelerate consideration of decontrol of newly discovered natural gas.

At the same time, both countries should strengthen other policies and programs that facilitate conservation efforts and alternatives development.

5. The United States and Japan should strengthen their cooperation for longer term energy supply security through aggressive joint programs of research, development, demonstration, and commercial application of new energy technologies. Such programs also lend themselves to international cooperation in the energy field under appropriate bilateral and multilateral arrangements. Indeed, mutually desired international projects can avoid unnecessary overlapping efforts by individual countries and help make efficient use of possibly limited financial resources of the countries concerned. Worthy of particular emphasis are projects in:

Conservation techniques

Coal combustion and transportation
Shale oil and tar sand development
Coal liquefaction
Coal gasification

Nuclear reactor safety
Nuclear-reactor-related technologies,
    including the breeder reactor

Solar energy

Geothermal energy

Fusion

6. The United States can and should assist Japan in reducing its dependence on oil by becoming a major supplier of coal for energy purposes. In order to do so, the United States should adopt policies that facilitate the reliable and competitive export of coal from East, Gulf, and West Coast ports, including the timely removal of impediments to more rapid environmental approvals and the timely development and improvement of the necessary infrastructure such as railroads, slurry pipelines, and port and harbor facilities. At the same time, early initiation of relevant joint studies would facilitate discussions toward equitable and mutually acceptable arrangements covering the long-term and stable supply of U.S. coal to the Japanese market.

7. Japanese investment in U.S. coal properties should continue for the mutual benefit of both Japan and the United States, as this could help secure a stable source of supply for Japan and provide more stable demand for the U.S. coal industry. Large-scale transactions in U.S. coal would assist in redressing a recurrent balance of payments problem.

8. Japanese cooperation and investment in the production of synthetic fuels from U.S. coal, shale, and other sources will further enhance the longer term prospects of energy supply security. The U.S. and Japanese governments should cooperate to develop a climate conducive to such cooperation and investment. U.S. action to allow export of produced synthetic fuels to Japan in return for such cooperation and investment is essential.[6] Successful implementation of this recommendation will require considerable political education within the United States in order to demonstrate that this will not compromise U.S. energy security.

9. It is of interest to both Japan and the United States that Japan make full use of nuclear power to reduce its use of oil. The United States should resolve the uncertainties created by its nuclear policy in a manner that will facilitate and encourage the use of increasing amounts of nuclear power in Japan as well as in the United States.

---

6. See Chapter 1, n. 20, which is relevant here.

In this regard, the United States must fully recognize Japan's desire for establishing its own nuclear fuel cycle and should be aware that its goals, for the time being, are to establish smooth reprocessing operations and to complete its own enriching plant under appropriate international safeguards. In this context, Japan and the United States should work closely to develop acceptable regional and international means to prevent proliferation.

10. The United States should take the initiative in formulating and carrying out joint programs with Japan and other interested countries whereby techniques of plant operation and management developed in such countries can be fully utilized to further enhance the safety and reliability of nuclear power generation. Also, the United States, in its move to amend the siting regulations of nuclear power plants, should take into consideration that these regulations can have substantial influence on the nuclear power programs of Japan and Western Europe and, in light of the present level of and possible future progress in nuclear safety technologies, make such regulations models that will facilitate and encourage the expanded use of nuclear power safely.

11. A regular means of exploring and discussing the entire range of bilateral energy issues between Japan and the United States should be instituted, involving representatives of related fields. Among the first items on the agenda of such a continuing dialogue should be the means of expanding U.S.-Japanese energy trade, which will contribute substantially to the security of Japanese energy supply, the creation of additional jobs in the United States, the improvement of U.S. economic conditions generally, and the amelioration of the undesirable U.S.-Japan trade imbalance.

12. To provide a suitable political climate for these policy recommendations to be put into practice smoothly, both Japan and the United States should endeavor to deepen recognition of the importance of U.S.-Japanese energy relationships among their respective peoples and their respective legislative bodies.

APPENDIX

The United States National Committee of the World Energy Conference (USNC/WEC), issued on February 18, 1981, a ten-point "action agenda" calling on policymakers to "reverse years of ineffectiveness and to move America along the road to energy security."

The USNC/WEC Board of Directors has released its study, *Toward a Responsible Energy Policy in the 1980's: Completing an Unfinished Agenda*, which reviews the energy problems of the last decade and recommends steps to be taken in the next ten years. The study's conclusions were concurred in by the American Gas Association, American Petroleum Institute, Atomic Industrial Forum, Edison Electric Institute, and the National Coal Association.

The statement, described by USNC/WEC as "a message to the new administration," said that recent studies indicate an average economic growth rate in the United States of 2.5 to 3 percent per year for the remainder of the century. This will necessitate energy consumption in the year 2000 at a level of 25 percent to 50 percent above 1980's level. "These increases in energy consumption would represent annual growth of 1 to 2 percent, modest by past standards, but essential if the nation is to achieve its most pressing national goals, including full employment, alleviation of poverty, and adequate national security," the study said.

The action agenda called for the following steps:

- Facilitate domestic oil and gas exploration and development;

- Promote efficient use of energy, making "pricing and investment encouragement the twin pillars of conservation policy";

293

- Remove obstacles to the development of nuclear power, which now include "unduly lengthy" licensing procedures, lack of government programs for storage of spent fuel and low level wastes, and failure to proceed with nuclear fuel processing and breeder reactor development;

- Develop a coordinated set of national policies that encourage the use of American coal at home and abroad;

- Encourage solar energy development by revising building codes and eliminating other institutional and economic barriers;

- Strike a balance between the need for environmental protection and the needs of economic growth and national energy security;

- Coordinate federal land use policies with national energy policy by returning to principles permitting individuals and privately owned companies, in competition, to develop natural resources on federal lands in a responsible and efficient manner and allowing the principle of multiple land use (i.e., federal lands should support more than one activity at a time, where practical);

- Recognize that energy fuel prices should reflect actual supply and demand conditions and permit regulated utilities to recover their full cost of doing business, including a return on equity that reflects fully the risks borne by shareholders;

- Encourage the development of a synthetic fuels industry; and

- Reduce vulnerability to supply interruptions through the Strategic Petroleum Reserve and by international cooperation through the International Energy Agency.

"If our nation chooses now to develop and use energy sources more effectively," the study continued, "we might reasonably expect in 10 years" to double our use of coal; stabilize oil production; increase significantly the availability of gas from conventional and nonconventional sources; triple the contribution of nuclear power; and obtain significant contributions from synthetic fuels and renewable sources.

The nation's energy problems, the statement pointed out, have their origins in a number of public policy failures—failure to coordinate activities of federal departments and agencies, with the result that conflicting actions adversely affect energy supply and demand; failure to assess realistically the costs and benefits of the most extreme environmental regulations; and failure to acknowledge the long-run consequences of efforts to superimpose government direction as a substitute for market forces.

"The reality of government's failures is at long last arousing all sectors of public opinion," it concluded. "This chance to establish a sensible energy policy must not be lost. If the comprehensive steps we recommend are taken, the benefits for America will be enormous."

GLOSSARY

ARAMCO	Arab-American Company
API	American Petroleum Institute
b/d	barrels per day
boe/d	barrels of oil equivalent per day
BNA	British North American Act
btu	British thermal unit
bcfd	billion of cubic feet (gas) per day
CED	Committee for Economic Development
CFE	Comision Federal de Electricidad
cf/d	cubic feet per day
COPEI	Social-Christian Party of Venezuela
DOE	U.S. Department of Energy
EC	European Communities
GATT	General Agreement on Tariffs and Trade
GWe	Gigawatts of electricity
GWhr	Gigawatts per hour
GDP	Gross domestic product
GW	Gigawatt
IMF	International Monetary Fund
IEA	International Energy Agency

295

IEP	International Energy Program
IOC	International Oil Company
JNOC	Japan National Oil Company
LNG	Liquefied natural gas
LDC	Less developed country
mcfd	thousand cubic feet per day
mtoe	metric ton of oil equivalent
MITI	Ministry of International Trade and Industry
mb/d	million barrels per day
MMCf/d	million cubic feet per day
MWe	Megawatt of electricity
mtce	metric ton of coal equivalent
mboe/d	million barrels of oil equivalent per day
NATO	North Atlantic Treaty Organization
NIEO	New International Economic Order
NEB	National Energy Board
NEP	National Energy Program
OPEC	Organization of Petroleum Exporting Countries
OAS	Organization of American States
OECD	Organization for Economic Cooperation and Development
OAPEC	Organization of Arab Petroleum Exporting Countries
PPR	Preferred production rate
Pemex	Mexican national petroleum company
PRI	Partido Revolucionario Institucional
RD&D	Research, development and demonstration
SPR	Strategic Petroleum Reserve
tcf	thousand cubic feet
toe	ton of oil equivalent
UAE	United Arab Emirates
WESTPO	Western Governors' Policy Office

INDEX

Accion Democratica, 230-31
"Acid rain," 28
Afghanistan, 101, 129
Africa, 73
African Development Bank, 8, 60
Agencies, and U.S. decisionmaking, 42-44
AID program, U.S., 261
Alaska, 109, 139, 174
Alberta (Canada), 27, 140-42, 144, 150, 158-60
Alfonso, Perez, 232-34
Algeria, 23, 25, 67, 114, 169
Allocation systems, 3, 35, 89
Alternative energy supply, 13-14, 287-90
  in Central America, 4
  and Japan, 269-70, 273-74
  and Japan-U.S. relationship, 284, 289-90
  in Latin America, 4
  in 1980s, 64-65, 67-76
  and policy recommendations, 5-6, 9, 53-54
  and U.S. energy policy, 2-3, 11-12, 47, 269-70
Andean Pact, 97, 232, 237
Arab-Israeli War, 24, 82, 87, 115, 117, 132-33

Arab Monetary Fund, 84
Argentina, 49, 106
Artic Islands, 27, 140-43
Asian Development Bank, 8, 60
Atlantic Council Energy Policy, 1, 247-48, 260, 287
Australia, 72-73, 257, 260

Bahrain, 30, 111, 114, 118
Banco Nacional de Mexico, 197
Banks, 8, 60, 84, 103-107, 197, 206, 235, 248. *See also* Debt; Financial aid
Battelle Memorial Institute, 248
Beaufort Sea (Canada), 140-43
Berti, Calderon, 228
Benancourt, Romulo, 230
Bilateral relations, 59
  Canada-U.S., 27-28, 138-39, 153-74
  France-Middle East, 23
  Japan-U.S., 16, 28-30, 248, 263, 167, 270-72, 274, 287, 289, 291
  Mexico-U.S., 25-26, 194-202, 202-212, 212-16
  in 1980s, 3, 24-32, 92-93
  OPEC-U.S., 30-32
  and preferential agreements, 24-25

Venezuela–U.S., 26–27, 231–38
238–45
Biomass, 4, 49, 53, 60, 284
Bond, Robert, 231
Brandt Commission, 107
Brazil, 15, 49, 99, 102, 106
British North American Act of 1867
(BNA), 147

Camp David accord, 129
Campeche Bay, 181, 183
Canada
coal resources, 257
energy policy, 49, 137, 140–49
energy resources, 72–73, 85, 138,
140–46, 149, 153, 257
and Middle East, 22
natural gas resources in, 72
in policy recommendations, 55,
59–60
politics in, 138–39, 146–49, 153
unconventional resources in, 27,
73, 85, 141–42
and U.S. energy trade, 138, 150–53
uranium resources in, 144–45,
170–72
and Venezuela, 242
Canada–U.S. relationship, 4, 27–28,
137–39, 149, 173–75
and bilateral relations, 138
and energy trade, 138, 150–53
environment and, 28, 138–39
and exports, 167–72
and investment, 28, 138, 160
and NEP, 161–65
and supply of energy, 138
Canadianization, 155–56
Caribbean, 232, 234, 237
Carter administration, 236, 269, 278,
282, 285
Casteneda, Jorge, 212
Central America, 4, 49, 201–202,
211–12
snf Venezuela, 232, 234, 237, 239
Chicontepec region, 181–83
China, 15, 17, 71
coal resources in, 73, 257
consumption of oil, 95, 99, 101–102
–Japan relationship, 251, 259
oil resources in, 71
Claimants, new, and international oil
trade, 4, 15, 64, 95, 98–102.

See also Developing countries;
USSR
Clark government, 157–58, 160
Coal exports, U.S., 6, 9, 47, 52, 57,
144, 172
Coal resources
in Canada, 144, 170, 172
in Mexico, 184
in 1980s, 67, 71, 73–74
in USSR, 100
in U.S., 73, 172, 257
in Venezuela, 224
Coal use
in Japan, 257, 264–65, 267, 269,
273–74
and Japan–U.S. relationship,
278–79, 281–82, 290
in U.S., 40, 268–69, 273–74,
278–79
Comission Federal de Electricidad
(CFE) (Mexico), 193–94
Commercial stockpiles, 21–22
Committee for Energy Policy Promotion (JAPAN), 247–48, 287
Congress, U.S., 5, 43, 51, 84
Congressional Research Service
(U.S.), 203
Consensus, need for, 87–88
Conservation, 287, 289
in Japan, 257, 266, 268–69
and Japan–U.S. relationship, 29–30,
273, 276, 284–86, 289
in 1980s, 64, 76
and policy recommendations, 6, 9,
47, 52, 56
in U.S., 40, 108–10, 257, 268–69
in Venezuela, 223, 240
Consumption
of coal, 67
of hydroelectric power, 67
of nuclear power, 67
Consumption of energy
vs. consumption of oil, 98
in France, 274–75, 284
Japan vs. U.S., 252, 257, 274–75,
284
by OECD, 67
in United Kingdom, 274–75, 284
in U.S., 274–75, 284
in Western Europe, 274–75, 284
Consumption of natural gas
in Mexico, 199

in Venezuela, 223, 239
in U.S., and Venezuela, 239
Consumption of oil, 67, 274–75
in China, 95, 99, 101–102
in France, 274
in Iraq, 124
in Italy, 274–75, 284
in Japan, 93, 266–67, 274–77
in Kuwait, 123
in 1970s, 15, 98, 117
in 1980s, 15, 95, 98–102
in UAE, 123
in United Kingdom, 274
in U.S., 40, 42, 83, 274, 277–78
in Western Europe, 83, 274–77
Continentalism, 28, 137–38, 150–51
Cooperation. See International
    cooperation
COPEI party, 230–31, 237
Cost, 25, 85, 223, 241–42
Council on International Energy
    Policy (U.S.), 5, 51
Crude oil resources/reserves
in Canada, 140–41, 148
and OPEC, 96–97
in Venezuela, 217–22
Cuba, 201–202, 211, 237–38

Debt. See also Financial aid
of developing countries, 103–106
in Mexico, 106, 186–88, 193, 197
in Venezuela, 226–27
Decisionmaking
in Canada, 146
international, 3, 42–46
in U.S., 3, 14, 39–46, 48
DeGolyer, 199
Demand for energy, 2, 11–12, 12–14,
    18, 47–48, 64–67, 179
Demand for oil, 15
in Brazil, 15
in Canada, 157
in Mexico, 205, 208
and the Middle East, 49, 68–70
new claimants, 4, 15, 64, 102
in 1960s, 116
in 1970s, 68–70, 117
in 1980s, 47–48, 64–67, 99, 102,
    274–75
vs. PPRs, 80–81
and U.S. policy, 3, 47–48

in U.S., 116, 239
in Venezuela, 221–22, 239
Department of Commerce (U.S.), 43,
    200
Department of Energy (DOE) (U.S.),
    5, 42–43, 46, 51–52, 243
–CFE study, 209
Department of Energy, Mines, and
    Resources (Canada), 141, 144
Dependence, on oil imports
in Canada, 173–74
in Japan, 9, 274–75, 281–82
and Japan–U.S. relationship,
    261–62, 273, 290
in U.S., 14–15, 112, 130–31,
    133–35, 139, 177–78, 274–75,
    284
Developing countries, 49, 64. See also
    OPEC; OIDCs
and consumption of oil, 15, 98–102
debt financing of, 103–107
and demand for oil, 48
energy in, 35–39, 45, 60–61
energy in the 1980s, 3, 12–15, 47,
    63–66, 95
and Japan–U.S. relationship,
    261–62, 274
and supply of oil, 1, 4, 35–39
and U.S. policy recommendations,
    8, 60–61
Diversification
in Japan, 267, 277, 280–81, 288
in the 1980s, 3, 34–35, 85, 97
in Venezuela, 224, 225, 243–44
Domestic development, in Saudi
    Arabia, 126–28, 134–35
Duarte, Napolean, 237

Eastern Europe, 99–101
Echeverria, 186, 192, 194–95, 197,
    201, 214
Economic growth, 13
in Canada, 148
in Japan, 257, 266
in Mexico, 190, 192, 197, 214
in the 1980s, 64
OECD, 67–68, 76, 78
in the U.S., 108, 258
in Venezuela, 226–28, 230–31,
    244–46

Economics, 22-23, 48, 65
  and Canada's energy policy,
    148-49, 153, 155, 158-60,
    163-65
  and Japan-U.S. relationship,
    261-66, 277
  and Mexico's policy, 177-79, 181,
    186-91, 198, 204-206, 212-16
  and importance of Middle East,
    112-13, 115-16
  in Middle East, 30, 48, 89-90
  and Middle East-U.S. relationship,
    112, 128-29
  and oil, 1, 31, 91
  and production policy in the Middle
    East, 121-27
  in Venezuela, 217-18, 225-28, 240,
    242, 245-46
Economy
  in Japan, 266
  international, 106-107, 116-19,
    129
  in Mexico, 186-91, 206-207,
    210
  in Venezuela, 218, 223, 224-25,
    227-28, 244-45
Electricity
  in Canada, 145-46, 170-71, 173
  in Japan, 267-68
  in Mexico, 193-94, 208-209
  in policy recommendations, 6, 53
  in Venezuela, 224
El Salvador, 237-38
Emergencies, 35, 45-46, 65, 88-89.
  See also IEA; Security; Stockpiles
  and Japan-U.S. relationship, 272,
    279-80, 288-89
Employment, U.S., and Hapan, 281,
    291
Energy Conservation Act (JAPAN),
    266
Energy demand. See Demand for
    energy
Energy development, 138, 155-56,
    161-62
  in Canada, 165-67
  in developing countries, 60-61
  in Mexico, 179, 185-86, 188, 199,
    214
  in Venezuela, 222-23, 229-31,
    239-41, 244-46
Energy efficiency, 48, 64, 108, 205

Energy end use, 2, 11-12, 13, 64
Energy industry, U.S., 3, 5, 44-46,
    57, 109-110
Energy policy
  in Canada, 138, 140-49, 158-59,
    165, 167-72, 173-75
  international, 3, 42-46
  in Japan, 265-70
  in Mexico, 185-94, 212-14
  in Venezuela, 228-31
Energy and foreign policy, U.S., 2-7,
    8-12, 14-22, 44-45, 50, 203,
    213-15, 263-65, 168, 277-79
  and demand for oil, 3, 47-48
  and energy industries, 3, 44-46
  vs. international arena, 3, 14-15
  options in international supply
    shortage, 3, 20-22
  policy recommendations, 5-7,
    7-8, 50, 132-35
Energy issues, 2, 11-12, 24-32,
    35-39
Energy problem, 2, 10-12, 14, 36
Energy production. See Production
    of energy
Energy resources
  in Canada, 138, 140-46, 148-49,
    153, 174
  in Japan vs. U.S., 251, 257
  in Mexico, 179-85, 204
  in 1980s, 64, 70-76
  in U.S., 29, 41, 46, 72-73, 75, 85,
    91, 257, 264, 274
Energy supply. See Supply of energy
Energy supply security. See Supply
    security
Energy trade policy, 3, 16, 81
  Japan-U.S. relationship, 260,
    281-82, 291
  international, 3, 16-17, 66-77,
    108-110, 209-211, 214-15,
    242-43, 261, 281-82
  in Mexico, 195, 200-202
  and Venezuela, 242-43
Environment, 28, 43, 109, 138-39,
    278
Environmental Protection Agency
  (EPA), 43, 109
European Community, 50, 56-59.
  See also OECD; Western Europe
Exporter-importer dialogue, 32, 48,
    60, 66, 83-85, 87

incentives for, 89-91
and pricing policy, 79
and technology transfer, 90
and U.S. policy, 4, 8
and Venezuela, 232-34, 236
Exporters, 65, 96-98, 108. *See also*
  Producers
Export-Import Bank, U.S., 43, 199
Exports, energy
  in Canada, 138, 147, 149, 150-53,
    167-72
  and Japan, 260, 268, 270-72
  and Mexico, 186-87, 189-91,
    194-96, 198, 202-208, 212-15,
    217
  U.S., 260, 268, 274
  from U.S. to Japan, 280-81, 288
  and Venezuela, 217-18, 219, 221,
    225-26, 245

Federal Energy Administration (FEA),
  46
Federal vs. provincial government, in
  Canada, 137, 146-51, 153, 155,
  158-60, 162-64
Federal government vs. state government, U.S., 40-41, 268
Fifth Development Plan (1976-80)
  (Venezuela), 227
Financial aid, and Venezuela, 234-35,
  237, 246. *See also* Banks; International financial system
Financial assets
  of Kuwait, 123
  in Middle East, 84, 131
  of Saudi Arabia, 126-27
  of UAE, 124
  and U.S. government, 129, 135
Foreign Investment Review Agency
  (Canada), 162
Foreign policy
  of Japan, 262, 265-68, 270-72
  of Mexico, 201-202, 209, 211-12
  of U.S., 2-4, 7-8, 44-45, 50, 213,
    215
  of Venezuela, 231-32, 234
Foreign sector. *See also* Investment;
  Nationalization
  in Canada, 28, 160
  in Japan, 257-59
  in Venezuela, 242-43

France, 18-19, 25, 49, 55, 274-75,
  284
  -Middle East relationship, 23, 87
Fuji Bank, 248

General Agreement on Trade and
  Tariffs (GATT), 129, 200, 210
Geothermal resources, 4, 13, 49, 53,
  184
Global Development Plan (1980-82)
  (Mexico), 189
Government policy. *See also* NEP
  in Canada, 137
  in Japan, 267-68, 290
  and Middle East relationship,
    115-16
  in Middle East, 117-20, 121-27
  in Venezuela, 222, 227-36, 240,
    243-45
Government, U.S., 268-69, 290
  and decisionmaking, 42-44, 48
  and the Middle East, 127-32
  policy recommendations for, 6,
    51-52, 137
  vs. private sector, 5-6, 8-9, 40,
    44-46, 48, 51, 60-61, 109-110,
    134
Government-to-government arrangements, 25, 84-85, 92-95,
  232-34
Gray, John E., 287
Grossling, Bernardo, 184, 221
GDP (Gross National Product), 188,
  197, 206-207, 225-26, 228.
  See also Economic growth

Herrera, Luis Campins, 226-27, 230,
  236-37, 239
Hydrocarbon Law of 1943 (Vene-
  zuela), 235
Hydrlcarbons Reversion Law of 1971
  (Venezuela), 235
Hydroelectric power, 4, 27, 49, 60,
  224. *See also* Electricity

Ikuta, Dr. Toyoaki, 248
Importer-exporter dialogue, 4, 8,
  32, 48, 60, 66, 79, 83-85, 87,
  89-91, 232-34, 236
Importers, 32, 83, 85, 89-91
Imports, energy, 7, 50, 57, 110.
  See also Oil imports

Import substitution, 190, 210
Industrial Development Plan (1979)
    (Mexico), 205
Industrialized world, 106–107, 261
    vs. OPEC, 89–91, 114–20, 135
    and PPRs, 81–82
    and supply/demand for energy, 1,
    12–14, 79
Industry. See also Private sector
    Japan, 29, 252, 267–68
    U.S., 6, 29, 51, 109–110, 252,
    268–69
Inflation, 31, 118
    in Mexico, 181, 186–88, 190–91,
    193, 206–207, 211
    in U.S., 4, 48
    in Venezuela, 226–27
InterAmerican Development Bank,
    8, 60, 235
Interests, international, imbalance of,
    85–87
Interests, U.S., 112–13, 127, 130–32,
    212
International arena
    in 1980s, 63–66, 76
    and nonenergy issues, 3, 16–18
    and policy recommendations, 54–61
    and supply security, 3, 18–20, 24,
    54–55
    and supply shortage, U.S. options in,
    3, 20–22
    effect of U.S. energy policy on, 3,
    15
International cooperation, 10, 49,
    56–59, 138, 174. See also Multi-
    lateral agreements
    and developing countries, 36–37
    and Japan–U.S. relationship, 49,
    269–70, 273, 277, 280–86,
    288–89
    and Mexico–U.S. relationship, 208
    and the Middle East, 24, 33
    and Venezuela–U.S. relationship,
    231–34, 236, 243
International Development Associa-
    tion, 129
International Energy Agency (IEA)
    emergency plan, 5, 8–9, 19–21, 32,
    35, 56, 263, 272, 279–80, 288
    and international oil market in the
    1980s, 97–98
    in policy recommendations, 51,
    56–57, 59

    and RD&D, 270
    role of, 88–89
International energy demand.
    See Demand for energy
International Energy Program, 19, 21
International energy production.
    See Production of energy
International financial system, 83,
    103, 234–35, 237. See also Debt;
    Financial aid
International Institute for Applied
    Systems Analysis, 18
International Monetary Fund (IMF),
    8, 37–39, 60–61, 103, 107, 129,
    181, 186, 199
International Nuclear Fuel Cycle Eval-
    uation, 283
International oil companies (IOC),
    25, 65, 84, 91–95, 97, 115, 118
    and Japan, 257–59, 263
    in Venezuela, 220, 229, 233, 235
International oil markets, 19–20, 27,
    93, 97–98, 115, 235, 242,
    265–66, 277
    and Japan–U.S. relationship, 260,
    272
    and the Middle East, 116–18, 120
International oil system, 65, 91–95,
    234–36
International security. See Security
International trade, 3, 16–18, 66–76,
    77, 242–43, 260, 281–82
    coal trade, 73–74
    energy trade, 66–76, 77, 108–110
    natural gas trade, 72
    nuclear power and, 74–76
    oil trade, 4, 15, 67–72, 77, 85–87,
    92–93
Institute of Energy Economics,
    247–48
Investment, foreign. See also Foreign
    sector
    and Canada–U.S. relationship,
    138–39, 149, 174
    and Japan–U.S. relationship, 280,
    290
    in Mexico, 198, 200–201
    and NEP, 155, 161–66, 174
    OPEC in U.S., 83–84
    in Venezuela, 227, 241–45
Iran, 25, 81, 84–85, 101, 114–15,
    127, 186, 262
    natural gas reserves in, 71–72

and PPRs, 81–82
production in, 114, 119–20
and U.S., 131
Iran–Iraq War, 23, 120, 130, 133
Iraq, 25, 30, 111, 114–15
–Mexico relationship, 183
oil production in, 118, 120, 123–24
–U.S. relationship, 128
Italy, 25
Iwasa, Yoshizanei, 287

Japan
–Australia relationship, 257, 260
–China relationship, 251, 259
consumption of oil in, 83, 266–67, 274–77
demand/supply of energy, 252, 257, 263–64, 267, 272, 274–77, 288
–Latin America relationship, 49
–Mexico relationship, 198, 200–201, 259
–Middle East relationship, 22–23, 85–87, 90, 109, 252, 259, 275–76, 282
and oil imports, 48, 83, 251–52, 275–76, 280, 288
Japanese Institute for Peace and Security, 260
Japanese Ministry of International Trade and Industry (MITI), 266, 270
Japan National Oil Corporation (JNOC), 257–59
Japan–U.S. relationship, 4, 16, 29–30, 49, 247–50, 272–74
improvements for, 279–87
issues in, 262–72
and joint policy recommendations, 8–10, 50, 56–59, 272–74, 277–79
policy objectives, 261–62
post–war, 250
and U.S. energy policy, 277–79
Joint venture, 229, 243

Klein, Milton, 248
Kuwait, 30, 111, 114
oil production in, 111, 117–18, 120, 122–23
–U.S. relationship, 128

Latin America, 4, 36–37, 49
Latin America Economic System, 232

LDCs. See Developing countries
Legislation, U.S., 40, 46
Libya, 25, 114
LNG, 29, 67, 69, 71–72. See also Natural gas

McNaughton, 199
"Majors." See IOCs
Market forces
and Canada's energy policy, 149–50, 153, 169
international oil, 19–20, 27, 93, 97–98, 116–18, 128, 242, 260, 265–66, 272, 277
and Japan–U.S. relationship, 261, 263, 266, 268
and Mexico–U.S. relationship, 195, 197–98, 203, 213
and Venezuela–U.S. relationship, 218, 233, 242–43, 245
Maximum revenue strategy, 122, 124–26. See also Production of oil
Methanol, 4, 49, 76
Mexico
and consumption of energy, 99, 208
debt of, 106
energy production polity, 185–94, 202–208
energy resources in, 179–85
exports, 207–208, 217
–Japan relationship, 259
natural gas resources in, 72, 183–84
in 1980s, 202–212
nuclear power in, 185, 209
oil resources in, 25–26, 71, 180–83
and policy recommendations, 59, 212–16
–U.S. relationship, 7, 25–26, 48, 59, 197–202, 202–216
uranium in, 185
vs. Venezuela, 217, 219, 237–38
Middle East, 48
–China relationship, 102
and consumption of oil, 68–70, 99
industrialized nations and, 114–20
in international oil trade, 68–71, 85–87
and international security issues, 22–24
–Japan relationship, 22–23, 85–87, 90, 109, 252, 275–76, 282
natural gas in, 71–72

oil reserves, 68–73, 77, 91, 111–12, 116
in post–war era, 114–16
–USSR relationship, 100–102
–U.S. relationship, 16–17, 30–32, 54–55, 112–13, 115, 252
Migration, and Mexico–U.S., 202–203, 209, 211–15
Military, U.S.,
and Japan, 251
and Mexico, 178, 213
in Middle East, 115, 131–33
Ministry of Energy and Mines (Venezuela), 223, 228–30, 240
Multilateral agreements
between Japan and U.S., 271–72, 289
in the 1980s, 3, 32, 36, 87
in policy recommendations, 50–51, 54–55
and Venezuela, 242

National Energy Board (NEB) (Canada), 140–43, 147–48, 165, 167
National Energy Commission (Mexico), 194
National Energy Program (NEP) (Canada), 137, 153–61
and exports, 167–72
incentives in, 155–56, 161–62, 166
and investment, 161–66, 113
pricing policy, 166–67
and taxes, 156, 159–60, 166
National energy program, in Mexico, 185–88, 194, 196, 207
National Industrial Development Plan (1979) (Mexico), 189, 210
National Institute of Nuclear Energy (Mexico), 193
Nationalism
in Canada, 149
in Mexico, 207
Nationalization
in Iran, 114
in Mexico, 178
in Venezuela, 220, 228–30, 232, 235–36
National security, and Japan, 277
National Security Council, 5, 51
NATO (North Atlantic Treaty Organization), 24, 55–56, 109

Natural gas
imports for U.S., 108
and Japan–U.S. relationship, 278
in Mexico's policy, 185–94, 196–98, 202–208, 212–15
in NEP, 155–57, 167–72
in policy recommendations, 6, 47, 52
Natural Gas Policy Act (1978) (U.S.), 278
Natural gas resources
in Canada, 27, 141–43, 148, 168–69
in Iran, 71–72
in Mexico, 72, 183–84
in Middle East, 71–72
in 1980s, 67, 71–72, 76
in USSR, 71, 100
in Venezuela, 223–24
Natural Resources Council (U.S.), 44
NEB. See National Energy Board
NEP. See National Energy Program
Netherlands, 72
Newfoundland, 27, 140–41, 160
New international economic order (NIEO), 106
Nicaragua, 237
Nixon, Richard, 150
Nonenergy issues, 3, 16–18. See also Energy trade; Strategic defense
Nonproliferation, 282–83
Nuclear power, 13
in Japan, 257, 263–65, 267
and Japan–U.S. relationship, 29–30, 273, 279, 282–84, 290–91
in Mexico, 185, 193–94
in 1980s, 67, 74–76
in 1990s, 75, 100
in policy recommendations, 6, 9, 47, 53, 57–58
in USSR, 100
in U.S., 46, 75, 264, 274
in Venezuela, 224
Nuclear Regulatory Commission (NRC), 43

OAPEC, 20, 82, 92–93
OAS, 36
OECD (Organization for Economic Cooperation and Development), 31–32, 47–48, 284
Declaration on International Investment and Multinational Enterprises, 162

growth, 67-68, 76, 78, 96-97
/IEA study, 74, 97
Oil Committee, 18
Oil
   new claimants for, 4, 15, 64, 95,
      98-102
   in 1980s, 63-66, 67-68
   in 1990s, 68
OIDCs, 103-107, 234-35. *See also*
   Developing countries
Oil import quotas, 233, 236
Oil imports, 11-12, 47-49
   in Canada, 157
   and developing countries, 2, 4, 48,
      98-102
   in international trade, 63, 66,
      85-87, 96, 111-12
   to Japan, 48, 83, 251-52, 275-76,
      280, 288
   from Middle East, 111-12, 138
   in 1980s, 63-65, 76-77
   and U.S. energy policy, 2-4, 47-49
   to Western Europe, 48, 275
Oil imports, U.S., 108-10, 251-52,
      274-77
   from Canada, 138, 150-51, 174
   and Japan, 280
   and Mexico, 208, 210
   from Middle East, 138
   from Venezuela, 138
Oil Import Task Force (U.S.), 150
"Oil in the ground" strategy, 121-22,
   126
Oil Market Revolution (1970-74),
   116-18
Oil policy
   in Mexico, 25-26, 180, 185-94,
      197-98, 202-208, 212-15
   in NEP, 155-57, 160, 167-72
   in Venezuela, 26-27, 217-18, 219,
      224-31, 231-38, 240-45
Oil price increases, 1, 65, 113-14,
   118-19
   and U.S. policy, 47-48, 128
Oil price shocks
   1973-74, 114, 128, 227, 235
   1978-79, 118-20
Oil production. *See* Production of oil
Oil resources. *See also* Crude oil
   resources
   in Canada, 167-70
   in Japan, 251

and Japan-U.S. relationship, 29, 251
   in Mexico, 25-26, 71, 180-93
   in Middle East, 68-73, 77, 91,
      111-12, 116
   in 1980s, 70-72, 76
   in Saudi Arabia, 68-71, 117
   in USSR, 100
   in U.S., 29, 72, 77, 91, 251
   in Venezuela, 26-27, 219-23
Oman, 30, 111, 118, 129
OPEC
   as cartel, 117, 120-21
   coal resources in, 73
   and consumption of oil, 15, 99,
      274-75
   and demand for oil, 68-70
   incentives for, 33-34
   vs. Mexico, 195-96
   and multilateral agreements, 32
   in 1980s, 65-66, 93, 99
   oil exports, 85-87
   and politics, 23-24, 38, 48, 89-90,
      121, 131
   PPRs, 79-82
   pricing policy, 78-79, 96-97,
      117-21
   and production policy, 33-34, 121
   and recycling, 83-84
   and technology transfer, 90
   and U.S. policy, 4, 8, 30-32, 48,
      50, 83-84
   and Venezuela, 217, 232-34, 236
   and the West, 90
Orinoco region, 26, 222-23, 229-31,
   238-46

Panama Canal Treaty, 237
Partido Revolucionario Institutional
   (PRI), 192-93
Pemex, 178, 180-81, 186-87, 190,
   193-94, 199-200, 205-206, 214
Perez, Carlos Andres, 227, 230,
   236-37
Persian Gulf. *See* Middle East
Petro Canada, 151, 156, 159, 162,
   164, 166
Petroleos, 220, 228-30, 239
Politics, 48, 65
   in Canada, 138-39, 146-49, 153,
      155, 158-60, 163-65, 173
   and Canada-U.S. relationship,
      138-39, 173-75

and developing countries, 4, 37, 45
and Japan–U.S. relationship, 261,
    266, 270, 274, 284–86, 290–91
and Mexico's policy, 179, 181,
    191–94, 203–206, 212–16
and importance of Middle East, 113,
    115–16
in the Middle East, 23–24, 30, 48,
    89–90, 121, 131
of oil, 1, 3, 10, 87, 91, 100, 102,
    113
influence on production of oil, 113,
    123–25, 127
and PPRs, 80–82
and supply security, 23–24
and U.S. policy, 51, 129
in Venezuela, 217–18, 228–31,
    239–40, 243–46
Population growth, 3, 18
in Japan, 267
in Kuwait, 123
in Mexico, 191
in UAE, 123
in U.S., 208
in Venezuela, 226
Portillo, Jose Lopez, 180–81, 186–89,
    191–92, 194–98, 201, 206, 215
Preferential agreements, 24–25, 82,
    84–85, 218, 232, 236
Preferred Production Rates (PPRs),
    65, 79–83, 89, 102, 111, 119,
    121–26
President's Select Commission on
    Immigration and Refugee Policy
    (U.S.), 211
Price
and economic motives, 121–27
and Japan, 265, 273
Middle East influence on, 112,
    117–18, 120–27
in 1960s, 116
in 1970s, 117–18
in 1980s, 65, 76, 78–79, 96
and OPEC, 121
and Saudi Arabia, 118–19, 124–26
vs. technooogy, 33
and U.S. interests, 130–32, 273
and Venezuela, 221–22, 227,
    239–41
Price decontrol, in U.S., 40, 45,
    277–78
Price increases. See Oil price increases

Price shock
of 1973–74, 114, 128, 227, 235
of 1978–79, 118–20
Pricing policy
in Canada, 151, 158–60
and Japan–U.S. relationship, 289
Mexico's, 195, 199, 205
in NEP, 155–56, 163–67
in policy recommendations, 9,
    52–53, 56
in Venezuela, 221–22, 227,
    233–35, 239–41
Private sector, 109–10
in developing countries, 37–39
and Japan–U.S. relationship,
    286–87
in Mexico, 199–200, 210
in U.S. policy, 8–9, 40, 44–46, 48,
    51, 56, 60–61, 109–10, 134
in Venezuela, 228–29, 231
Producers. See also Exporters
incentives for in 1980s, 3, 33–39,
    92–95
in 1970s, 91–92
and PPRs, 80–82
and U.S. policy, 128–29, 132–35
Production
of coal, 13
of energy, 4, 13–14, 48–50, 59, 99
of natural gas, 13
Production of oil, 13, 33, 72.
    See also PPRs
in China, 102
in Iran, 119–20
in Kuwait, 117–18, 120
in 1960s, 116
in 1970s, 117–19
in 1980s, 64–65, 67–70, 72–73
in Saudi Arabia, 111–12, 117–20
in U.S., 72, 108, 111
in USSR, 72, 100–101
Production of oil, in the Middle East,
    30–33, 79–82, 111–12, 117–18,
    120–27
and economic motives, 121–27
and OPEC, 33–34, 121
and policy recommendations,
    134–35
and U.S. policy, 128–29, 130–32
Production policy
in Mexico, 179, 181–82, 186–91,
    191–209, 212–15

in Middle East, 117–27
in 1980s, 96–97, 113
in Venezuela, 219–21, 223, 228,
    235–36, 239–40, 245–46

Qatar, 30, 111, 114, 118

Rand study, 182, 204
Reagan administration, 44, 238, 278
Recycling, 3, 34, 83–84
Refinery modernization, in Venezuela,
    221, 239, 245–46
Reforma region, 181, 183, 195
Regionalism, 3, 16–17, 97
in Canada, 147–49
in Japan, 261, 291
in Venezuela, 236–38
RD&D, 26–27
and bilateral agreements, 26–27, 30
in policy recommendations, 5, 9,
    51–52, 56
and Japan–U.S. relationship,
    269–70, 273, 284, 288
and Venezuela–U.S. relationship,
    242–43

Saudi Arabia, 25, 30–31, 111–12
vs. Mexico, 177, 182–83, 202
natural gas resources in, 72
oil production in, 81–82, 112, 121,
    124–27
oil resources in, 30–31, 70–71,
    111–12
pricing policy and, 77, 118–21
–USSR relationship, 100
–U.S. relationship, 128–31, 134
Schlesinger, James, 199
Security
in the Middle East, 109, 131–32
and importance of Middle East,
    115–16
in the 1980s, 3, 22–24
influence on oil production, 113,
    123, 125, 127
and U.S.–Middle East relationship,
    112, 129
and U.S. policy recommendations,
    109, 133–34
Serrano, Jorge Diaz, 186
Sixth Development Plan (1981–85)
    (Venezuela), 220–21, 227
Social issues
and Mexico's policy, 179, 186–91,
    192

in the Middle East, 89–90, 131
influence on production, 123–25
and U.S. energy policy, 41
in Venezuela, 225–28, 244–45
South Korea, 106
Soviet Union. See USSR
SPR. See Strategic petroleum reserve
Stockpiles, 18–22, 272, 288–89
Strategic defense, 3, 17, 29–31, 66,
    113, 260, 263
Strategic Petroleum Reserve (SPR), 7,
    21–22, 54, 88–89, 130
Substitution
in Canada's energy policy 157–58,
    169
in Japan, 29–30, 257, 263–64
in Mexico, 185
in 1980s, 71–76, 108, 110
in policy recommendations, 6, 9, 47
in U.S., 29–30, 40, 46, 257
Supply/demand, 89–91
in 1970s, 91–93
in 1980s, 93–95
Supply of energy, 12–14, 63–66,
    68–76, 92–95
and Canada–U.S. relationship, 138,
    173–75
international, 4, 12–15
and Japan, 263–64, 267, 272,
    274–11
and Japan vs. U.S., 252, 257, 288
and Mexico–U.S. relationship,
    212–14
vs. oil, 68–72
and unconventional oil, 72–73, 76
and U.S., 109–110, 138, 173–75
Supply of oil, 1–3, 10–12
and bilateral relations, 24–32
in Canada, 152–53
in developing countries, 1, 4, 35–39,
    99
and international oil markets,
    95–98, 235
and IOCs, 97
and the Middle East, 25, 30–32,
    138, 274
in thr 1980s, 12–14, 63–66, 77–91,
    90–91, 98–99
in the 1990s, 68
and PPRs, 80–82
and preferential agreements, 24–25
and producer incentives, 33–34
and Venezuela, 235–36

Supply security, 1–3, 10, 12, 18–20, 24, 54–55
Supply security, U.S.
  and Japan, 288–89
  and Mexico, 25, 202, 208, 213–14
  and Venezuela, 26, 233, 245
Synfuel Corporation, 40
Synthetic fuels, 40, 45, 47, 53, 57, 79, 274, 290

Taxes
  in Canada's NEP, 156, 159–60, 166
  in Japan, 266
  in U.S., 46
  in Venezuela, 228–29, 235, 240
Technical constraints
  and Japan–U.S. relationship, 284–86
  in Mexico, 204–205
  and U.S.–USSR relationship, 17
  and Venezuela, 223, 240, 242–43, 245
Technology transfer, 33, 81, 90, 203, 214
Texas Railroad Commission, 115
Three Mile Island, 269, 282
Tinker Foundation, 248
Tokyo Summit, 97
Trade policy. See Energy trade policy; International trade
Trade Reform Act of 1974 (U.S.), 236, 242
Treaty of Rome, 32
Trudeau, Pierre, 137, 147, 149, 153, 155, 157–62, 166, 168–69
Truman, Harry, 115

Unconventional resources, 13, 27, 59, 72–73, 76, 85, 91, 141–42
Unemployment
  in Japan, 272
  in Mexico, 189–91, 211
United Arab Emirates (UAE), 30, 111, 114, 118, 123, 128
United Kingdom (U.K.), 49, 86–87, 274–75, 284
United Nations (U.N.), 201
USSR (United Socialist Soviet Republics), 25
  coal resources in, 73
  and consumption of oil, 15, 95, 99–101, 274–75

  and demand for oil, 48
  and Latin America, 49
  and the Middle East, 100–102, 113, 129
  natural gas resources in, 71, 100
  in the 1980s, 64
  nuclear power in, 100
  oil production in, 48, 72, 100–101
  –U.S. relationship, 7, 17, 54–55, 133–34
  –Western Europe relationship, 4, 7, 17
United States (U.S.)
  –Caribbean, 36–37
  –Central America, 4, 49
  –China relationship, 17
  coal exports, 9, 47, 52, 57, 144, 172
  coal resources in, 73, 257
  consumption of energy in, 274–75, 284
  consumption of oil in, 40, 42, 83, 274, 277–78
  –Latin American relationship, 4, 49
  nuclear power in, 29, 46, 75
  and oil imports, 63–66, 88, 108–110
  oil production in, 72, 108, 111
  oil resources in, 29, 72, 77, 91, 251
  –OPEC relationship, 4, 8, 30–32, 50, 83–84
  role in the 1980s, 108–110
  strategic reserves, 88–89
  unconventional resources in, 73, 85
  –USSR relationship, 17
  uranium resources in, 29, 264, 274
  –Western Europe relationship, 4, 56–59
U.S.–Canada relationship, 4, 8, 27–28, 59–60, 137–39, 149, 173–75
  and energy investments in NEP, 161–65
  and energy trade, 150–53
  and exports, 167–72, 174
U.S.–Japan Coal Conference, 282
U.S.–Japan relationship, 4, 16, 23, 29–30, 56–59, 247–50, 272–74
  improvements for, 279–87
  issues in, 262–72
  and joint policy recommendations, 287–91

policy objectives, 261–62
policy recommendations, 272–74
post–war, 250
and U.S. policy, 263–65
U.S.–Mexico relationship, 7, 25–26,
    48, 59, 177–79, 197–202, 212–16
and electricity, 208–209
and Mexico's foreign policy, 209,
    211–12
and Mexico's trade policy, 200–202,
    209–11
and migration, 209, 211
and nuclear power, 209
and oil and gas production, 202–208
and U.S. policy, 203, 215
U.S.–Middle East relationship, 7,
    16–17, 22–23, 85–87, 111–13
conflicts and interrelations, 130–32
demand for oil, 68–70, 116
in the 1970s, 113–20
policy since 1974, 128–29
policy recommendations and,
    54–55, 132–35
U.S.–Venezuela relationship, 7,
    26–27, 59, 217–19, 231–38,
    238–45, 245–46
Uranium resources
in Canada, 144–45, 170–72
in Mexico, 185
in U.S., 29, 264,274

Venezuela
and developing countries, 246
energy resources in, 26, 73, 85, 91,
    219–24
and Mexico, 183, 201, 206

in the 1980s, 238–45
oil policy, 219, 224–31
Venezuela–U.S. relationship, 26–27,
    217–19, 231–38, 245–46
in 1980s and 1990s, 238–45
policy recommendations for, 7, 48,
    59
Venezuelan Investment Fund, 227

Western Coal Export Task Force, 282
Western Europe, 49
consumption of energy in, 83,
    274–75, 284
–Middle East relationship, 22,
    85–87
oil imports, 48, 83
oil resources in, 77
policy recommendations for, 4,
    8–10, 50
–USSR relationship, 4, 7, 17
–U.S. relationship, 4, 7
West Germany, 23, 25, 49, 86,
    274–75, 284
Western Governors' Policy Office
    (WESTPO)
Wilson, Carroll, 74
World Bank, 8, 60–61, 103, 107,
    129, 191, 235, 246
and energy development in develop-
    ing countries, 37–39
World Energy Conference study, 12
World energy trade. See International
    energy trade
World oil markets. See International
    energy markets